WOOD TECHNOLOGY

IN THE

DESIGN OF STRUCTURES

ROBERT J. HOYLE, Jr., P.E.

Lecturer in Civil Engineering
and
Wood Technologist

Washington State University

MOUNTAIN PRESS PUBLISHING COMPANY

MISSOULA, MONTANA

Library of Congress Catalog No. 72-96102

ISBN No. 0-87842-039-8

Third Edition

Second Printing — October, 1973

MOUNTAIN PRESS PUBLISHING COMPANY
287 West Front Street
Missoula, Montana 59801

PREFACE

The adoption of new lumber size and quality standards in 1970 has made a new textbook on the design of timber structures timely. The inclusion of basic material on the general types of all wood structural materials in a single volume, for the convenience of students and teachers, is a key feature of this book. A particular effort is made to provide the rationale for allowable properties assignment and the numerous adjustment factors used in practice. In general the book presents the design methods which are commonly recommended and accepted, with illustrative examples and figures to better show the principles involved.

The book is a comprehensive elementary treatment of wood structural design. Its purpose is to prepare the student for practical structural design tasks in the choice of wood structural materials and their proportions to meet prevailing code requirements. Numerous departures from authoritarian regulations, where they appear technically sound and economically advantageous, are discussed. No art or science can develop under a closely regulated discipline. It is an objective to illustrate accepted practice and to encourage innovation in structural concepts for wood in engineering, architectural, and building practice.

While basically a teaching document, the book can serve as a design manual with a variety of commonly needed data conveniently at hand.

Much of the material in the book is not original with the author. It draws upon the publications of the forest products industry, the wood preserving and laminating industries, model building codes, standards associations, and the forest products research laboratories of the United States, Canadian, Australian, and British governments as well as many universities. The courtesies which these groups have extended in allowing the use of copyrighted materials are deeply appreciated.

Many individuals have given generously of their time and talent to examine portions of the manuscript and offer guidance. I should like to thank George Atherton, Jim Johnson, Stanley Corder, Anton Polensek, and Helmuth Resch of Oregon State University; Alan A. Marra of the University of Michigan; Ralph H. Gloss and David R. Norcross of the Timber Engineering Company; Russell P. Wibbens and Thomas A. Brassell of the American Institute of Timber Construction; Robert A. Holcombe and John P. Shope of the National Forest Products Association; Fred L. Werren, Billy Bohannon, Robert L. Ethington, Wallace Youngquist, Kenneth C. Compton, Thomas Lee Wilkinson, Ed Kuenzi, and Ivan Orosz of the U.S. Forest Products Laboratory; Lajos J. Nemeth of Potlatch Forests, Inc.; Neal I. Pinson and Byron L. Foreman of the Western Wood Products Association; David Countryman and James P. Elliott of the American Plywood Association; M. Dee Strickler of Washington State University; Stanley K. Suddarth of Purdue University; F. Alan Taylor of the Western Forest Products Laboratory of Canada; James E. Bihr of the International Conference of Building Officials; and L. G. Booth of the Imperial College, London.

To George G. Marra of the College of Engineering Research Division at Washington State University, I am particularly indebted for his encouragement concerning the objectives of this project.

My closest associate in this work has been my wife, Rosemary, who has made an invaluable contribution to the phraseology and logic of many portions of the descriptive language and composition.

I am also appreciative of the many associates, who, during my tenure as an industrial researcher and teacher, have profoundly affected my views and knowledge.

Robert J. Hoyle
Pullman, Washington
November 15, 1972

TABLE OF CONTENTS

Chapter	Title	Page

CHAPTER 1

INTRODUCTION

An understanding of materials is a key to good engineering design. This book will deal as much with wood as a material as it will with design methods themselves. Design formulas, design conceptions, and the performance criteria which structures must meet to be serviceable and safe are really independent of the material to be used. Beam and column formulas for one material are basically like those for another. The service loadings a structure must bear are more a matter of environment and purpose than of material. Some materials, because of their properties and costs, tend to dominate particular types of structures. This is why high-rise buildings favor the use of steel and concrete, whereas wood tends to dominate single-family dwellings and low-rise apartments.

At one time timber was the predominant structural material in mill buildings. Today there is a healthy competition between steel, aluminum, concrete, masonry and timber in these buildings. This is more a matter of economics than of performance capability, and often a wood deck will be combined with steel beams or bar-joists, masonry walls, and concrete floors; or a wood frame will be enclosed in a metal sheathing. We will consider the various factors that affect the choice of a material from time to time in this book.

Wood and masonry are both ancient building materials and their use has been more traditional than technical. The metals are of more recent origin and are produced from a materials technology. To meet the competition of metals, a technology of wood has arisen during the past 50 to 75 years, which is growing steadily. The favorable cost position of wood has not demanded an application of this technology until quite recently. Today cost factors are motivating the use of technology in timber design, and in addition, pressing needs for housing are making the use of an efficient technology a matter of public policy. It is in the application of good engineering practices, using knowledge to the greatest advantage, and depending as little as possible upon unduly high factors of safety, that engineers and architects have the chance to extend the utility of the world's timber supply to meet the needs of people as extensively as they can.

Let us look at a few statistics. In 1914, the nation's production of softwood lumber and plywood reached a peak of about 42 billion board feet a year. A board foot is a piece of roughly sawn green (unseasoned) lumber, one-inch thick by twelve inches by twelve inches, or the product of that basic unit. For example, the seasoning and machine dressing processes make this into a piece three-quarters of an inch by eleven and one-quarter by twelve inches. This is also a board foot on the seasoned and finished basis. Lumber is generally sold in thousand board foot units, which weigh about a ton (seasoned and dressed), give or take ten percent depending on the particular species of wood involved.

A rate of production near 42 billion board feet a year has been sustained year by year on a balanced growth and cut basis since that time. The way this 42 billion board feet is used is shown by the bar graph in Figure 2. Sixteen billion board feet for residential construction, 6.1 billion board feet for non-residential construction, 5.6 billion board feet for remodeling and upkeep purposes, 4.7 billion for manufactured products of all kinds, 4.6 billion for shipping, and 5.4 billion for farm, railroad and various miscellaneous purposes.

At current use rates, the 16 billion board feet will produce about two million homes. We need more than two million new homes a year. There are three ways to get them: Grow more wood; use substitutes; or use less wood per house. Foresters can grow more wood per year and they will, maybe as much as fifty percent more over a period of 75 to 150 years. Wood substitutes will be used, but they will not be able to provide the sheer volume required, so we are faced with using less wood per structure of any kind, and using it more intelligently with greater effectiveness. This could mean smaller houses, an example of which are many of the mobile homes; or equal size houses constructed more efficiently. It is not difficult to appreciate that wood constitutes a huge building resource that cannot be ignored and will not be easily displaced by substitutes in the face of our growing needs. It requires skillful design to use it properly to meet these needs, not only here at home but all over the world. So traditional building methods must change, and we are seeing this already in the form of the factory-built house and the prefabricated building. However, the design of these factory-builts is still very traditional, not only outwardly, but in the basic frame of the structure. This consists of a framework of 2 x 4 studs, sills and plates; 2 x 6 and 2 x 8 rafters; and of 2 x 10 and 2 x 12 floor joists. Engineering methods,

NOMINAL
2"x6"
6"
12"
GRAIN
2"
1 1/2"
12"
5 1/2"
NOMINAL
1"x 12"
12"
12"
GRAIN
1"
3/4"
12"
11 1/4"

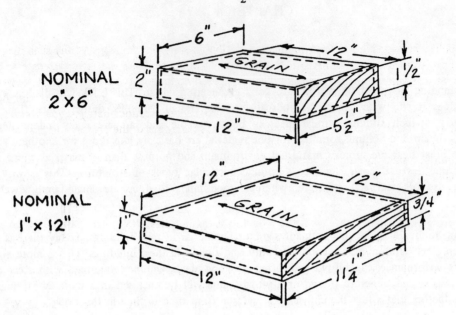

Figure 1. Examples of the board foot solid outlines are rough sawn and unseasoned. Broken outlines are dressed and seasoned.

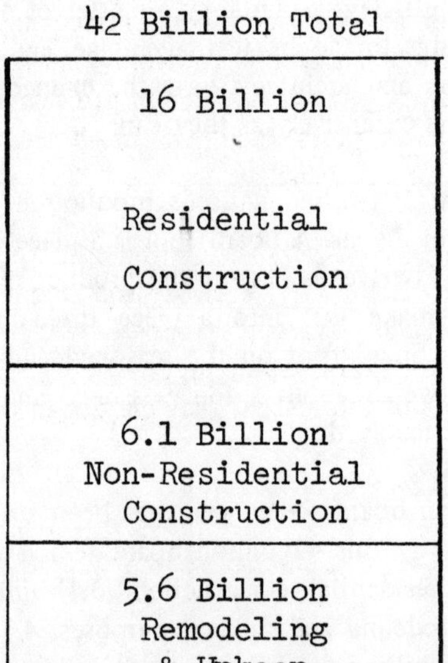

42 Billion Total
16 Billion
Residential Construction
6.1 Billion
Non-Residential Construction
5.6 Billion
Remodeling & Upkeep
4.7 Billion
Manufactured Products
4.6 Billion
Shipping
5.4 Billion
Farm, Railroad & Miscellaneous

Figure 2. Annual Consumption Softwood Lumber and Plywood.

when they are applied to wood houses are predicated on the assumption that none of the sheathing, flooring or gypsum wall covering contribute anything to the structural performance. Joist and rafter strength is calculated as though no covering was nailed to the framing. The reason this situation exists is that most engineers do not know of a better way to do the job. They don't know how rigid the connections between the sheathing and framing are, nor do they adequately understand the rigidity of the connections between the various members of a truss connected with metal plates or with plywood gussets, so they make the assumption that all of the joints are pin-connected and free to rotate under stress. Engineers could figure out how rigid these connections are, but generally the amount of time and money available for designing a wood structure does not permit that degree of refinement in engineering. As we change from building houses one by one on the job site, to building them on a production line in factories, the engineering required to make these refinements is going to become economical.

Studies made in the laboratory and also on full-size structures, show that there is a great deal of joint rigidity in wood structures. This causes real performance far above the calculated performance. This is an extremely challenging area for engineers to work in. It has been estimated that right now, today, we could reduce the amount of wood in structures by twenty to thirty percent by applying the technology we now have. A twenty to thirty percent saving per house would extend our wood supply for housing by twenty-five to forty-three percent. That will be a very worthwhile accomplishment when it has been achieved. We have reason to be optimistic about what engineers can do to meet some of our pressing needs for living space.

As civil engineers and architects, you may not expect to be engaged in housing construction. Many of you will, however, one way or another. As members of public building departments, some of you will make decisions about the application of building codes to housing. Opportunities for employment as building designers and builders of volume produced housing are on the increase. If you should find yourselves in the area of non-residential construction, the portion of the wood consuming market that utilizes the 6.1 billion board feet of lumber each year, you are going to need to apply this technology to get performance and economy for your clients and employers. You may be designing heavy construction projects using laminated timber, heavy decking, concrete formwork, and preservatively treated poles or pilings. In all these types of work, a good knowledge of timber technology will make you a more effective engineer.

One of the principal problems associated with the introduction of change in the building industry arises from the fact that many of the engineers in the code agencies and in the building departments of cities do not understand wood sufficiently well to evaluate the new proposals with confidence. If you find yourself in a position of this kind, perhaps some of the information in this book will be useful to you. I hope, by these remarks, I have been able to indicate some of the reasons that the design of timber structures can be a rewarding capability.

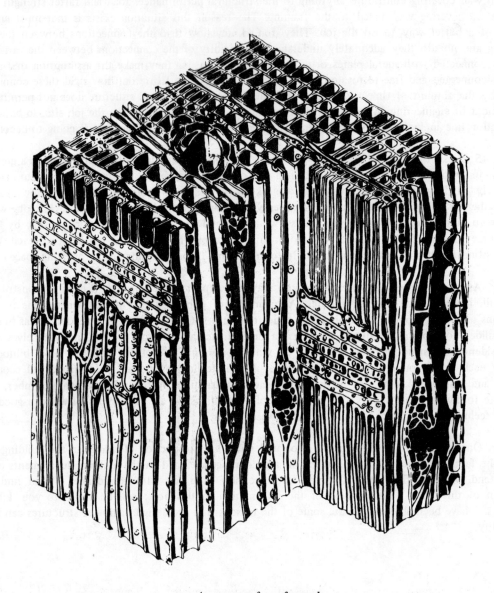

Anatomy of a softwood

Photo courtesy U.S. Forest Products Laboratory, Forest Service, U.S.D.A.

CHAPTER 2

PHYSICAL CHARACTER OF WOOD

Wood, being a biological material, is immensely varied in its structure. This variation is a matter of degree and there is a pervading and fundamental pattern to the structure of wood. This structure can be inspected with a relatively low-power hand lens. Figure 3 shows a cube of wood with the grain pattern on the three principal faces. The curved lines on the top face represent portions or arcs of the concentric annual rings of growth. These are readily visible to the naked eye and can also be seen in the frontispiece of this book. The top face of the cube is a transverse section, or cross-section. The other two faces show approximately parallel lines representing the side-grain of wood. The left face is in a plane which is tangent to the annual rings and is called a tangential-section. The right hand face is in a plane which closely coincides with the radius of the tree and is called a radial-section. The three axes of this cube, the T or tangential axis, the R or radial axis, and the L or longitudinal axis are sometimes used to denote the directional characteristics of wood properties.

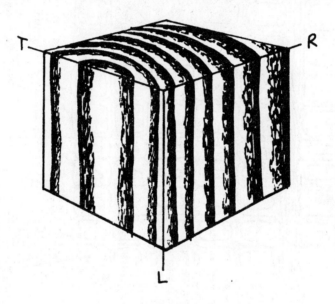

Figure 3. Anisotropic axes of wood

The enlarged transverse and tangential sections depicted in Figure 4 are typical of softwoods such as pine, spruce, larch, fir, hemlock, cedar, redwood and a few other commonly used coniferous species. These sections, drawn to a scale of fifty to one hundred times their actual size, show important features which help to explain the way wood behaves structurally. In the transverse section the radial direction is vertical and the tangential direction is horizontal. The top of the sketch is toward the outside of the tree, toward the bark. The bottom of this cross-section is toward the center or pith of the tree. Here you will see some cells of large size and thin wall thickness. These are called springwood or earlywood cells since they form early in the year when the tree is growing rapidly. Above these, in the sketch, the cells become flatter and smaller, somewhat thicker-walled, but of about the same width. These are summerwood or latewood cells and their walls become quite heavy at the end of the growing season. Above this we observe the beginning of another growing season, large, thin-walled cells characteristically followed by flatter cells with thicker walls as the outside of the annual ring is approached.

The large and oval-shaped structure with the distorted cells around it is a resin canal. As a conduit for resin it has a different function in the life process of the tree than the other cells which have a structural purpose and conduct liquids or store food. The resin canal is a particular feature of the pines, spruces and larch

6

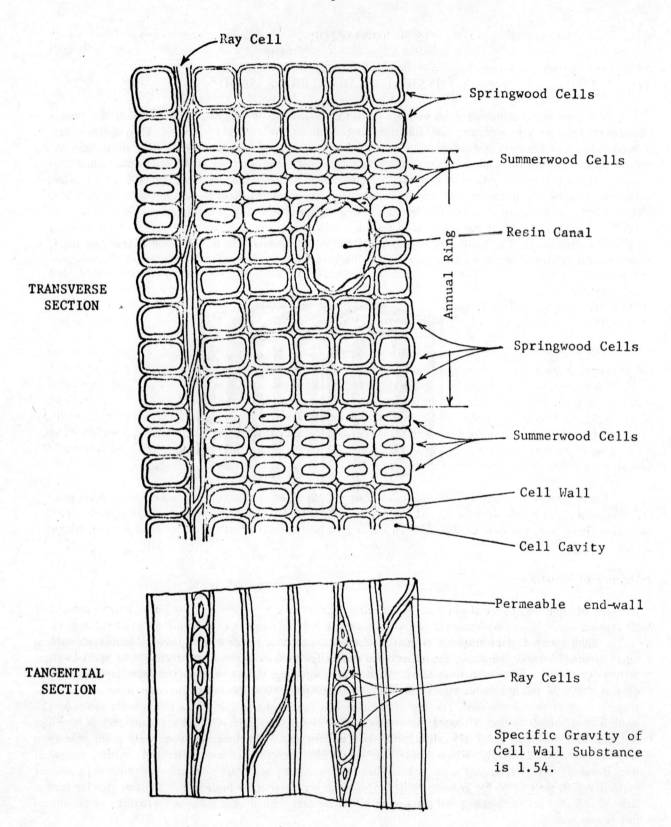

Ray Cell

Springwood Cells

Summerwood Cells

Resin Canal

Annual Ring

TRANSVERSE
SECTION

Springwood Cells

Summerwood Cells

Cell Wall

Cell Cavity

Permeable end-wall

TANGENTIAL
SECTION

Ray Cells

Specific Gravity of
Cell Wall Substance
is 1.54.

Figure 4.   Wood Anatomy

and is often visible and useful in identifying the species of wood. The true firs hemlocks, cedars and redwood do not have resin canals. Douglas fir, an important structural wood and not a true fir, has resin canals. Hardwoods are of more complex structure than softwoods, not so uniformly arranged and with a greater variety of cell types.

You probably appreciate the structural efficiency of round or rectangular tubes. The tube-like cells in wood account for its high strength to weight ratio. These tubes are really chains of cells whose end-walls contain perforations or valve-like openings that permit the passage of liquids, and are believed to have a function that enables the pumping system of the tree to lift water more than 34 feet that atmospheric pressure alone is ordinarily able to accomplish. Surface tension and capillary action, or course, also play important roles in lifting fluids form the soil to the leaves. The structure and physiology of wood and trees are explained in fascinating detail by William M. Harlow in his book, "Inside Wood—Masterpiece of Nature."

The specific gravity of the substance comprising the cell walls is 1.54. This is an important fact to remember. Any cell wall, be it a thick one or a thin one, is composed of a complex cellulose-lignin compound with a specific gravity of 1.54. This is a density of 96 pounds per cubic foot, and is heavier than water. Most wood is lighter than water and will float. The actual density of wood depends on the relative amounts of solid cell wall substance and cell cavity space present. Examined in cross-section, dense woods have a large relative area of cell wall while light woods have relatively small cell wall area.

The mechanical properties of this cell wall substance are fairly uniform. Its elastic modulus and tensile and compressive strengths are reasonably uniform. The strength, like the density, of a particular piece or species of wood is related to its anatomy. If you could measure the dimensions of all the cells and cell walls in a wood section, you could estimate its strength in tension and compression on the basis of the actual cross-sectional area of the walls, its bending strength on the basis of the section modulus[1] and its stiffness on the basis of the moment of inertia of the grid-like cross-section of the solid wall substance. Species with thick cell walls or large proportions of summerwood would be dense and strong. Those with thin-walled cells and/or small proportions of summerwood would be light and of lower strength.

Other growth features of wood also affect strength. Knots, knot-holes, sloping and distorted grain, splits and checks, all have influences that depend on the size of the lumber in which they are found as well as their own size. They are not minute anatomical features, and we will consider their effects in the chapter on lumber grades.

Influence of Moisture

In addition to the actual structure of the cell system, wood's properties are affected by its environment. Most materials are affected by temperature-moisture. Wood is quite sensitive to moisture either as vapor in the air or as liquid water. In fact, moisture is perhaps the most important environmental factor that affects wood. Keep in mind that wood is a highly hygroscopic material. Dry wood placed in a very humid space will take on moisture. Wet wood will give up some of its moisture to a drier atmosphere. You should know how moisture content is measured and expressed, and how it is related to wood's design properties.

The moisture content of wood is the weight of water in the wood, expressed as a percentage of the completely dry weight of the wood. If a piece of completely dry wood is placed in a humid room until its weight increases ten percent, it is said to have attained a moisture content of ten percent. Simple stated:

$$\frac{\text{The weight of moist wood} - \text{The weight of dry wood}}{\text{The weight of dry wood}} \times 100 = \text{Percent M.C.}$$

---

[1] For readers who are not familiar with section properties of rectangular cross-sections of width, "b," by depth, "h,": Section Modulus is $bh^2/6$ and Moment of Inertia is $bh^3/12$.

The moisture content of wood in a living tree is in the order of 30 to 90 percent in the heartwood portion, and may be as high as 200 percent in the sapwood portion.

Heartwood is the older wood in the central portion of a tree, which has ceased participating actively in the physiology of the tree life. Sapwood is the newer wood, which occurs in the form of a band immediately within the bark and extending inward for a few to many annual rings of growth. The size of the sapwood portion varies greatly with the species. Southern pine trees have very extensive sapwood, comprising most of the stem in trees up to 10 or 12 inches in diameter. Douglas fir, on the otherhand, exhibits sapwood in only the outer inch or two of the radius. In the living tree, the sapwood specializes in physiological functions of growth, and the heartwood functions structurally. Fortunately, the structural properties of wood cut from living trees and dried or seasoned, are about the same, whether it is from the heartwood or the sapwood portion. Aside from the color effect of the heartwood, which is important for certain appearance uses of wood, no distinction is made between heart and sap portions in structural grading. Heart and sap portions have different permeabilities and susceptibilities to treatment and to decay, sapwood being generally more permeable.

The moisture content of wood in the exterior walls of a building is likely to be around ten or twelve percent. Wood furniture, or wood trim, in a heated building in most parts of the United States is likely to be six or seven percent. (Table 1 and Figure 5) The wood in a ship or a marine piling, exposed directly to liquid water, may be 100 percent moisture contant or more. For an explanation of these differences it is helpful to know how water occurs in wood.

Water in wood is found in the cell cavity and also in the cell wall itself. The water in the cavities is called *free* water. It is held in the cavities primarily by capillary forces and can be extracted rather easily in a warm and dry atmosphere which sets up a vapor pressure differential and produces a migration of vapor molecules. The water in the cell walls is called *bound* water and is held in the walls by forces at the molecular level. In the cell wall, water molecules attach themselves to sites in the cellulose chain molecule. It takes considerably more energy to detach these water molecules from the cellulose chain than it does to evaporate and drive off the free water in the cell cavities. Because of this difference, the free water in the cell cavities is driven off first when wood is seasoned, and the bound water is driven off last. (See Figure 6)

When both free water and bound water are present, the wood is regarded as green or unseasoned. If free water is removed leaving only the bound water, the wood is said to be at its *fiber saturation point* (F.S.P.). The fiber saturation point is the moisture content of wood with fully saturated cell walls but empty cell cavities. This is generally at a moisture content of 30 percent, but it can vary somewhat with the species in the range of 20 to 30 percent. The fiber saturation point is important because shrinkage, swelling and strength-changes due to moisture occur in the range of fiber saturation to completely dry.

Recalling the anatomy of wood, there is obviously more room for water in the cell cavities than in the cell walls. The specific gravity of wood is in the order of 0.3 to 0.6, again dependent upon species, with a within-species variation of about 20 percent of the mean specific gravity. The specific gravity of cell wall substance is 1.54. It is evident then that 1.54 material must enclose substantial air volume to form a 0.3 specific gravity material. Actually, 80 percent of the volume would be cell cavities, in this instance. Since the cell cavities can be completely occupied by water, but the cell walls can only take on a small volume of water, most of the water in completely saturated wood must be free water. As a matter of fact, the ratio of free water to bound water in wood is in the order of five-to-one or more. This explains where the moisture is in wood. What determines the amount of water a piece of wood will retain?

The moisture content of wood is the result of an equilibrium condition between the forces that hold water in the wood, and the vapor pressure of the surrounding environment. A completely dry piece of wood can only remain dry if kept in a space completely free of water vapor. At 20 percent relative humidity and 70 degrees Fahrenheit, which is a dry environment by ordinary standards, wood comes into equilibrium at about 4 percent moisture content. At 50 percent relative humidity and 70 degrees Fahrenheit, the *equilibrium moisture content* (EMC) is about 9 percent. At 75 percent relative humidity and 70 degrees, it is about 14 percent, and at 100 percent relative humidity the equilibrium moisture content approaches fiber saturation, perhaps 25 percent.

Table 1. Recommended Moisture Content Values for Various Wood Items at the Time of Installation.

Use of Lumber	Moisture content (percentage of weight of ovendry wood) for --					
	Dry southwestern States[1]		Damp southern Coastal States[1]		Remainder of the United States[1]	
	Average[2]	Individual pieces	Average[2]	Individual pieces	Average[2]	Individual pieces
	Percent	Percent	Percent	Percent	Percent	Percent
Interior finish woodwork and softwood flooring	6	4-9	11	8-13	8	5-10
Hardwood flooring	6	5-8	10	9-12	7	6-9
Siding, exterior trim, sheathing, and framing[3]	9	7-12	12	9-14	12	9-14

[1] For limiting range, see Figure 4

[2] In general, the moisture content averages have less significance than the range in moisture content permitted in individual pieces. If the moisture content values of all the pieces in a lot fall within the prescribed range, the entire lot will be satisfactory as to moisture content, no matter what its average moisture content may be.

[3] Framing lumber of higher moisture content is commonly used in ordinary construction because material of the moisture content specified may not be available except on special order.

U.S. FOREST PRODUCTS LABORATORY REPORT 1655

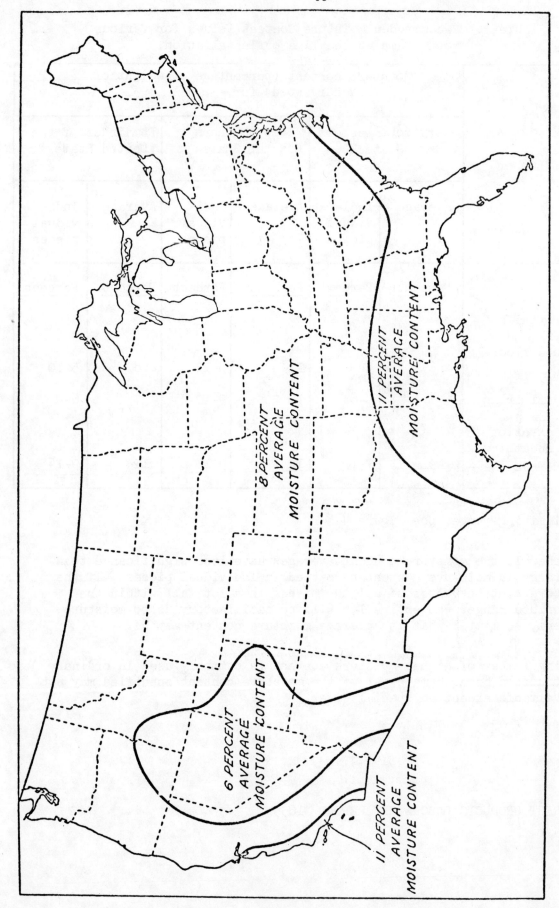

Figure 5. Recommended moisture content averages for interior-finishing woodwork for use in various parts of the United States.

Courtesy of U. S. Forest Products Laboratory

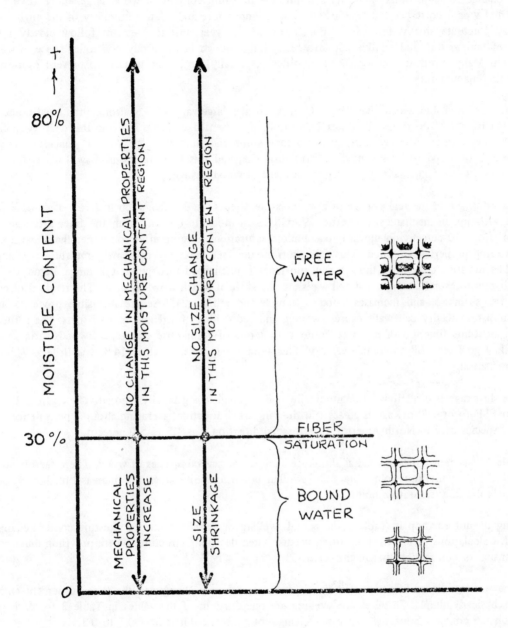

Figure 6. Diagram Indicating Moisture Content Ranges
Where Size and Strength Changes Occur.

Since there is always a time lag between the attainment of a particular relative humidity and the establishment of equilibrium, wood rarely comes to its EMC before the atmospheric relative humidity and temperature change to some other value. As a result, the moisture content of wood is generally at or near the equilibrium that would correspond to the average daily temperature and relative humidity of the environment it is in. It may fluctuate slowly throughout the course of the year, but it does not follow closely the daily fluctuations of temperature and relative humidity. Left long enough in uniformly controlled space, it will come to equilibrium. Many furniture factories are humidified, especially during the winter, to prevent over-drying of the wood during manufacture.

Charts are available which give the EMC of wood at a large variety of environmental conditions. Such a chart, provided by the U. S. Forest Products Laboratory is presented as Table 2. From this chart, you can pick out the EMC associated with any atmospheric temperature and humidity. We will be concerned about the moisture content of wood to be specified for structural use, and this EMC relationship will be useful for that purpose. So now we see what makes the moisture content of wood change.

This brings us to the real essence of how moisture affects the designer's job in terms of wood shrinkage, swelling and variation in mechanical properties. Variations in moisture content from the fiber saturation point, that is, from about 30 percent on upward to complete saturation, have no effect on either the dimensional size or the engineering properties of wood. This follows from the fact that only cell cavity moisture is changing in this range. The moisture content of the cell wall substance is unchanged throughout this range. Below the FSP, it is cell wall moisture that changes, and cell walls are the stuff of which wood is made. The removal of cell wall moisture causes shrinkage and increases wood's strength and stiffness. These are reversible processes and the addition of moisture to dry cell walls causes swelling and reductions of strength and stiffness. The shrinkage of wood is a straight-line function of moisture content. In terms of volumetric change, softwoods shrink about 11 percent, as they go from FSP to completely dry. This amount can be as much as 14 and as little as 7, but 11 is a good generalization.

This shrinkage is directional. Longitudinally it is so small it is generally ignored. The figure is 0.1 to 0.3 percent from FSP to dry. Shrinkage is greatest in the tangential direction, averaging about 7 percent for most of the structural species used in North America. In the radial direction it is 4.5 to 5.0 percent.

Table 3 lists tangential and radial shrinkage factors for several species of wood. These factors are based on size at the fiber saturation point, the fully swollen condition. Size does not increase further if moisture content exceeds the fiber saturation point.

Using the information in Table 3 the actual swelling or shrinkage due to moisture content changes can be calculated. Calculations of this kind are often needed when designing structures where provision must be made for any expansion or contraction that might occur.

Since size is a linear function of moisture content and only changes in the 0 to 30 percent range, this calculation is basically simple. Shrinkage or swelling are one-thirtieth of the values in Table 3 for each percent change in moisture content. For longitudinal size change they are one-thirtieth of 0.1 to 0.2.

Shrinkage of Douglas fir from green to 12 percent moisture content in the tangential direction is:

$$7.8 \left(\frac{30-12}{30} \right) = 4.68\% \text{ of the green size}$$

In the radial direction the shrinkage is:

$$5.0 \left(\frac{30-12}{30} \right) = 3.0\% \text{ of the green size}$$

Wet bulb depression (°F.)

Temperature dry-bulb (°F.)	1	2	3	4	5	6	7	8	9	10	11	12	13	14	15	16	17	18	19	20	21	22	23	24	25	26	27	28	29	30	32	34	36	38	40	45	50
30	89	78 *16.9*	67 *12.9*	57	46 *9.0*	36	27	17	6																												
35	90	81 *16.8*	72 *13.9*	63 *11.9*	54	45	37	28	19 *4.6*	11	3																										
40	92	83 *17.6*	75 *13.9*	68	60 *10.3*	52	45	37	29 *5.0*	22	15	8	1																								
45	93	85 *18.5*	78 *14.8*	72	64 *11.2*	58	51	44	37 *6.2*	31	25	19 *1.9*	12 *2.9*	6																							
50	93	86 *18.3*	80 *15.6*	74	68 *12.0*	62	56	50	44 *7.5*	38	32	27 *4.2*	21 *2.9*	16 *3.9*	10	5																					
55	94	88 *19.0*	82 *16.3*	78	73 *12.7*	68	63	54	49 *8.5*	48	43	38 *5.7*	34 *4.8*	24 *3.9*	19	14 *1.5*	9	5																			
60	94	89 *19.5*	83 *16.5*	80	75 *13.4*	71	66	60	53 *9.3*	53	48	43 *6.0*	39 *4.8*	30 *5.3*	26	21 *3.6*	17	13	9	5																	
65	94	89 *19.9*	84 *17.1*	81	77 *13.9*	72	68	63	56 *9.9*	56	51	48 *6.5*	44 *5.3*	36 *6.3*	32	27 *4.9*	24 *2.5*	20	16	13 *1.7*	9	6	2														
70	95	90 *20.3*	86 *17.8*	82	78 *14.4*	74	70	64	59 *10.4*	59	54	51 *7.0*	47 *5.7*	40 *7.1*	37	33 *5.6*	29 *3.6*	25	22	19 *2.3*	15	11 *1.4*	8 *0.4*														
75	95	90 *20.6*	87 *18.2*	86	79 *14.9*	72	73	66	62 *11.0*	62	57	54 *7.4*	50 *6.0*	44 *7.7*	41	37 *6.0*	34 *4.3*	31	28	24 *3.0*	21	18 *2.3*	15 *2.0*	12	10	7											
80	95	91 *20.9*	87 *18.5*	86	80 *15.2*	74	74	70	64 *11.5*	66	61	57 *9.7*	53 *6.5*	50 *8.6*	44	41 *6.9*	38 *4.9*	35	32	29 *3.7*	26	23 *2.9*	20 *4.5*	18	15	12 *1.7*	10	7	5	3							
85	96	91 *21.0*	88 *18.7*	87	81 *15.7*	75	76	71	66 *11.8*	63	59	55 *9.8*	57 *6.9*	53 *9.0*	47	44 *7.6*	41 *5.7*	38	35	33 *4.5*	30	28 *3.6*	25 *4.6*	23	20	18 *2.4*	15	13	11 *0.3*	9	4						
90	96	92 *21.2*	89 *18.9*	85	82 *15.9*	78	72	72	69 *12.5*	66	61	57 *10.0*	59 *9.5*	55 *9.3*	49	47 *8.0*	44 *6.3*	41	39	36 *5.0*	34	31 *4.0*	29 *5.6*	26	24	22 *2.6*	19	17	14 *1.7*	13	5 *1.3*	1 *0.4*					
95	96	92 *21.3*	89 *19.0*	85	83 *16.1*	79	75	72	69 *12.8*	69	65	62 *10.5*	60 *9.6*	56 *9.5*	52	49 *8.2*	46 *6.7*	44	42	39 *5.4*	36	34 *4.6*	32 *6.1*	30	28	24 *2.9*	23	20	17 *2.4*	14	10 *2.3*	5 *1.0*					
100	96	93 *21.3*	90 *19.0*	89	83 *16.3*	80	77	73	71 *12.9*	69	66	63 *10.6*	62 *9.7*	58 *9.8*	54	51 *8.4*	49 *7.0*	47	44	41 *5.8*	39	37 *5.1*	34 *6.2*	32	30	28 *3.6*	26	24 *4.8*	22 *3.3*	20	14 *2.6*	10 *1.6*	5 *0.7*	2			
105	96	93 *21.4*	91 *19.0*	90	83 *16.5*	81	77	74	73 *13.5*	70	67	63 *11.0*	63 *10.1*	60 *9.9*	56	53 *8.6*	50 *7.3*	48	46	44 *6.0*	42	40 *5.4*	37 *6.4*	36	34	31 *4.1*	29	26 *4.8*	24 *3.7*	23	17 *2.9*	13 *1.9*	10 *1.3*	6 *0.4*	4		
110	97	93 *21.4*	91 *19.1*	90	84 *16.6*	82	79	75	74 *14.0*	71	68	65 *11.1*	65 *10.4*	61 *10.0*	58	54 *8.8*	52 *7.6*	50	48	46 *6.4*	44	42 *5.7*	40 *6.7*	38	36	34 *4.5*	32	29 *5.2*	28 *4.0*	26	20 *3.2*	17 *2.3*	14 *1.7*	11 *0.7*	7		
115	97	94 *21.4*	91 *19.0*	91	85 *16.8*	82	80	77	75 *14.1*	72	69	67 *11.5*	65 *10.7*	62 *10.4*	60	58 *9.0*	54 *8.0*	52	51	47 *6.8*	45	45 *6.5*	43 *7.2*	40	38	36 *4.8*	34	32 *5.4*	31 *4.6*	29	23 *3.4*	20 *2.9*	17 *2.1*	14 *1.4*	11		
120	97	94 *21.4*	91 *19.0*	88	85 *16.8*	82	80	78	76 *14.5*	73	70	68 *11.5*	66 *10.8*	63 *10.6*	61	58 *9.3*	55 *8.4*	53	51	49 *7.0*	47	45 *6.6*	44 *7.3*	41	40	38 *5.2*	36	34 *5.8*	32 *4.8*	31	25 *3.7*	22 *3.0*	20 *2.5*	17 *1.8*	14		
125	97	94 *21.3*	91 *19.0*	91	86 *16.9*	82	80	77	77 *15.0*	74	72	69 *11.5*	67 *11.0*	64 *10.6*	63	59 *9.4*	57 *9.0*	55	53	51 *7.3*	48	47 *6.9*	45 *7.4*	43	42	40 *5.5*	38	36 *6.0*	34 *5.1*	33	27 *4.0*	25 *3.4*	22 *2.9*	19 *2.1*	17		
130	97	94 *21.2*	91 *18.9*	91	86 *16.9*	83	81	78	76 *15.4*	75	73	70 *11.8*	68 *11.0*	66 *10.6*	64	60 *9.7*	58 *9.0*	56	54	52 *7.5*	50	48 *7.0*	47 *7.5*	45	44	42 *5.9*	40	38 *6.0*	37 *5.6*	35	29 *4.2*	27 *3.6*	24 *3.1*	21 *2.4*	19		
140	97	95 *21.0*	91 *18.8*	89	87 *16.9*	84	82	79	78 *15.4*	77	74	71 *11.9*	70 *11.3*	67 *10.8*	66	62 *9.8*	60 *9.6*	58	56	54 *7.7*	53	51 *7.3*	49 *7.7*	47	46	44 *6.1*	43	41 *6.2*	40 *6.0*	38	32 *4.5*	30 *3.9*	27 *3.4*	24 *2.7*	22		
150	98	95 *20.7*	93 *18.6*	89	87 *16.8*	84	84	80	79 *15.4*	77	75	72 *12.0*	72 *11.5*	68 *11.0*	67	64 *10.0*	60 *9.7*	60	58	56 *7.8*	54	53 *7.5*	51 *7.8*	49	48	46 *6.3*	45	43 *6.3*	42 *6.1*	41	35 *5.1*	33 *4.4*	30 *3.8*	27 *3.1*	25 *2.5*	19	14
160	98	95 *20.2*	94 *18.4*	92	90 *15.8*	88	85	83	81 *13.6*	80	78	76 *12.7*	74 *12.7*	72 *10.9*	69	65 *10.1*	63 *8.9*	62	60	60 *7.9*	59	57 *7.7*	55 *8.0*	53	52	50 *6.7*	49	48 *6.5*	45 *6.3*	45	38 *5.4*	36 *4.6*	35 *4.3*	33 *3.5*	31 *3.1*	24	21
170	98	95 *19.8*	93 *18.1*	91	89 *15.8*	88	86	82	82 *12.7*	80	79	77 *12.5*	75 *11.9*	74 *9.7*	72	67 *9.6*	65 *8.6*	63	62	60 *7.8*	58	57 *7.6*	55 *7.6*	53	52	49 *6.4*	48	46 *6.4*	44 *6.2*	43	40 *5.2*	38 *5.2*	38 *4.9*	35 *4.6*	33 *4.4*	26	24
180	98	96 *19.8*	94 *17.5*	91	89 *14.5*	87	85	81	83 *12.1*	79	77	75 *11.0*	73 *10.4*	72 *9.4*	70	68 *8.8*	67 *8.4*	65	63	62 *7.7*	60	58 *7.0*	57 *7.0*	55	54	52 *6.2*	51	50 *5.9*	48 *5.8*	47	42 *5.1*	44 *5.2*	42 *4.6*	40 *4.6*	38 *4.5*	30	26
190	98	96 *19.7*	94 *16.9*	92	90 *14.2*	88	85	84	84 *12.0*	80	78	76 *10.9*	75 *10.5*	73 *9.2*	71	69 *8.6*	68 *8.1*	66	65	63 *7.4*	62	60 *6.8*	58 *6.8*	57	55	54 *6.2*	53	51 *5.9*	49 *5.6*	49	44 *5.3*	44 *5.3*	42 *4.5*	41 *4.5*	39 *4.3*	32	28
200	98	96 *18.1*	94 *16.4*	92	90 *13.8*	88	86	84	82 *11.8*	80	79	77 *10.3*	76 *9.6*	74 *9.1*	72	70 *8.4*	67 *8.1*	67	66	64 *7.2*	63	61 *6.6*	60 *6.5*	58	57	55 *6.0*	54	53 *5.7*	52 *5.6*	51	46 *5.3*	46 *4.8*	45 *4.3*	43 *4.3*	41 *4.4*	34	30
210	98	96 *17.7*	94 *16.0*	92	90 *13.0*	87	86	83	82 *11.1*	81	79	78 *10.8*	76 *9.9*	73 *9.0*	73	71 *8.3*	70 *8.0*	68	67	65 *7.1*	64	63 *6.9*	61 *6.5*	60	59	57 *5.9*	56	54 *5.5*	53 *5.4*	52	50 *5.7*	47 *5.1*	45 *4.6*	43 *4.6*	42 *4.2*	36	32

[1] Relative-humidity values in roman type.
[2] Equilibrium-moisture-content values in italic type.

Table 2. Relative Humidity[1] and Equilibrium Moisture Content[2] Table for Use with Dry-Bulb Temperatures and Wet-Bulb Depressions.

From Wood Handbook, USDA Agriucltural Handbook #72, by the Forest Products Laboratory, 1955.
Courtesy U. S. Forest Products Laboratory

EMC

Table 3. Shrinkage Factors for Several Common Softwoods
and Hardwoods

The following data are taken from the Wood Handbook 1955 Edition, Table 39.
Many other species are included in that reference.

Species	Percent Shrinkage Fiber Saturation to Oven-dry % of size @ F.S.P.	
	Tangential	Radial
Douglas fir	7.8	5.0
Douglas fir south	6.2	3.6
True firs:		
Grand	7.5	3.4
White	7.1	3.2
Balsam & Subalpine	7.4	2.9
California red	7.2	4.0
Noble	8.2	4.5
Pacific silver (and commercial Hem-fir)	9.8	4.6
Western hemlock	7.9	4.3
Western larch	8.1	4.2
Western red cedar	5.0	2.4
Pines:		
Eastern white	6.0	2.3
Idaho (western) white	7.4	4.1
Ponderosa	6.3	3.9
Lodgepole	6.7	4.5
Sugar	5.6	2.9
Southern	7.8	5.5
Engelmann spruce	6.6	3.4
Redwood	4.9	2.2
Oak:		
Red (many varieties)	10.0	5.0
White	9.0	5.3
Hard maple	9.5	4.9
Yellow birch	9.2	7.2
Cherry	7.1	3.7
Walnut	7.8	5.5
Beech	11.0	5.1
Mahogany (true)	5.0	3.6
Luaun, red	8.0	3.3

When lumber is manufactured randomly with respect to the T and R directions, as is commonly the case, the shrinkage can be estimated as:

$$\left(\frac{7.8+5.0}{2}\right)\left(\frac{30-12}{30}\right) = 3.84\% \text{ of the green size}$$

In the longitudinal direction, the maximum shrinkage from green to 12 percent will be:

$$0.2\left(\frac{30-12}{30}\right) = 0.12\% \text{ of the green size}$$

Shrinkage of Hem-fir from 15 percent to 10 percent moisture content presents a slightly more complex calculation, because the shrinkage must be obtained in terms of the size at 15 percent rather than at the fiber saturation point. The obvious method is to compute size at each of these moisture contents and express the shrinkage as the difference in percent of the size at 15 percent. As an example consider the tangential shrinkage.

Shrinkage from FSP to 15% is: $9.8\left(\frac{30-15}{30}\right) = 4.9\%$ of the size green

Shrinkage from FSP to 10% is: $9.8\left(\frac{30-10}{30}\right) = 6.53\%$ of the size green

Shrinkage from 15% to 10% is: 6.53 - 4.9 = 1.63% of the size green, or at the FSP. To obtain shrinkage as a percent of the size at the 15 percent moisture level of a further calculation is required:

$$\frac{1.63 \times \text{Size at FSP}}{\text{Size at 15\%}} = \frac{1.63 \times 1.0}{1.0-0.049} = \frac{1.63}{0.951} = 1.72\% \text{ of size at 15\%MC}$$

This illustrates the procedural steps. A simplified formula for obtaining the shrinkage or swelling on the basis of some initial moisture content other than 30 percent is:

$$\text{Shrinkage in percent of size at } M_i = \frac{100S(M_i-M_f)}{30 + S(M_i-30)}$$

where: S = Shrinkage factor/100
M_i = Initial moisture content in percent
M_f = Final moisture content in percent

Using this formula the tangential shinkage from 15 to 10 percent would be:

$$\frac{100 (0.098) (15-10)}{30 + 0.098(15-30)} = 1.72\%$$

By using S equal to 0.046 for the radial direction, S equal to 0.072 for the random direction, and S equal to 0.002 for the longitudinal direction, other appropriate shrinkage values may be calculated.

Swelling is the reverse of shrinkage. If, in the above Hem-fir example, the swelling of an initially 15 percent moisture content piece for a 5 percent increase in moisture content is wanted, the calculation for the tangential direction would be:

$$\frac{100\ (0.098)\ (15-20)}{30 + 0.098(15-30)} = -1.72\%$$

The negative sign denotes negative shrinkage, or swelling.

Plywood, because of its cross-laminated construction, does not show as much size change due to moisture fluctuations as does lumber in the directions perpendicular to the grain. Softwood plywood, in the direction perpendicular to the grain direction of the face plies, has a shrinkage factor of 0.67 percent from FSP to the oven-dry condition. In the parallel to face grain direction however, the factor is 0.45 percent, on the average. With reference to thickness, the shrinkage factor is the same as that for lumber in the radial direction given in Table 3.

If wood had the same shrinkage coefficients in both the radial and tangential directions, our problems of warping and distortion would largely vanish. It is because tangential shrinkage exceeds radial shrinkage that wood which is squared by the saw when it is green becomes distorted when it is dried. Figure 7 illustrates some characteristic distortions. The best way to avoid these distortions is to use wood that is planed square or rectangular after it has been seasoned to within a few percent of the moisture content it will have in service. Builders who do not specify and insist upon properly seasoned wood may expect some warping problems to develop.

The strength properties are improved by drying. The amount of this improvement depends upon the species and the particular properties. For the softwoods we generally use, the bending strength of completely dry wood exceeds that of wood at FSP by about 150 percent. The longitudinal compression strength of dry wood exceeds green wood by about 200 percent. For shear the excess is 100 percent; and for elastic modulus, about 50 percent. Be sure to note that these are all large improvements.

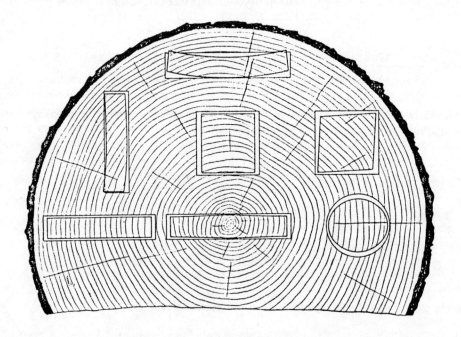

Figure 7. Characteristic shrinkage and distortion of flats, squares, and rounds as affected by the direction of the annual rings. Tangential shrinkage is about twice as great as radial.

In normal exterior service the E.M.C. of wood is 10 to 15 percent. This about half-way between fiber saturation and dry conditions. The strength improvements are roughly half of the above values given for dry wood. ASTM Standard D2555 has a table of these factors for most North American species. The manufacturers of plywood and lumber publish tables of design information for wood which take into account the specifications for manufacturing and the ordinary conditions for use. When you see different strengths recommended for the same grade of lumber, you will probably discover that the manufacutring specification for the stronger lumber requires a higher degree of seasoning at the mill.

Thermal Expansion

The effect of temperature on the length of a piece of lumber is very small. For Douglas fir the longitudinal expansion is 1.8×10^{-6} inches per inch, per degree Fahrenheit temperature change. This is a good factor for estimating structural softwood length change due to temperature. For some hardwood species the expansion coefficient may be as high as 2.5×10^{-6}, longitudinally.

In the tangential direction, specific gravity has an effect. For structural softwoods the tangential coefficient of linear expansion is $45 \times 10^{-6} \times$ specific gravity. Radially the value is $31 \times 10^{-6} \times$ sp. gr. The denser structural softwoods have specific gravities of 0.5 to 0.6, so the tangential and radial thermal coefficients are about 23.8×10^{-6} and 17×10^{-6}.

More detailed information on a wider variety of species may be found in "Textbook of Wood Technology" Volume II, by Brown, Panshin, and Forsaith.

The thermal expansion of steel (7×10^{-6}) and aluminum (13×10^{-6}) exceed that of wood longitudinally by four to seven times. In structural design, thermal expansion coefficients of wood are usually only of interest when the structure will be quite dry but subject to large temperature changes, because wood dimensional change due to moisture usually exceeds that due to temperature.

Thermal Conductivity

As an insulator, wood is superior to most of the common structural materials. This insulating effect should not be overlooked in design, as it contributes to the operating economy of buildings. Heat transfer losses depend on surface areas, and the direction of heat transfer is usually across the grain rather than along it. The conductances of seasoned Douglas fir and southern pine are about 0.875 BTU per hour per sq. ft. per degree Fahrenheit for a one-inch thickness at 12 percent moisture content. For lower density species it may be as low as 0.70, and for exceptionally light species such as balsa wood the conductance at 12 percent moisture content is 0.34, comparable with most insulating materials used in construction.

A formula for conductance across the grain is:

$$k = S(1.39 + 0.028M) + 0.165$$

k = conductance, BTU/hr., sq. ft., degree F., inch thick
s = specific gravity
M = percent moisture content

In a direction parallel to the grain, thermal conductivity is about 2.5 times as great as across the grain.

Because thermal conductivity is so low for wood, expansion resulting from temperature change occurs very slowly. For structural beams exposed to winter weather at their ends, for instance, the total thermal contraction is much less than that for an uninsulated metal structural member. When fire raises the temperature, unprotected steel responds very much faster, in terms of expansion and strength loss, than does wood.

The thermal conductances of steel and aluminum are 310 and 1400 BTU per hour per sq. ft., per degree F. per inch thickness, hundreds of times greater than wood. The "Wood Handbook" published by the Superintendent of Documents, Washington, D.C. contains a very useful chapter on the thermal characteristics of wood products under the heading, "Thermal Insulation."

Electrical Properties

The electrical properties of wood are important for several reasons. As an electrical insulator, wood serves as tool handles and as poles supporting electric power lines. Wood also is processed electrically and its moisture content is often monitored on the basis of its electrical resistance.

The specific resistance of oven-dry wood is very high (3 x 10^{17} to 3 x 10^{18} ohm-cm. for a one centimeter cube). At 16 percent moisture content this resistance is 10^8 ohm-cm. Over the range of 7 to 25 percent moisture content the electrical resistance of wood varies by a factor of 100,000. At low moisture content wood is a good electrical insulator, but its resistance is comparable to water, when the wood is wet.

The dielectric constant of wood varies from about 4.2 when it is oven-dry to that of water, 81, when it is wet or green. At moisture contents below 12 percent wood has a low dielectric constant. Layers of wood coated with wet glue and placed in a dielectric field absorb energy principally in the glue, effecting a cure. This is an industrial process used in the manufacture of glued laminated wooden beams, furniture, and hardwood plywood. Small pieces of green wood can be seasoned by placing them in a dielectric field. Pieces of structural size, however, have not been successfully seasoned in this way on a commercial scale. Electrical energy is absored into green wood faster than moisture can migrate from the minute cellular structure and internal pressures, which can not be relieved, develop rather quickly and explode the wood. Dielectric heating is effective in the latter stages of drying, for levelling out the moisture among pieces, and for other specialized applications. Microwave energy has also been used successfully in this way, but not commercially.

CHAPTER 3

MECHANICAL PROPERTIES OF WOOD

Material Variability

Designers assume substantial responsibility for safety and performance of structures. It is really not sufficient that they simply go "by the book" in choosing design stresses. Handbooks are great conveniences and their use is not to be criticized, provided the user understands the basis for the "numbers" in the handbook tables. Knowing that, he may proceed with the use of recommended design properties when their basis fits his purpose, or he may alter those values when his judgment tells him he has a situation where that basis is not realistic. This is true both in the application of design properties, and the acceptance of the design load criteria found in handbooks. We are no longer satisfied to simply direct the student to the "recommended practices," but feel he needs further background so he can make the kind of judgments and decisions on which a design will be founded. That sort of judgment is fully as important a contribution to a design as skillful stress analysis and refined mathematical technique.

Discrepancies between a design and its performance may arise out of a poor understanding of the variability of the material. While a comprehensive treatment of the statistical mathematics used in handling variability is beyond the scope of this text, its application to the development of allowable properties for design will illustrate the utility of the methods.

Wood, like all other materials, displays a characteristic variability. In its simplest form, one might consider the frequency distribution of ultimate bending strength values of 1000 clear straight grained pieces of a species of wood such as western larch.

Figure 8 is a histogram, with each vertical bar representing the number of pieces with an ultimate bending strength in the range which that bar spans on the horizontal axis. Thus, 40 pieces would break in the range 7450 to 7550 psi, 24 pieces each in the ranges 6450 to 6550 psi and 8450 to 8550 psi, 5 or six in the ranges 5450 to 5550 psi and 9450 to 9550 psi, with almost no chance of any in the ranges below 4500 or above 10,500 psi. This type of distribution is typical of wood, steel and concrete, although the values will differ from one material to another. This is a normal distribution of the kind obtained from a large random sampling of an infinitely large and unbiased population of material. The area under the curve (the sum of all the bars) represents the total sample of 1000 pieces, in this case.

Experience with these kinds of distributions tells us that if the difference between the mean value and either of the extremes is divided into three equal parts, the resulting quantity can be very useful in making predictions about the number of pieces that can be expected to exceed any particular bending strength. This value, one-third the range from mean to extreme, is called a *standard deviation*.

For example, 67 percent of the pieces will lie in the range of the mean plus or minus one standard deviation. Ninety-five percent will be in the range of the mean plus or minus two standard deviations; and 98 percent will be in the range of the mean plus or minus 2.33 standard deviations.

The means and standard deviations of each of the properties of the principal commercial woods in the United States and Canada, given in ASTM Standard D2555, serve as the basis for developing allowable design stresses. Table 4 lists a few of the species and their standard deviations, from this ASTM Standard.

Using this kind of information, strength levels can be selected for any desired probability of occurrence. As an example, 98 percent of clear wood samples of unseasoned western larch may be expected to have bending strengths in the range $7652 \pm 2.33 \times 1001$, or between 5320 and 9984 psi. Only one percent would fail below 5320 psi, while the other one percent would be stronger than 9984 psi. The bending strength value of the average minus 2.33 standard deviations (5320 for western larch) is often called the one percent exclusion value,

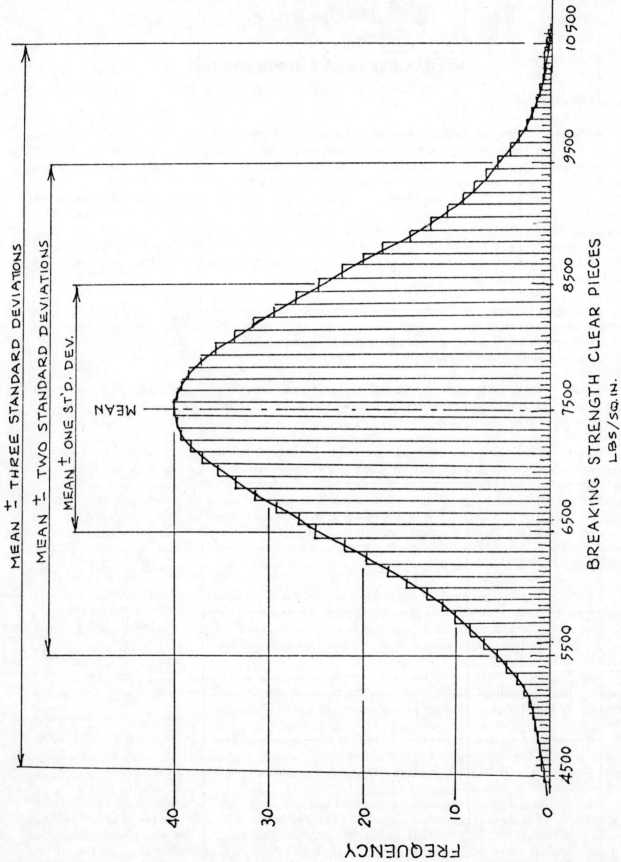

FIGURE 8. - A NORMALLY DISTRIBUTED POPULATION OF 1000 TESTS.

Table 4. Clear Wood Strength Values and Standard Deviations for Several Species of Wood (Unseasoned).

Species	Modulus of Rupture and Tension Parallel Avg. psi	Standard Deviation psi	Modulus of Elasticity Avg. 1000 psi	Standard Deviation 1000 psi	Compression Parallel to Grain Avg. psi	Standard Deviation psi	Shear Strength Avg. psi	Standard Deviation psi	Compression Perpendicular at Proportional Limit Avg. psi	Standard Deviation psi	Specific[1] Gravity Avg.	Standard Deviation
Douglas fir												
Coast	7665	1317	1560	315	3784	734	904	131	382	107	0.45	0.057
Interior West	7713	1322	1513	324	3872	799	936	137	418	117	0.46	0.058
Interior North	7438	1163	1409	274	3469	602	947	126	356	100	0.45	0.049
Interior South	6784	908	1162	200	3113	489	953	153	337	94	0.43	0.045
Southern pine												
Longleaf	8670	1387	1598	352	4300	774	1037	145	479	134	0.54	0.054
Slash	8570	1371	1588	349	4210	758	958	134	529	148	0.54	0.054
Loblolly	7340	1174	1406	309	3490	628	850	119	389	109	0.47	0.047
Shortleaf	7300	1168	1391	306	3430	619	851	119	353	99	0.46	0.046
Western hemlock	6637	1088	1307	258	3364	615	864	105	282	79	0.42	0.053
Western larch	7652	1001	1458	249	3756	564	869	85	399	112	0.48	0.048

[1]Based on volume when green and weight at 12 percent moisture content.

DATA FROM ASTM D2555-70, by permission

meaning that only one piece in 100 is likely to have a lower bending strength. Other levels of exclusion, such as 2.5 percent, 5 percent, 10 percent or 20 percent might be desired, depending upon the consequences of failure in the application. Various exclusion levels for the bending strength property of western larch are illustrated in Table 5.

Table 5. Bending Strength Exclusion Level Values for Western Larch
An Example

Exclusion Level	Number of Standard Deviations	Exclusion Value
50.0%	0	7652 psi
20.0%	0.68	6971 psi
10.0%	1.28	6371 psi
5.0%	1.65	6000 psi
2.5%	1.96	5690 psi
1.0%	2.33	5320 psi
0.1%	3.00	4650 psi

Using the figures in the second column of this table and the averages and standard deviations for any of the properties of any of the species, exclusion values at any of the levels in the first column for clear, straight-grained wood can be readily estimated.

It is of some interest to look at the variability of several common structural materials, as illustrated in Figure 9 and Table 6.

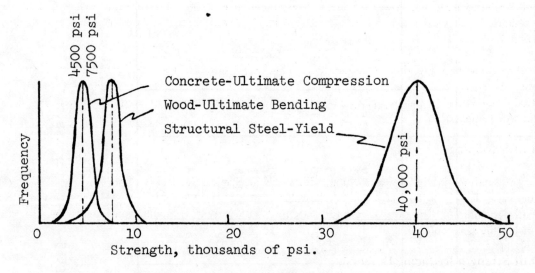

Figure 9. Variability of Properties of Three Common Materials.

Table 6. Properties of Three Materials and Their Variability
(Examples)

Material	Property	Average	Standard Deviation	Coefficient of variation
Unseasoned Wood	Bending Strength	7,500	1,200	16%
Concrete	Compression Strength	4,500	540	12%
Structural Steel	Tensile Strength	40,000	3,600	9%

These values in Table 6 are given to illustrate in a general way the relative variability of various materials. While they differ, they are all of the same general order of magnitude, wood being somewhat higher in variability than the others, owing to the fact that it is not subject to control in its process of growth. The coefficient of variation in Table 6 is the standard deviation expressed as a percentage of the average. It is a common term for expressing variability of a material.

Other Factors Affecting Design Properties

As a starting point for establishing design values for bending strength for wood, the 5 percent exclusion value on ultimate bending strength is customarily used.*The decision to use the 5 percent exclusion value is based on the consequences of failure in a framed wood structure composed of many closely spaced joists, rafters, studs, etc., i.e., fairly conventional wood building practice. In the case of laminated timber structures, where large pieces may be widely spaced, a condition that precludes the possibility of nearby members sharing the load of members of low line strength, a one-half percent exclusion level is used. The 5 percent exclusion level on western larch, for example, was about 6000 psi (Table 5). This is considerably higher than the design allowable bending stress of western larch. The highest grade of western larch is 2100 psi in bending, so there must be other considerations. These factors are set forth in ASTM D245, "Establishing Structural Grades for Visually Graded Lumber."

There are basically three considerations: (1) An increase in the property value due to the effect of seasoning; (2) The effect of the strength reducing defects permitted in the grade of lumber involved; and, (3) A general adjustment factor which is the composite result of a systematic consideration of other influences known to affect wood strength.

Effect of Seasoning

Information on the way seasoning affects the mechanical properties of wood, from ASTM D245 is reproduced in Table 7. To establish an allowable bending stress for lumber manufactured to 19 percent maximum moisture content, the increase for seasoning is 25 percent. Seasoning adjustments for other properties are found in the same column.

Effect of Strength Reducing Defects

Techniques for visually estimating the degree to which the growth features of wood reduce its performance from that to be expected from clear, straight-grained material have been developed and used over a period of forty years. In retrospect, it seems remarkable that such methods were not developed earlier. No doubt the rapid growth of our technological approach to life in only the past 100 years accounts for the late beginning.

---

*Five percent exclusion value all properties except compression perpendicular to grain and elastic modulus. As the latter are not ultimate properties, their averages are the basis for allowable values.

Table 7. Modification of Allowable Unit Stresses for Seasoning
Effects for Lumber Four Inches and Less in Nominal
Thickness.

Property	Percentage Increase in Allowable Stress Above That of Green Lumber When Maximum Moisture Content is:	
	19 Percent	15 Percent
F_b Extreme Fiber in Bending (Modulus of Rupture)	25	35
F_t Tension Parallel to Grain	25	35
F_v Horizontal Shear	8	13
$F_{c\perp}$ Compression Perpendicular to Grain	50	50
F_c Compression Parallel to Grain	50	75
E Modulus of Elasticity	14	20

These adjustment factors apply to all the principal structural wood
species. Exceptions are: Eastern red and incense cedar, Eastern
hemlock, subalpine fir and redwood, species not widely used for
structural work. Adjustment factors for these exceptions are given
in ASTM D245-69

ASTM D245-69, by permission

By measuring the effect of knot size, grain deviation and general slope, end splits, seasoning checks, and shakes (shakes are checks following the curve of growth rings, appearing as ring separations), and systematically codifying these characteristics, strength ratio estimating tables have been developed. These are published in ASTM D245. Structural lumber grade descriptions are written to fit strength ratios established from these tables. In the case of the No. 1 Structural grade of joists and planks, the bending strength ratio is 46 percent.[1] Other grades have other bending strength ratios as indicated by Table 8.

The strength ratios for all properties of a grade are not the same. For No. 1 Structural J. & P., these ratios are 62% for compression parallel, 50% for shear, 31% for tension, and 100% for elastic modulus and compression perpendicular-to-grain.

One must bear in mind the strength ratio of a grade is the minimum strength ratio permitted in that grade. Within any single grade the strength ratio of pieces will vary from the minimum permitted up to the minimum permitted by the next higher grade. Furthermore, since minimum strength ratios for all of the properties of a piece do not occur simultaneously, some pieces that might be in one grade on the basis of the

---

[1] The strength ratio factors for bending in Table 8 differ from the strength ratios in Table 11, due to inclusion of a depth effect factor in the Table 8 values.

Table 8. Strength Ratios of WWPA & WCLIB Grades (1970 Rules)

Grade Name[3]	Strength Ratio For					
	F_b[1]	F_t	F_v	$F_{c\perp}$	F_c	E[2]
Light Framing & Studs						
Construction	32	19	50	100	56	80
Standard	18	10	50	100	46	80
Utility	9	5	50	100	30	80
Studs	24	14	50	100	30	80
Structural Light Framing And Appearance						
Select Structural	63	37	50	100	78	100
No. 1	54	31	50	100	62	100
Appearance	54	31	50	100	74	100
No. 2	44	26	50	100	49	90
No. 3	24	14	50	100	30	80
Structural Joists and Planks And Appearance						
Select Structural	54	36	50	100	69	100
No. 1	46	31	50	100	62	100
Appearance	46	31	50	100	74	100
No. 2	38	25	50	100	52	90
No. 3	22	14	50	100	33	80
Beams & Stringers						
Select Structural	61	41	50	100	75	100
No. 1	51	34	50	100	63	100
Posts and Timbers						
Select Structural	57	38	50	100	79	100
No. 1	46	31	50	100	69	100

[1]These values include a depth factor component for grades of lumber 4" and less in thickness. For 5" and thicker lumber, size effect adjustments are proper.

[2]Called a "Grade Quality Factor" since E is not a strength property.

[3]For "Dense" grades (not shown), a 17 percent increase is allowed for all properties except E. E may be increased 5 percent for "Dense" grades.

minimum strength ratio for compression, as an example, may be forced down into the next lower grade on the basis of the strength ratio in flexure. For such pieces, the compression strength ratio may actually be above the minimum value for the higher grade. Circumstances of this kind extend the range of strength ratios in any grade somewhat above the threshold value for the next higher grade.

The point of all this is to call attention to the fact that strength ratios also have distributions, centering about the mean strength ratios of each grade. This is significant in terms of the real factor of safety in structural lumber. If strength ratios are normally distributed, in the fashion of Figure 8, and if the minimum strength ratio is at the 5 percent exclusion level of the distribution, then the probability of the product of strength ratio and clear wood stress each at its 5 percent exclusion level occurring simultaneously is 0.05 x 0.05, or 0.0025 or 0.25/100. Thus the real probability of pieces occurring at the allowable strength value published by the grading agencies would be in the order of one-fourth of one percent. This is a very respectable level, in terms of safety of designs for construction purposes.

Adjustment Factors

The third consideration in allowable design strength development mentioned on page 23 is the general adjustment factor. It brings together in one number, several phenomena that are known to affect each of the mechanical properties of wood, as summarized in Table 9.

Table 9. Elements of the Adjustment Factor.

	Property	Normal Duration of Load Factor	Manufacture and Use Factor	Stress Concentration	End Position	ℓ/d	Adjustment Factor
F_b	Bending	10/16	10/13	-	-	-	1/2.1
F_c	Compression Parallel to Grain	2/3	4/5	-	-	-	1/1.9
F_v	Shear	10/16	8/9	4/9	-	-	1/4.1
F_t	Tension Parallel to Grain	10/16	10/13	-	-	-	1/2.1
$F_{c\perp}$	Compression Perpendicular To Grain	11/10	10/11	-	2/3	-	1/1.5
E	Elastic Modulus	1	-	-	-	1/0.94	1/0.94

The duration of load effect that exists for all of the properties except elastic modulus, is a highly relevant feature of timber design. It enters into every design problem, not only as it affects allowable design properties, but as it affects the modification of those properties for each specific application. This is sufficiently important to deserve the thorough explanation presented beginning on page 31. The mechanical properties of wood are load and time dependent. The maximum stress that a wood member will withstand permanently without failure, is only half as large as the value it will sustain for a few seconds, as in the form of a series of short term impacts. Between these extremes of load duration, the permissible load varies according to a fairly well-defined relationship, depicted in Figure 10.

The clear wood strength properties are established from laboratory tests of close to five minutes duration from zero load to failure.

The "Normal" duration of load condition adopted as a basis for structural timber design properties fits the concept that the maximum load on structures will have a *cumulative* duration not exceeding ten years over its entire life of possibly 100 years or more. The normal duration of load factors in Table 9 are ratios of laboratory test strength to normal duration strength. Compression perpendicular-to-grain is the only wood design property based on proportional limit strength. The normal duration of load adjustment for proportional limit strength is small, because proportional limit values at laboratory load conditions are only about 6/10 of ultimate strength.

You will also note that there is no load duration effect for elastic modulus. The elastic modulus shows a load duration effect only under extremely rapid load rates (strain rates of 2 inches/second and higher), well above anything anticipated in building structures, and an error in the deflection calculation is so transitory as to be unimportant in structural design.

The manufacture and use factors in Table 9 come from a consideration of such things as the effect of fastenings driven into members in use, the possibility of broken edges or other damage, possible machine skip in dressing, small end splits that could occur after construction, and drilling of holes for wiring and plumbing in ordinary wood frame buildings, probability of error in grading, and shrinkage variability.

The stress concentration factor is listed separately because it is due to the shape and behavior of the standard shear test specimen rather than load duration, manufacturing or use practices.

The span-depth (ℓ/d) factor used to adjust elastic modulus arises from the influence of internal shear deformation in bending members. The apparent elastic modulus of pieces with uniform loads at typical ℓ/d ratios in the 18-24 range encountered in practice, is somewhat higher than the value obtained from the standard 2" x 2" x 30" test specimens loaded at mid-point on 28" spans. Under laboratory test conditions (ASTM D143), the value of E is 94 percent of the value at ℓ/d = 21 with uniformly distributed load as generally assumed for design of building structures.

Allowable Design Properties

The influences of seasoning, strength ratio, and general adjustment factor are applied as shown in Table 10, to produce the design properties. In the case of bending strength, a depth factor is also applied which, for nominal 12-inch dimension, is 0.86. Depth factor is a strength reducing phenomenon mentioned in the chapter on design of flexural members.

The values in the last column of Table 10 would be rounded off to the nearest 50 psi for all strength properties except shear, which would round to nearest 5. Elastic modulus is rounded to the nearest 100,000 psi.

The foregoing has been an illustrative example using western larch. The allowable values will not agree exactly with those for No. 1 Structural western larch given in Chapter 5 because western larch is combined with Douglas fir, a very similar species, growing on the same forest sites, as permitted by the procedures of ASTM D245.

28

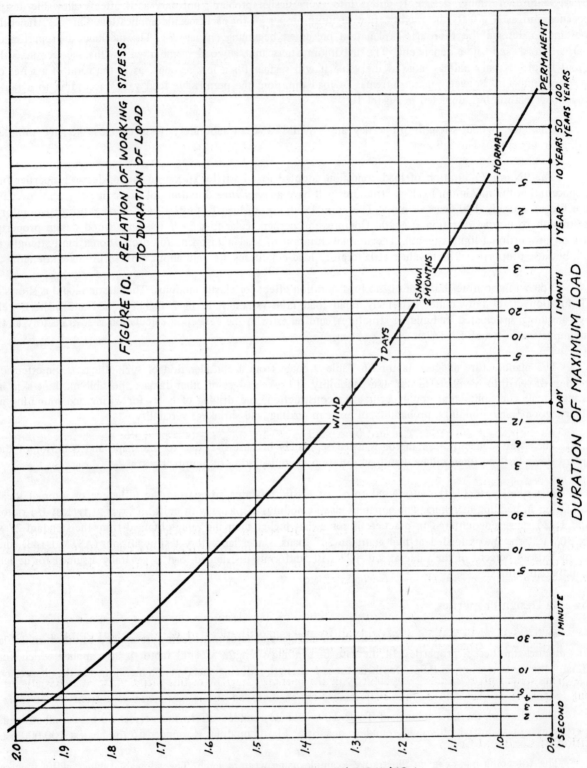

FIGURE 10. RELATION OF WORKING STRESS TO DURATION OF LOAD

Table 10. Allowable Properties for a Sample Stress Grade.

Property	Clear Wood[1] Strength Value psi	Strength Ratio ÷ 100 (Minimum)	Seasoning Increase for 19% Max. M.C.	General Adjustment Factor	Depth Effect	Allowable[2] Property psi
F_b	6000	0.54	1.25	1/2.1	0.86	1,660
F_c	2826	0.62	1.50	1/1.9	-	1,380
F_v	729	0.50	1.08	1/4.1	-	96
F_t	6000	0.31	1.25	1/2.1	-	1,100
$F_{c\perp}$	399	1.00	1.50	1/1.5	-	399
$E \div 1000$	1458	1.00	1.14	1/0.94	-	1,770

[1] Unseasoned, 5% Exclusion value, except E and $F_{c\perp}$ which are average values.

[2] For use at 19% maximum moisture content.

The purpose of this rather extended development of allowable stresses is to enable the student to obtain some grasp of this systematic process. Structural wood properties are neither vague nor unreliable. With the quality controls that are required of the lumber producers, legally grade marked lumber is as reliable as any other commodity type material used in building construction.

Considering the combined effect of strength ratio and clear wood strength probabilities, the factor of safety with recommended values averages 2.5. In over 99 percent of cases it will exceed 1.25, while in one percent of cases it will exceed 5. If a designer has an application where risks differ substantially from those judged reasonable for building construction, the recommended properties can be modified, using Table 5 as a guide. A quotation from ASTM D245 is appropriate here:

"It is assumed to be the final responsibility of the designing engineer to relate design assumptions and working stresses, and to make modifications of design stresses to fit a particular use, subject to the requirements of any applicable building code."

This statement is entirely compatible with the opening paragraph of this chapter. The responsibility for making judgments of this kind is what distinguishes architecture and engineering professions from the building trades.

Duration of Load and Creep

Ordinarily one might assume that if a structure is proof tested to the full service loading without any evidence of instability or failure, it could be relied upon to carry that load indefinitely. In the case of wood structures this assumption can be false, because the strength properties of wood are time-dependent. The stress which this material will carry continuously for a period of ten years is only 75 percent of the stress that would produce failure in a 24-hour test. These relationships are set forth as a curve in Figure 10 and are widely used as the basis for adjusting the expected service loads for designing.

The duration of load adjustment practices used by timber designers are not difficult to describe. First, however, some background on the time-dependent behavior of wood can be a useful aid to understanding certain observation and research findings that, from time to time, appear in such a way as to concern the designer about the soundness of common practices recommended to him.

Clear wood strength values, examples of which are given in Table 4, are for a very special condition of loading, i.e., zero to ultimate, in five minutes. This is called "short term" loading. Allowable stress for short term loading is 164 percent of the 10-year, or "normal" load strength, and 182 percent of the permanent load strength.

A wood member carrying a constant load may fail at a stress well below the "short term" ultimate value it would display in the laboratory, if imposed for sufficient duration. Loads causing the "short term" ultimate stress would produce failure in less than five minutes. Lower loads, producing lower stresses would be sustained for greater periods of time. It is not known if there exists some level of stress below which wood members would never fail, for never is forever and we have no way of verifying such a stress level. However, the curve in Figure 10, based on tests over a period of ten years, does, if projected, suggest that a stress level of 55 percent of the short term ultimate will be sustained for over 100 years. Permanent loads on most structures are considerably less than 55 percent of short term ultimates so it is no surprise to find examples of timber structures carrying their permanent loads for periods of 500 years or more.

Among the various design criteria for housing structures by the Federal Housing Administration, the highest ratio of dead (permanent) to maximum load is 0.5. The permanently applied stress for such a structure is about 28 percent of the short term ultimate. So, although the behavior of structures under permanent loading at high stress levels can cause progressive deformation and ultimate failure, it is emphasized that the stresses generally recommended are low enough to give indefinitely long expected life.

The curves in Figure 11 from "The Structural Use of Timber" by Booth and Reece indicate these various types of behavior. A wood member stressed at less than 55 percent of its short term ultimate would follow curve OADE. It would deflect to point A immediately upon application of the load, then over a period of time would creep fairly rapidly to D, then creep more and more slowly, eventually stabilizing at E. At a stress level of perhaps 70 percent of short term ultimate, it would follow OBGH to failure. Initial deflection would be to point B, with creep starting at B, proceeding at a diminishing rate to G, and then accelerating to failure at H. Curve OCF is for a yet more highly stressed condition, perhaps 90 percent of the short term ultimate.

The ratio C/e is called the "proportional creep." The initial deflection is e, and the additional deflection is C. This ratio appears to be about 1.0 for either seasoned wood that remains dry, or green wood that remains unseasoned. Under the permanently applied portion of load, a timber would be expected to eventually creep to a

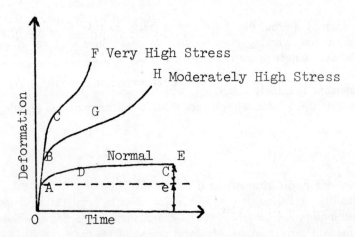

Figure 11.   Deformation with Time.   Courtesy SPON (London)

total deformation roughly twice the initial deflection. It would take several years for this to develop. If the load is removed after creep has occurred, most of the initial elastic portion of the deformation would recover, but the creep would remain as a permanent set.

In a structure where very specific constraints exist on the maximum deflection which can be accepted, the designer generally designs for one-half that initial deflection using the recommended value of elastic modulus. Alternatively, in laminated timber, camber equal to, or greater than, the dead load deflection may be built into the member, to compensate for dead load deflection and creep and to provide for drainage of flat roofs. See page 90.

In cases where members are installed *completely green* and season while under load, proportional creep of 3.5 is fairly typical, in some instances going as far as 7 times the initial deflection, over a period of two to three years.

Even seasoned members exhibit proportional creep greater than 1.0, if placed in an environment conducive to moisture content fluctuation. Proportional creep in the order of 1.25 is likely.

In all the above circumstances, the stress level should be substantially below 56 percent of the estimated short term ultimate strength, and in practice a level of 35 percent would be judicious in view of the variability in strength properties mentioned earlier in this chapter.

Research on very small green beams, less than 1/2" x 1/2", which seasoned and also cycled in moisture content, failed at stresses of about 25 percent of short term ultimate. They did not fail at 12 percent of short term ultimate. This has generated apprehension on the part of some people. Wood in structural sizes, however, cannot respond to moisture cycling rapidly, like these tiny test beams, and we have more basis for confidence than for apprehension about the behavior of ordinary structures.

Figure 11 does suggest a useful observation. Pieces in which creep has ceased increasing are not likely to fail as long as the permanent load is not raised. On the other hand, pieces that show any evidence of an increasing rate of creep appear headed for ultimate failure unless the stress can be reduced. (See page 90.)

For efficient use of wood, designers adjust the allowable strength properties in the light of expected durations of load. ASTM D245 offers the most authoritative guidance on this procedure, and all the recommended practices conform to this Standard.

The recommended allowable stresses are for "normal" load duration, meaning that the full value may be applied steadily for ten years, or intermittently for a longer period as long as the sum of time periods at this stress does not cumulatively exceed ten years.

Ninety percent of the allowable stress will be sustained on a permanent basis, without failure. An important point to make at this juncture, is that a member which supports the full allowable stress continuously or cumulatively for ten years will continue to support 90 percent of that stress for an indefinitely long time. This concept is sometimes difficult to accept, but research and experience bear it out.

The following stress levels are generally recommended for various load durations of less than ten years:

Two months duration, commonly applied to maximum snow load	1.15 X Normal
Seven day duration, used in hurricane zones	1.25 X Normal
Wind loading, in areas where hurricanes do not occur regularly	1.33 X Normal

Seismic loads	1.33 X Normal
Impact loads (very occasional)	2.0 X Normal

From Figure 10, you will note that wind loading corresponds to a cumulative duration of maximum wind load not to exceed 15 hours. Likewise, the cumulative duration of seismic load over the life of the structure should not exceed 15 hours at maximum intensity. Figure 9 suggests impact loads be limited to cumulative duration of a very few seconds, *clearly not providing for regular and frequent* impact loads of high intensity.

The determinations of maximum stress due to wind, seismic load and impact are crucial elements of design that are discussed in the chapter on Design Criteria for Timber Structures.

Attention is directed again to the ability of the wood structure to carry stresses of several different levels, provided that cumulatively none of them exceed the duration defined by Figure 9.

A wood structure then could sustain loads that would cause all of the following stress levels during its life, as long as the duration limits are not exceeded:

90% of Normal	Permanently
100% of Normal	For 10 years, cumulative
115% of Normal	For 2 months, cumulative
125% of Normal	For 7 days, cumulative
133% of Normal	For 15 hours, cumulative
200% of Normal	For 2 seconds, cumulative

Controlling Loads for Design

Structures are ordinarily subject to a variety of loads, usually relatively low permanent loads with higher loads of shorter duration. A designer must note which of these would control his design. Individuals may develop their own preferred method of doing this, but the method must provide for the effect of duration of load on allowable stress as described in the foregoing section. Several examples will illustrate procedures that are used.

Example 1: Determine the controlling load duration for a factory roof located in a region where the maximum snow loading is 30 lbs. per sq. ft. and the maximum wind loading is 14 lbs. per sq. ft. pressure. The dead load of the roof structure is 20 lbs. per sq. ft., including all equipment, piping, ductwork, etc. If the cumulative duration of maximum snow does not exceed 2 months, and the probability of maximum wind loading is less than a cumulative 15 hours as previously discussed, the amount of load on the structure for these various durations will be:

	Permanent	Two Months	15 Hours
Dead Load	20	20	20
Snow Load	--	30	30
Wind Load	--	--	14
	20	50	64

Since these are all uniformly distributed design loads, the stresses the various loads will produce are directly proportional to each load. The allowable stresses are 90% of normal for permanent, 115% of normal for two-month, and 133.3% of normal for 15 hrs. (wind).

Equations for the required section modulus per foot of width of this structure, assuming a simple span support arrangement, are:

Permanent Load

$$S = \frac{w\ell^2}{8(0.9F_b)} = \frac{20}{0.9}\frac{\ell^2}{96F_b}$$

w = lbs/lineal inch when ℓ is in inches and F_b in psi.

Snow Load (two months)

$$S = \frac{w\ell^2}{8(1.15F_b)} = \frac{50}{1.15}\frac{\ell^2}{96F_b}$$

Wind Load (15 hours)

$$S = \frac{w\ell^2}{8(1.33F_b)} = \frac{64}{1.33}\frac{\ell^2}{96F_b}$$

In these equations $\dfrac{\ell^2}{96 F_b}$ is common to each and the section modulus requirements are proportional, among the various load conditions to $\dfrac{20}{0.9}$, $\dfrac{50}{1.15}$, $\dfrac{64}{1.333}$ or 22.2, 43.5 and 48.1. The combination of loads that will require the greatest section modulus is Dead Load and Snow Load and Wind Load, so the 15 hour duration controls.

A more direct way to reach this conclusion would be to divide the various loads combinations by their duration of load factors as follows:

	Permanent	Two Months	15 Hours
Dead Load	20	20	20
Snow Load	--	30	30
Wind Load	--	--	14
	$\dfrac{20}{0.9}$ = 22.2	$\dfrac{50}{1.15}$ = 43.5	$\dfrac{64}{1.333}$ = 48.1

Having determined that 64 P.S.F. for wind duration controls, one may carry forward the design using either 64 P.S.F. and 1.333 F_b; or 48.1 P.S.F. and F_b.

Example 2: A consideration commonly accepted in most parts of the U.S. is that maximum snow and maximum wind will not occur simultaneously, but that maximum wind is only likely to coincide with half the maximum snow load. If one accepts this, on the basis of weather records in the region, the analysis would produce a different result, as follows:

	Permanent	Two Months	15 Hours
Dead Load	20	20	20
Snow Load	--	30	15
Wind Load	--	--	14
	$\dfrac{20}{0.9}$ = 22.2	$\dfrac{50}{1.15}$ = 43.5	$\dfrac{49}{1.333}$ = 36.7

In this case the controlling conditions for design are 50 P.S.F. for two-months duration with allowable bending stress at 1.15 F_b; or 43.5 P.S.F. with F_b; either combination of load and allowable stress producing the same required section modulus.

Instances occur where the dead load may control if the structure is extremely heavy, and carries small or infrequent live loads.

The method of simply dividing loads by duration of load factors can be used only if all loads are distributed in the same way, i.e., all uniformly distributed. Dead load is generally uniformly distributed, however, live loads might be differently disposed.

Example 3: Consider the case of a deck supporting a parked car, which may be assumed to be on the deck 60 percent of the time over the life of the structure. The load per wheel on the car is 700 lbs., distributed over a deck width of 12 inches. Dead load of the structure might be 60 P.L.F. With a wheelbase of 10 feet, a total simple span of 20 feet, and an assumed life of the structure of 50 years, the controlling load would be developed as follows:

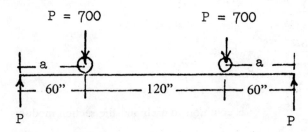

Figure 12.

Stress caused by the parked car:

$$f_b = \frac{M}{S} = \frac{Pa}{S} = \frac{700 \times 60}{S} = \frac{42000}{S}$$

Stress caused by the dead load:

$$f_b = \frac{M}{S} = \frac{wl^2}{8S} = \frac{60}{12} \frac{(240)^2}{8S} = \frac{36,000}{S}$$

	Permanent	30 Years
Dead load stress	36,000/S	36,000/S
Live load stress	---	42,000/S
	$\frac{36,000}{0.9S} = \frac{40,000}{S}$	$\frac{78,000}{0.96S} = \frac{80,412}{S}$

This analysis shows that the 30 year load is the largest effective design load. The point to be made is that when all loads are not distributed in the same fashion, it is necessary to either compare stresses, or convert the concentrated loads to equivalent uniformly distributed loads to make the comparison.

A uniformly distributed load equivalent to the parked car would be:

$$\frac{w\ell^2}{8} = Pa$$

$$w = \frac{8Pa}{\ell^2} = \frac{8 \times 700 \times 60}{(240)^2} = 5.833 \ \frac{lbs.}{in.} \ \text{or 70 P.L.F.}$$

Then:

	Permanent	30 Year
Dead Load	60	60
	--	70
	$\frac{60}{0.9} = 66.6$	$\frac{130}{0.97} = 134$

Design for 135.4 PSF uniformly distributed load and stress F_b

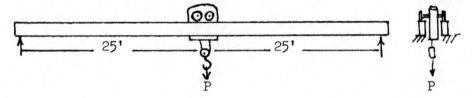

Figure 13.

Example 4: A pair of large laminated timbers support a traveling hoist. Each beam weighs 150 lbs. per lineal foot. The hoist weighs 500 lbs. It is estimated that the operating conditions will require the hoist to support loads at various cumulative durations as follows:

2000 lbs.	5 years
4000 lbs.	1 year
6000 lbs.	3 months
12000 lbs.	Maximum acceleration loading not to exceed 6 hours cumulative duration.

Assuming these loads will all occur when the hoist is at the mid-point of a 50-foot span, the controlling load for design is obtained by converting the uniform loads to an equivalent concentrated load and proceeding as before.

		Permanent	5 Years	1 Year	3 Months	6 Hours
Dead Loads:	Beams	7500	7500	7500	7500	7500
	Hoist	500	500	500	500	500
Live Loads		----	2000	4000	6000	12000
		8000	10000	12000	14000	20000
Duration of Load Factor		0.9	1.025	1.08	1.13	1.38
Quotients		8900	9800	11,100	12,400	14,500

The structure will be designed for maximum concentrated load of 14,500 lbs. using "normal" stress values or 20,000 lbs., using 1.38 x normal stress values.

CHAPTER 4

GRADES AND SIZES OF STRUCTURAL LUMBER

In the United States softwood lumber is manufactured in conformance with PS20-70, a Product Standard developed under procedures established by the U. S. Department of Commerce. Representatives of manufacturers, distributors and users of lumber, as participating members of the American Lumber Standards Committee, administer PS20-70 with respect to enforcement of the proper use of grade marks, updating of the Product Standard to assimilate advancing technology, and determining the technical adequacy of grading rules, testing procedures and quality control.

Grading rules are written descriptions of the maximum strength reducing growth and manufacturing characteristics of the grades. The preparation of grading rules is a function of the several rules writing agencies—manufacturers associations representing producers of the various species marketed commercially. These agencies have established a National Grading Rule for Softwood Dimension[1] Lumber, a common framework of sizes, grades and grade names. Under this system the physical description of each grade is independent of the geographic region in which it is produced or the species to which it is applied. This simplifies the task of knowing the physical description of each grade. At one time some differences in the descriptions of a grade existed between regions, and different names were used for basically similar grades. A standardization of grades has been accomplished, greatly simplifying the tasks of persons interested in the measurement of lumber quality.

Because the physical descriptions of most U.S. lumber grades are now alike, the stress ratings must necessarily vary with species. A piece of No. 1 Structural Joist & Plank of Douglas fir meets the same descriptive requirements as one of western hemlock or lodgepole pine. Each of these species, however, has a different specific gravity and has different mechanical properties of clear wood. Therefore, the bending strength, for example, differs by species. Douglas fir, of the grade mentioned, has a bending strength of 1500 psi while western hemlock's is 1200 psi and lodgepole pine's is 1100 psi.

The strength properties recommended for design are published in the rule books of the grading agencies. Tables A1 through A7 found in Appendix A are from the 1970 Standard Grading Rules of the Western Wood Products Association (WWPA).[2] An inspection of these tables will show how the design properties vary with species. It will also indicate how some species that may be marketed and produced in mixture are grouped together for grading and stress rating. This grouping is necessary because it is virtually impossible for many users, and even for some producers to reliably separate them by species on the basis of physical appearance.

Douglas fir and larch often look alike, have similar properties, and are marketed under one grouping. This does not mean shipments of Douglas fir-larch will always contain some of each species, but they may. The properties given for this group are applicable whether the shipment is a mixture or is entirely of one or of the other species.

Douglas fir South from the southern part of Douglas fir's natural range. It is genuine Douglas fir of slightly lower strength and considerably lower elastic modulus, as contrasted to the Douglas fir-larch group. Because of this distinct geographical source, all mills in that region mark their Douglas fir as Douglas fir South.

Hem-fir is a combination grade of western hemlock and a variety of true firs which often grow in mixed forest stands and can become mixed in manufacturing.

Mountain hemlock is a variety of western hemlock of somewhat lower elastic modulus, and different strength properties. In some regions where it grows, western hemlock and true firs do not exist. Mills in those regions can reliably identify their mountain hemlcok and mark it accordingly.

---

[1]Softwood dimension lumber is lumber nominal 2" to and including 4" thick, in widths 2" and larger.

[2]Appendix A gives property information on all species of structural lumber produced in the United States. The discussion is limited to the species of one regional group for convenience only.

There are other regions where mountain hemlock, true firs, and western hemlock occur in the same general forest area. This leads to problems of identification, so a *Mountain hemlock-Hem-Fir* species grouping is used, with safe design properties for this combination based on the lowest recommended design value for any of the species in that mix.

In certain producing areas *subalpine fir,* with somewhat lower design properties than other true firs is found in the forests. When it is the only true fir in the area, it is graded as subalpine fir. It has lower properties than any other species graded under WWPA rules, but is still commercially useful. The volumes available are usually small, however, and mills may have difficulty accumulating enough subalpine fir to justify marketing it as a distinct and separate species. Under those circumstances, they may put it into a group with other true firs, hemlocks, pines and spruces. Such a group goes by the name *White Woods* with stress ratings of the low line subalpine fir species. Sometimes the harder Douglas fir, larch, and even the softer cedars are also included along with the species of White Woods, in which case the group is called *Mixed Species,* is so labeled and offered for sale.

These White Woods and Mixed Species groupings are rather uncommon and would be unlikely to appear on the market in any volume.

Generally in design work an engineer or architect would specify the commonly available species or species groups, Douglas Fir-Larch, Hem-Fir or Southern Pine.

A detailed discussion of grade rules will not be attempted. They are published in the rule books. The design stress and elastic modulus properties for the various lumber and timber grades are based on procedures set forth in ASTM Standard D2555—Methods for Establishing Clear Wood Strength Values, and ASTM D245—Methods for Establishing Structural Grades for Visually Graded Lumber, published by the American Society for Testing and Materials.

Visually Stress Graded Dimension Lumber

The terms "dimension lumber" refer to lumber in the thickness range of 2" to 4" nominal size.

Dimension lumber is produced in two width categories and five use categories, as described in Table 11.

The Southern Pine Inspection Bureau (SPIB) and the West Coast Lumber Inspection Bureau (WCLIB) list "Dense" grades of Select Structural, No. 1, No. 2 and No. 3. The strength ratios of these dense grades are the same as above, but by invoking an added limitation on minimum number of growth rings per inch in the radial growth direction, and a minimum percentage of summerwood, a strength increase (17%) for density is permitted. WWPA Rules permit the grading of dense grades, but their properties are not listed in the stress-rated lumber property tables. Increases in the listed property values for grades meeting the density requirements are mentioned in Chapter 5. In the SPIB grade rules there is a "medium grain" No. 2 grade, intermediate between Dense and normal or open grain (5% increase in strength).

Machine-Stress-Rated Lumber (MSR)

A method of grading lumber based on nondestructive testing has been in official use since about 1963. This system is a recognized procedure per PS20-70 and the National Grading Rule. Grading machines measure the stiffness of pieces by a mechanical test procedure. Areas of weakness due to knots, sloping grain, and low density are identified by a rapidly applied bending test which continually scans the lumber for stiffness, using this property as a basis for strength estimating.

Machine-stress-rated lumber is produced primarily in thicknesses of 2" nominal or less and in widths from 4" to 12" nominal. With the exception of shear and compression perpendicular, design values (Appendix Table A6) are independent of species. MSR grades may differ in appearance from species to species for any one stress-rated grade. A piece of 1500f-1.4E Douglas fir, for example, will have larger knots than a piece of 1500f-1.4E white fir.

Table 11. Dimension Lumber Grades, Uses and Widths.

Width Category	Use Category	Grade Name	Bending Strength Ratio
2"-4"	Light Framing	Construction	34%
2"-4"	Light Framing	Standard	19%
2"-4"	Light Framing	Utility	9%
2"-4"	Light Framing	Economy	None
2"-4"	Studs	Stud	26%
2"-4"	Studs	Economy Stud	None
2"-4"	Structural Light Framing	Select Structural	67%
2"-4"	Structural Light Framing	No. 1	55%
2"-4"	Structural Light Framing	No. 2	45%
2"-4"	Structural Light Framing	No. 3	26%
2"-4"	Structural Light Framing	Economy	None
2"-4"	Appearance	Appearance	55%
6" & wider	Structural Joists & Plank	Select Structural	65%
6" & wider	Structural Joists & Plank	No. 1	54%
6" & wider	Structural Joists & Plank	No. 2	45%
6" & wider	Structural Joists & Plank	No. 3	26%
6" & wider	Structural Joists & Plank	Economy	None
6" & wider	Appearance	Appearance	54%

This grading system has two particular virtues. It provides readily interchangeable grades, permitting easy substitution of one species for another, and it identifies and makes available higher strength material than is possible by visual grading methods. It also eliminates any issue of species identification as a determinant of strength.

It is expected that this ability to identify lumber accurately will increase the demand for, and use of, machine-stress-rated grades. At present MSR lumber is used primarily for structural specialities such as trusses of various types and for laminating lumber of high quality. The machine-stress-rated grades are listed in Table A6 of the Appendix All species are not available in all grades. The principal MSR grades that several softwoods will produce are shown in Table 12. The 1500F-1.4E, 1800F-1.6E and 2100F-1.8E grades are commonly available.

Machine-stress-rated lumber does have some visual limitations on edge knot size, end split, wane (round edges), warp, checks, shake, and skips in surfacing. These limitations are standardized and are relatively simple for mills to apply and for users to verify.

Table 12. MSR Grade Potential of Various Species.

MSR Grade	Douglas fir	Western larch	Western hemlock	True firs	Engelmann spruce	Pines	Cedars
900f - 1.0E				X	X	X	X
1200F - 1.2E			X	X	X	X	X
1500f - 1.4E	X	X	X	X	X	X	X
1800f - 1.6E	X	X	X	X	X	X	X
2100f - 1.8E	X	X	X	X	X		
2400f - 2.0E	X	X	X				
2700f - 2.2E	X	X	X				
3000f - 2.4E	X	X					
3300f - 2.6E	X	X					

Stress-Rated Boards (Visual)

Stress-rated lumber less than 2" nominal thickness is useful in light trusses and for framing in the design of mobile homes and factory-built sectional buildings. Efficiently designed structural components using glued lumber and plywood also utilize stress-rated boards to advantage.

This type of product is furnished in the Structural Light Framing (2"-4" wide) and Structural Joist & Plank (6" & wider) categories, with the same design properties given in the tables for these dimension grades.

Stress-rated boards bear the symbol "SRB" as a part of their grade mark.

Visually Stress-Graded Timbers

Lumber 5" and more in nominal thickness is classified into Beam & Stringer and Post & Timber grades. These grades are not included in the National Grading Rules, and consequently one may expect some differences in the visual characteristics from region to region.

The widths of Beam & Stringer grades exceed their thickness by 2" nominal or more. The widths of Post & Timber grades exceed their thickness by less than 2" nominal. Posts & Timbers are often square.

The stress-rated grades of Beams & Stringers are Select Structural and No. 1. Grades of No. 2 and No. 3 are also manufactured but are not stress-rated. The same grade names are used for Post & Timber grades.

Beams & Stringers emphasize bending strength, whereas Posts & Timber emphasize compression parallel to grain, in keeping with their primary intended use. An inspection of Table A5 illustrates this difference. Grade for grade, the extreme fiber stress in bending is greater for Beams & Stringers, and compression parallel to grain is greater for Posts & Timbers. Beams & Stringers can be used as compression members at the compression stresses recommended for them, and Posts & Timbers can be used as flexural members at their stress-ratings, although not quite as efficiently as would be possible if used for the purpose for which the rules are made.

Visually Stress-Graded Decking

To insure against the development of shrinkage gaps between courses of decking, tongue and groove decking is only offered seasoned to 15 percent maximum moisture content.

The two decking grades are:

SELECTED DECKING

COMMERCIAL DECKING

These are stress-rated grades per Table A7 of Appendix A. Elastic modulus and bending strength are the principal design properties for decking, but if compression perpendicular to grain values are needed for bearing calculations, or shear strength is required for design, this author recommends using the values published for Select Structural and No. 1 Structural Joist & Plank adjusted to MC-15. This will be discussed in Chapter 5.

Other Types of Lumber Grades

Non-stress-rated material graded strictly for appearance and non-structural uses is also manufactured. A large variety of specialties, flooring, siding, paneling, stepping, etc., are found in the rule books. Factory Lumber for box manufacture and mouldings, and Shop Lumber graded on the basis of yield of clear cuttings for furniture and millwork use, are also in the rule books. These grades are not of particular interest for structural use and are outside the scope and purpose of this particular publication.

Lumber Sizes

Nominal lumber sizes are the sawn sizes before either seasoning or planing has taken place. Actual size of dressed unseasoned timber is somewhat less than the rough sawn size. Lumber that is dressed and seasoned is smaller than dressed-unseasoned material.

Nearly all lumber is dressed to smooth surfaces to facilitate grading and produce uniform sizes to make fabrication easier.

Rough[3] sawn lumber or lumber surfaced on only the edges or only the wide faces can be purchased. This is sometimes done in the interests of economy. Large sizes in the Beam & Stringer and Post & Timber grades are purchased rough more often than dimension lumber or boards. Persons ordering rough sawn lumber should familiarize themselves with the rule book provisions on rough lumber sizes.

Both seasoned and unseasoned lumber are readily available. The advantages of seasoned lumber are pointed out in various places in this book. Green or unseasoned lumber is somewhat lower in price than seasoned material, and in instances where the advantages of seasoning do not justify the cost, it may be specified.

The cost of seasoning increases with lumber size, being roughly proportional to the square of the thickness. Time required for seasoning is also a consideration and it is impractical to season timber thicker than nominal four-inch size without incurring intolerable delays in delivery. Beam & Stringer and Post & Timber grades are not normally seasoned during the manufacturing process.

---

[3]Note: In Europe the term rough lumber is not favored. Domestic supplies of timber are more limited than in North America, much wood is imported, and the utmost economy is practiced in the use of wood. Producers precision saw timber for construction to avoid the obvious waste incurred in surfacing. It is likely that such practice will become more common in North America as time goes by.

For lumber less than nominal 4" thickness, seasoning is practical and common.

Seasoned lumber has a maximum moisture content as it leaves the mill of 19%. Such material averages about 15% with a variation of plus or minus about 4% M.C.

Unseasoned lumber may be material that has never been purposely seasoned, or lumber that has been air-dried or kiln-dried to some extent, but not enough to bring the maximum moisture content below 19%. Unseasoned lumber may be marked S-GRN.

Lumber less than nominal 4" thickness is produced to a size standard which gives the user the same size at any particular moisture content to which it may come when it reaches equilibrium with the environment in service. An unseasoned 2 x 4 is produced to 1 9/16" x 3 9/16". A seasoned 2 x 4 is 1 1/2" x 3 1/2". In building construction these pieces will both come to about 10 or 12% moisture content in service, and will be the same size at that moisture level.

It is a requirement of PS20-70, that all surfaced and seasoned lumber be marked "S-DRY". Lumber not so marked is always assumed to be unseasoned. The one exception to this is the authorization of a mark, "MC 15". This mark is used on material that has been exceptionally well-seasoned to 12% average, 15% maximum moisture content. MC-15 material is produced by the same size standard as S-DRY lumber.

The S-DRY standard lumber sizes are 1/2-inch less than nominal from 2" to and including 6" nominal, and 3/4-inch less for sizes greater than 6". S-DRY lumber below 2" nominal is 1/4-inch below nominal size.

Surfaced unseasoned dimension lumber is 7/16-inch less than nominal size from 2" to 4", 3/8-inch less through 6" widths, and 1/2-inch less for greater nominal widths. For nominal sizes less than 2", surfaced-unseasoned material is 7/32-inch less than nominal.

These standard sizes are summarized in Table 13.

Under certain circumstances, a customer may want lumber surfaced to some size less than these standards. If this is done, PS20-70 requires that the actual size be included as a part of the grade mark. As an example, a piece of 1 1/2" x 5 1/4" surfaced dry lumber would be marked S-DRY 5 1/4".

The widths of MC-15 decking are measured at the face, excluding the tongue. Standard decking widths are one-inch off nominal through 6-inches and 1 1/4-inch off for wider sizes. Thickness conforms to the aforementioned dry sizes.

Decking and glued-laminated timber are not required to conform to these standards. They are sold on an "actual size" basis. The nominal size system is not used for glued-laminated structural specialties.

Table 13. Lumber Sizes

NOMINAL AND MINIMUM-DRESSED SIZES OF BOARDS, DIMENSION, AND TIMBERS

(The thicknesses apply to all widths and the widths to all thicknesses)

Item	Thicknesses			Face Widths		
	Nominal	Minimum Dry[1]	Dressed Green[1]	Nominal	Minimum Dry[1]	Dressed Green[1]
		Inches	Inches		Inches	Inches
Boards---------	1	3/4	25/32	2	1-1/2	1-9/16
	1-1/4	1	1-1/32	3	2-1/2	2-9/16
	1-1/2	1-1/4	1-9/32	4	3-1/2	3-9/16
				5	4-1/2	4-5/8
				6	5-1/2	5-5/8
				7	6-1/2	6-5/8
				8	7-1/4	7-1/2
				9	8-1/4	8-1/2
				10	9-1/4	9-1/2
				11	10-1/4	10-1/2
				12	11-1/4	11-1/2
				14	13-1/4	13-1/2
				16	15-1/4	15-1/2
Dimension--------	2	1-1/2	1-9/16	2	1-1/2	1-9/16
	2-1/2	2	2-1/16	3	2-1/2	2-9/16
	3	2-1/2	2-9/16	4	3-1/2	3-9/16
	3-1/2	3	3-1/16	5	4-1/2	4-5/8
				6	5-1/2	5-5/8
				8	7-1/4	7-1/2
				10	9-1/4	9-1/2
				12	11-1/4	11-1/2
				14	13-1/4	13-1/2
				16	15-1/4	15-1/2
Dimension--------	4	3-1/2	3-9/16	2	1-1/2	1-9/16
	4-1/2	4	4-1/16	3	2-1/2	2-9/16
				4	3-1/2	3-9/16
				5	4-1/2	4-5/8
				6	5-1/2	5-5/8
				8	7-1/4	7-1/2
				10	9-1/4	9-1/2
				12	11-1/4	11-1/2
				14	13-1/4	13-1/2
				16	15-1/4	15-1/2
Timbers--------	5 and thicker	not made S-Dry	1/2 off	7 and wider	not made S-Dry	1/2 off

[1]Dry lumber is defined as lumber which has been seasoned to a moisture content 19 percent or less. Green lumber is defined as lumber having a moisture content in excess of 19 percent.

CHAPTER 5

DESIGN PROPERTIES OF STRUCTURAL LUMBER

The recommended design values for the six basic properties of wood needed by designers are for normal load duration, as published. These values are for timber that will be used under dry conditions as in most covered structures.

The development of design strength properties for safe use in building and construction has involved a consideration of the risks and consequences of structural failure. These factors are discussed in Chapter 3. If a designer plans to use wood for other purposes, for example in the design of a highly stressed tower, a key structural member of a wooden ship, the spar of an aircraft wing, the propellor of a wind tunnel, or some critical element of a machine, he should familiarize himself with the methods of derviation of design stresses and apply such added limitations on strength values as may be judged appropriate. For general construction purposes, the recommended design values represent a balance between safety and economy that has, by experience over a long period of time, proven acceptable.

The elastic modulus property given for design is an average value for the species and grade. Load sharing between members supporting a deck, or between decking material joined together by tongues and grooves or by nailing, averages out the variation between pieces. Deflection is generally not highly critical in design as far as structural failure is concerned. If maximum deflection is highly critical to a particular design, a 50 percent reduction in the elastic modulus would insure that the computed deflection would not be exceeded with a confidence considerably exceeding 99%. The need to apply this kind of reduction factor is extremely rare, but is mentioned here to indicate that designers faced with very special problems can alter values developed for general construction to suit other end-use purposes.

Nondestructive test equipment and methods are also available for certifying the stiffness of important structural members. Machine-stress-graded lumber has some advantages where flexural behavior is a crucial element of design, because the extremes of elastic modulus within a machine stress grade are not great.

Single and Repetitive Member Systems

Tables A1, A2 and A3 list single member and repetitive member design values for extreme fiber stress in bending. Single member values are for use when there is no connection between members, to constrain them to deflect in unison, i.e., they are able to deflect independently of one another. Under these circumstances, the full design load on a particular member would apply independently of its deflection with reference to other members of the system.

Single member structures are quite unusual. Widely spaced supported building frames would be an example. The crossarm on an electric utility pole would be another example. Widely spaced beams supporting a roof deck on purlins that are not continuous over more than one span would also be of this type.

Most timber structures have uniformly spaced members which are constrained by continuous connecting purlins, stiff decking, and bridging, to deflect as a unit. In a roof system, for example, all rafters, even though they be of the same grade, vary in their strength and stiffness, within the range encompassed by the grade. To deflect in unison, each assumes a portion of the uniformly distributed design load proportional to its elastic modulus. Since elastic modulus and strength are correlated in wood, the stronger pieces bear the greatest loads.

As a result, the system does not fail when the load contiguous to the weakest member reaches a value that would exceed its design value. Adjacent stronger pieces relieve the weaker pieces of some of its load. The degree to which this type of behavior occurs obviously depends on the stiffness of the distributive deck system, the spacing of the members, and the variability of the stiffness and strength of the joists.

For wood structural systems with three or more members spaced within 24-inches of one another and connected by lumber or plywood sheathing, it has been established in theory and confirmed by test that a strength increase of 15% in bending may be safely assumed. The bending stresses for repetitive loading are 115% of those for single member loading.

Actually, with a knowledge of joist variablity, spacing and continuity of the connection, stress increases as much as 50% above those for single member loading can be determined. This, however, involves a degree of design sophistication and material selection supervision beyond that which would be economically justified for most timber designs at the present time. Consequently, the 15% repetitive load sharing increase is the general practice.

The repetitive stress ratings for wood published by the WWPA (Appendix A) are not found in the property tables of all grading rules, but some provision for the 15% increase is usually found elsewhere in the rule book.

Single member bending stresses are assumed for members spaced more than 24-inches on centers or not interconnected by an adequate load distributing structure.

This concept is, of course, applicable to members in compression or tension, even though repetitive values for those properties are not published or recommended by the grading agency.

Section Properties for Design

The section properties for design are based on the surfaced-dry dimensions of stress rated boards and dimension lumber, regardless of whether the lumber is manufactured to the seasoned or unseasoned size standards. The tabulated design stresses apply to any manufacturing moisture content if the service conditions in use are dry.

For 5" and thicker lumber, the section properties are based on the standard unseasoned sizes, and the design values given are applicable to structures that will be dry in service.

Table A8 in the Appendix lists the section properties of the most commonly used lumber sizes.

Effect of Depth

The depth of a bending member measured in the direction of load, influences the bending strength. This is discussed in Chapter 9 on beams and flexural members.

The grading rules are written on the basis that Stress Rated Boards, Dimension, and Beams & Stringers will be loaded on the narrow face.

For planks loaded on the wide face, bending strength values of Boards and Dimension may be increased per Table 14. Beams & Stringers are not graded for use loaded on the wide face, and no adjustments for that type of use are available.

Table 14. Adjustment Factors for Depth Effect for Extreme Fiber Stress in Bending for Use as Plank.

Lumber Width	When Used as Plank, Nominal Thickness			
	1"	2"	3"	4"
2" to 4"	1.19	1.10	1.04	1.00
6" and wider	1.32	1.22	1.16	1.11

Effect of Moisture Content

For MC-15 lumber that will not exceed 15 percent moisture content in use, design properties may be increased per Table 15. MC-15 lumber is 15 percent maximum (12 percent average) moisture content. Since it is manufactured to the same standard size as 19 percent maximum (15 percent average) moisture content lumber, increased strength and elastic modulus are justified on the basis of the added wood substance in MC-15 lumber.

Dimension lumber, 2" to 4", which is used at moisture content conditions above 19 percent, suffers a loss in intrinsic property values, not compensated by the section property gain due to dimensional swelling. Adjustment factors for this service condition are listed in Table 15. Stress Rated Boards, used above 19 percent should be adjusted the same amounts.

Five-inch and thicker timbers have different adjustment factors than dimension lumber when used above 19 percent. These reductions listed in Table 15 are (except for $F_{c\perp}$) smaller, because the strength and elastic modulus properties published for this thick lumber were reduced for checking and shrinkage defects expected to occur when these heavy sections seasoned in dry service. The service checking reductions are essentially equal to the difference between green and seasoned wood property values.

Table 15. Adjustment Factors for Design Properties for Service Moisture Content

	F_b	F_t	F_v	$F_{c\perp}$	F_c	E
MC-15 Lumber Used Below 15%	1.08	1.09	1.05	1.00	1.17	1.05
Nominal 2" to 4" Thick Lumber Used Above 19%	0.86	0.84	0.97	0.67	0.70	0.97
Nominal 5" and Thicker Lumber Used Above 19%	1.00	1.00	1.00	0.67	0.91	1.00
MC-15 Decking Used Above 15%	0.79	----	----	----	----	0.92
S-DRY Decking Used Dry	0.93	----	----	----	----	0.95

Shear Parallel-to-the-Grain

Prior to the establishment of the National Grading Rules, the design stress in shear parallel-to-the-grain, (sometimes called horizontal shear) recommended for design use, was based upon the amount of end split permitted for each grade. This caused endless discussion as to the effect that changes in end split due to seasoning between the time the lumber was graded at a mill, and used by a consumer, might have on the validity of the recommended value. To circumvent this difficulty, the value of F_v now recommended is based on the most severe end split conceivable. The user may increase this value to conform to his own specification for the acceptable end split he wishes to permit or expects will occur, in the material going into his design.

Table 16 lists shear stress increases for limited end split.

LMBR. ADJ.

Table 16. Shear Stress Increase Factors for End-Split.*

	Nominal 2" Lumber	Nominal 3" and Thicker Lumber
No split	2.00	2.00
1/2 x wide face	1.66	----
1/2 x narrow face	----	1.68
1 x wide face	1.34	----
1 x narrow face	----	1.36
1 1/2 x wide face or more	1.00	----
1 1/2 x narrow face	----	1.04
2 x narrow face or more	----	1.00

* For 2"-4" thick lumber manufactured to 19% maximum moisture content, these factors are applied to the recommended value of F_v. For 2" to 4" lumber manufactured to moisture content above 19%, these factors are applied to 0.97 F_v. For 5" and thicker lumber, these factors are applied to the recommended value of F_v.

CHAPTER 6

SOFTWOOD PLYWOOD—GRADES AND SIZES[1]

Plywood is such a familiar product that we sometimes fail to realize it is a relatively recent development in the array of structural materials at our disposal. Historically, decorative veneer was known to artisans of the Egyptian civilization. Wood veneer was used extensively in the 19th century as a means of obtaining attractive surfaces for furniture. Manufactured products made from veneers layed up in the cross-grained configuration and moulded over curved forms appeared as furniture, sewing machine cabinets and luggage in the late 1800's. Moulded plywood was important in the early manufacture of aircraft, quite extensively as late as the 1940's, and to a limited extent today.

Flat plywood paneling was produced early in this century for both decorative and utilitarian purposes, using cold-setting adhesives of low to moderate durability. By 1948 plywood production was about 1,800 million square feet per year in the U.S.A. with about half of this volume as softwood plywood for house construction.

The development of low cost and durable adhesives made softwood plywood production a reality and encouraged its growth in competition with lumber for sheathing of floors, walls, and roofs of buildings. The advent of synthetic resin adhesives which cure rapidly when heated, and have exceptional durability, gave further impetus to structural plywood as a commodity in North America. Softwood plywood production in the United States was over 15 billion square feet per year in 1968 and has continued to grow. The sheathing market formerly served by nominal 1" lumber has almost completely been captured by plywood. Almost all well-integrated forest products companies have plywood divisions today. Lumber and plywood are mutually compatible building materials for structural use.

Plywood Sizes and Constructions

The unit of plywood measure is a piece one foot square by 3/8" thick. Plywood statistics are reported on the thousand square foot, 3/8" thick basis (MSF 3/8" or simply MSF). A shipping unit is a 30" high stack of 4' x 8' sheets. This unit contains 2560 sq. ft. 3/8"-basis, and weighs approximately 2800 lbs.

While other panel sizes are not common, 4' x 9' and 4' x 10' panels are produced. A very few mills are able to make panels to 5' widths. Twelve-foot long panels are available from some mills. Because the production volume of sizes different than 4' x 8' is small, the unit price for these special sizes is greater by about 25 percent. Therefore, designs that require special sizes are usually avoided in conventional construction as much as possible.

The grain direction of the veneer on the outer faces of panels is parallel to the long dimension. A few mills have veneer lathes long enough to cut the 10' and 12' veneer required by long panels. Some mills, however, make long panels by scarf jointing 8' panels end-to-end and cutting them to the new length. Other mills scarf joint veneer for faces, centers and backs.

The demand for panel size versatility in plywood like that found in the hardboard and particleboard industry is stimulating plywood producers to develop processes that will expand the variety of widths and lengths.

Plywood construction terminology given in Figure 14 will be helpful in understanding the discussion to follow. Crossband layers have grain direction at 90 degrees to faces, centers, and backs. All material between the faces and backs is referred to as "core."

---

[1]Chapters 6, 7, and Tables 18-21 make extensive use of information published by the American Plywood Association, 1119 A Street, Tacoma, Washington 98401. APA has conducted extensive research to aid the consumer in the engineered use of plywood. Its field offices throughout the United States are staffed to furnish help to architects, engineers, and builders.

Virtually all softwood plywood in the United States conforms to U.S. Department of Commerce Product Standard PS 1-66, or subsequent revisions of that document. In Canada softwood plywood is produced to Canadian Standards Association Specifications CAS 0120 (Douglas fir) and CSA 0151 (other softwoods).

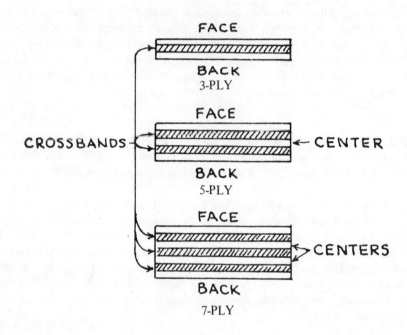

Figure 14. Plywood Construction Terminology

Plywood constructions may be 3-ply up to 1/2" thick. There is no rule against 3-ply 3/4" thick but little is currently produced. A small amount of 3-ply 5/8" thick has been produced and used.

Five-ply construction begins at 1/2" and is used in panels up to 13/16" thick. Panels 7/8" and thicker are 7-ply construction.

Panels of 1/2" thickness are commonly produced in both 3-ply and 5-ply constructions.

One construction is made with an even number of plies. This is 4-ply. The two inner plies are placed with grain parallel to one another to form a laminated crossband between the face and back.

Ply constructions for different sizes are summarized in Table 17.

Unlike lumber, construction plywood is never supplied as an unseasoned product. Dryness is essential to good gluing. Furthermore, a cross-laminated product manufactured unseasoned would develop enormous internal stresses due to the shrinkage differences between veneer in opposing layers. Flatness is an essential feature of panel products and flat panels require careful seasoning of the veneer prior to layup and gluing. Plywood veneer is usually seasoned to 10 percent maximum moisture content, which makes it suitable for nearly all dry-use situations.

Plywood Grades

Softwood plywood is manufactured in two types—*Exterior type* with 100 percent waterproof glue and *Interior type* with fairly moisture-resistant glue. Veneers used in the inner plies of Interior type plywood may be of lower grade than those in Exterior type. Specify Exterior type for all exposed applications. Interior type plywood glue bonds, while moisture resistant, are not permanently waterproof. Interior type may be used wherever it will not be subject to continuous exposure to moisture or extreme humidity that would cause more than 15 percent maximum moisture content.

The wide variety of plywood grades are divided into two general categories, the *appearance* grades in Table 18 and the *engineered* grades in Table 19.

Appearance grades are determined by the grade of veneer (N, A, B, C or D) used for the face and back of the panel. The designation Exterior or Interior is an integral part of the grade mark, generally indicating the type of glue used.

Engineered grades are particularly intended for construction purposes and are designed for maximum structural performance per unit of cost. Appearance grades, although they have allowable stresses for design, have generally higher grade face veneers and other appearance features not essential to engineered use. The engineered grade marks do not always include face and back veneer grades. There are very specific veneer quality requirements for these grades.

Brief descriptions of veneer grades are listed in Table 20.

PS 1-66 is sufficiently broad in coverage to provide for over 50 species of many different strengths. These species have been grouped on the basis of stiffness, into five classifications, each with a group number as listed in Table 21. *The group number in the grade-trademark is based on the species used in the face and back. An exception* to this occurs in the case of engineered grades explained in footnotes 4 and 5 to Table 22, whereby Group 2 species of outer plies are permitted in plywood identified as Group 1, and Group 4 species of outer plies are permitted in plywood identified as Group 3, if they meet special extra thickness and construction requirements.

Grades of particular interest for structural design are Structural I, Structural II, and Standard. These are unsanded grades, not intended for paint-holding surfaces or overlays.

Grades for Engineered Structural Design

Structural I and Structural II are made only with Exterior glue, yet they are designated as Interior grades. PS 1-66 requires that all plywood intended for permanent exposure to weather or moisture have a minimum of C grade veneer. Structural I and II may have D grade backs and inner plies, in which case they do not qualify for that kind of exposure. As an added assurance of performance in structures they are made with Exterior glue and are marked *Interior grade*, with *Exterior Glue* footnoted to the grade stamp.

Table 17. Ply Construction of Various Plywood Thicknesses

Thickness	3	4	5	7
5/16	X			
3/8	X			
1/2	X	X	X	
5/8	X	X	X	
3/4			X	
13/16			X	
7/8			X	X
1				X
1 1/8				X

TABLE 18

Guide to appearance grades of plywood (1)

Type	Use these terms when you specify plywood (2)	Description and Most Common Uses	Typical Grade-trademarks	Face	Back	Inner Plys	\<Most Common Thicknesses (inch)(3)\>					
							1/4	5/16	3/8	1/2	5/8	3/4
Interior Type	N-N, N-A, N-B INT-DFPA	Cabinet quality. One or both sides select all heartwood or all sapwood veneer. For natural finish furniture, cabinet doors, built-ins, etc. Special order items.	N N · G 1 · INT DFPA PS 1 66 ; N A · G 2 · INT DFPA PS 1 66	N	N,A, or B	C						3/4
	N-D-INT-DFPA	For natural finish paneling. Special order item.	N D G 3 INT DFPA PS 1 66	N	D	D	1/4					
	A-A INT-DFPA	For interior applications where both sides will be on view. Built-ins, cabinets, furniture and partitions. Face is smooth and suitable for painting.	A A · G 3 · INT DFPA PS 1 66	A	A	D	1/4		3/8	1/2	5/8	3/4
	A-B INT-DFPA	For uses similar to Interior A-A but where the appearance of one side is less important and two smooth solid surfaces are necessary.	A B · G 4 · INT DFPA PS 1 66	A	B	D	1/4		3/8	1/2	5/8	3/4
	A-D INT-DFPA	For interior uses where the appearance of only one side is important. Paneling, built-ins, shelving, partitions and flow racks.	A-D GROUP 3 INTERIOR DFPA	A	D	D	1/4		3/8	1/2	5/8	3/4
	B-B INT-DFPA	Interior utility panel used where two smooth sides are desired. Permits circular plugs. Paintable.	B B · G 3 · INT DFPA PS 1 66	B	B	D	1/4		3/8	1/2	5/8	3/4
	B-D INT-DFPA	Interior utility panel for use where one smooth side is required. Good for backing, sides of built-ins. Industry: shelving, slip sheets, separator boards and bins.	B-D GROUP 3 INTERIOR DFPA	B	D	D	1/4		3/8	1/2	5/8	3/4
	DECORATIVE PANELS	Rough-sawn, brushed, grooved or striated faces. Good for paneling, interior accent walls, built-ins, counter facing, displays and exhibits.	DECORATIVE B D G 1 INT DFPA	C or btr.	D	D		5/16	3/8	1/2	5/8	
	PLYRON INT-DFPA	Hardboard face on both sides. For counter tops, shelving, cabinet doors, flooring. Hardboard faces may be tempered, untempered, smooth or screened.	PLYRON · INT DFPA			C & D				1/2	5/8	3/4
Exterior Type	A-A EXT-DFPA (4)	Use in applications where the appearance of both sides is important. Fences, built-ins, signs, boats, cabinets, commercial refrigerators, shipping containers, tote boxes, tanks, and ducts.	A A · G 4 · EXT DFPA PS 1 66	A	A	C	1/4		3/8	1/2	5/8	3/4
	A-B EXT-DFPA (4)	For use similar to A-A EXT panels but where the appearance of one side is less important.	A B · G 1 · EXT DFPA PS 1 66	A	B	C	1/4		3/8	1/2	5/8	3/4
	A-C EXT-DFPA (4)	Exterior use where the appearance of only one side is important. Sidings, soffits, fences, structural uses, boxcar and truck lining and farm buildings. Tanks, trays, commercial refrigerators.	A-C GROUP 2 EXTERIOR DFPA	A	C	C	1/4		3/8	1/2	5/8	3/4
	B-B EXT-DFPA (4)	An outdoor utility panel with solid paintable faces.	B B · G 1 · EXT DFPA PS 1 66	B	B	C	1/4		3/8	1/2	5/8	3/4
	B-C EXT-DFPA (4)	An outdoor utility panel for farm service and work buildings, boxcar and truck lining, containers, tanks, agricultural equipment. Also as base for exterior coatings for walls, roofs.	B-C GROUP 3 EXTERIOR DFPA	B	C	C	1/4		3/8	1/2	5/8	3/4
	HDO EXT-DFPA (4)	Exterior type High Density Overlay plywood with hard, semi-opaque resin-fiber overlay. Abrasion resistant. Painting not ordinarily required. For concrete forms, cabinets, counter tops, signs and tanks.	HDO A A G 1 EXT DFPA PS 1 66	A or B	A or B	C plgd		5/16	3/8	1/2	5/8	3/4
	MDO EXT-DFPA (4)	Exterior type Medium Density Overlay with smooth, opaque, resin-fiber overlay heat-fused to one or both panel faces. Ideal base for paint. Highly recommended for siding and other outdoor applications. Also good for built-ins, signs and displays.	MDO B B · G 2 · EXT DFPA PS 1 66	B	B or C	C (5)		5/16	3/8	1/2	5/8	3/4
	303 SIDING EXT-DFPA (7)	Grade designation covers proprietary plywood products for exterior siding, fencing, etc., with special surface treatment such as V-groove, channel groove, striated, brushed, rough-sawn.	303 SIDING 16 oc GROUP 4 EXTERIOR DFPA	(6)	C	C			3/8	1/2	5/8	
	T 1-11 EXT-DFPA	Exterior type, sanded or unsanded, shiplapped edges with parallel grooves 1/4" deep, 3/8" wide. Grooves 2" or 4" o.c. Standard, other spacing optional. Available 8' and 10' lengths and MDO. For siding, paneling, fences, chimney enclosures.	T·1-11 GROUP 1 EXTERIOR DFPA	C or btr.	C	C					5/8	
	PLYRON EXT-DFPA	Exterior panel surfaced both sides with hardboard for use in exterior applications. Faces are tempered, smooth or screened.	PLYRON · EXT DFPA			C				1/2	5/8	3/4
	MARINE EXT-DFPA	Exterior type plywood made only with Douglas fir or western larch. Special solid jointed core construction. Subject to special limitations on core gaps and number of face repairs. Ideal for boat hulls. Also available with HDO or MDO faces.	MARINE A A EXT DFPA PS 1 66	A or B	A or B	B	1/4		3/8	1/2	5/8	3/4

(1) Sanded both sides except where decorative or other surfaces specified.

(2) Available in Group 1, 2, 3, 4, or 5 unless otherwise noted.

(3) Standard 4x8 panel sizes, other sizes available.

(4) Also available in STRUCTURAL I (face, back and inner plys limited to Group 1 species).

(5) Or C-Plugged.

(6) C or better for 5 plys; C-Plugged or better for 3 ply panels.

(7) Stud spacing is shown on grade stamp.

By permission, American Plywood Association

TABLE 19.

Guide to engineered grades of plywood

Use these terms when you specify plywood (2)	Description and Most Common Uses	Typical Grade-trademarks	Face	Back	Inner Plys	Most Common Thicknesses (inch) (3)
Interior Type						
STANDARD C-D INT-DFPA (1) (4)	Unsanded sheathing grade for wall and roof sheathing, subflooring; also industrial uses such as pallets. Also available with intermediate glue (9) or exterior glue. Specify intermediate glue where moderate construction delays are expected; exterior glue where durability is required in long construction delays. For permanent exposure to weather or moisture, only Exterior-type plywood is suitable.	STANDARD 32/16 INTERIOR DFPA; STANDARD 32/16 INTERIOR EXTERIOR GLUE	C	D	D	5/16 3/8 1/2 5/8 3/4 7/8
STRUCTURAL I C-D INT-DFPA and STRUCTURAL II C-D INT-DFPA (9)	Unsanded structural grades where plywood strength properties are of maximum importance. Structural diaphragms, box beams, gusset plates, stressed-skin panels, containers, pallet bins. Made only with exterior glue. STRUCTURAL I limited to Group 1 species for face, back and inner plys. STRUCTURAL II permits Group 1, 2, or 3 species.	STRUCTURAL I 32/16 INTERIOR EXTERIOR GLUE DFPA	C (6)	D (7)	D (7)	5/16 3/8 1/2 5/8 3/4 7/8
UNDERLAYMENT INT-DFPA (4) (1)	For underlayment or combination subfloor-underlayment under resilient floor coverings, carpeting in homes, apartments, mobile homes. Use UNDERLAYMENT with ext. glue where moisture may be present, such as bathrooms, utility rooms. Sanded or touch-sanded as specified.	UNDERLAYMENT GROUP 1 INTERIOR DFPA	C Plugged	D	(8) C & D	1/4 3/8 1/2 5/8 3/4
C-D PLUGGED INT-DFPA (4) (1)	For built-ins, wall and ceiling tile backing, cable reels, walkways, separator boards. Not a substitute for UNDERLAYMENT, as it lacks UNDERLAYMENT's punch-through resistance. Unsanded or touch-sanded as specified.	C-D PLUGGED GROUP 2 INTERIOR DFPA	C Plugged	D	D	5/16 3/8 1/2 5/8 3/4
2-4-1 INT-DFPA (5) (1)	Combination subfloor-underlayment. Quality base for resilient floor coverings, carpeting, wood strip flooring. Use 2·4·1 with exterior glue in areas subject to moisture. Unsanded or touch-sanded as specified.	2·4·1 GROUP 2 INTERIOR DFPA	C Plugged	D	C & D	(available 1-1/8" or 1-1/4")
Exterior Type						
C-C EXT-DFPA (4)	Unsanded grade with waterproof bond for subflooring and roof decking, siding on service and farm buildings, crating, pallets, pallet bins, cable reels.	C-C 32/16 EXTERIOR DFPA	C	C	C	5/16 3/8 1/2 5/8 3/4 7/8
UNDERLAYMENT C-C Plugged EXT-DFPA (4) and C-C PLUGGED EXT-DFPA (4)	For UNDERLAYMENT or combination subfloor-underlayment under resilient floor coverings where particularly severe moisture conditions may be present, as in balcony decks. Also use for tile backing where severe moisture conditions exist. For refrigerated or controlled atmosphere rooms, pallets, fruit pallet bins, reusable cargo containers, tanks and boxcar and truck floors and linings. Sanded or touch-sanded as specified.	UNDERLAYMENT GROUP 3 EXTERIOR C-C PLUGGED DFPA; C-C PLUGGED GROUP 4 EXTERIOR DFPA	C Plugged	C	C (8)	1/4 3/8 1/2 5/8 3/4 7/8
STRUCTURAL I C-C EXT-DFPA	For engineered applications in construction and industry where full Exterior type panels made with all Group 1 woods are required. Unsanded.	STRUCTURAL I 32/16 EXTERIOR DFPA	C	C	C	5/16 3/8 1/2 5/8 3/4 7/8
B-B PLYFORM CLASS I & CLASS II (9) EXT-DFPA	Concrete form grades with high re-use factor. Sanded both sides. Edge-sealed. Mill-oiled unless otherwise specified. Special restrictions on species. Also available in HDO.	B-B PLYFORM CLASS I EXTERIOR DFPA	B	B	C	5/8 3/4

(1) Also available with exterior or intermediate glue.
(2) All grades except PLYFORM available tongue and grooved in panels 1/2" and thicker.
(3) Panels are standard 4x8-foot size. Other sizes available.
(4) Available in Group 1, 2, 3, 4, or 5.
(5) Available in Group 1, 2 or 3 only.
(6) Special improved C grade for structural panels.
(7) Special improved D grade for structural panels.
(8) Ply beneath face a **special** C grade which limits knotholes to 1".
(9) Check dealer for availability in your area.

PLYWD GRADES

By permission, American Plywood Association

Note: A number of the symbols in the first column of Table 18 and 19 are proprietary names for products made by APA member mills. Other mills make similar products meeting the specifications set forth in PS1-66, and marketed by different designations. For example: Plyform Class I & II is Concrete Form Plywood, Class I and II, per PS1-66.

TABLE 20

Veneer grades used in plywood
(Summary...see PS 1 for complete specifications.)

Veneer Grade	Limiting Characteristics	
N Intended for Natural Finish	Presents smooth surface. Veneer shall be all heartwood or all sapwood free from knots, knotholes, open splits, pitch pockets, other open defects, and stain, but may contain pitch streaks averaging not more than 3/8" wide blending with color of wood. If joined, not more than two pieces in 48" width; not more than three pieces in wider panels. Joints parallel to panel edges and well-matched for color and grain. Repairs shall be neatly made, well-matched for color and grain, and limited to a total of six in number in any 4' x 8' sheet.	• Maximum of three "router" patches not exceeding 3/4" x 3-1/2" admitted. No overlapping. • Shims admitted not exceeding 12" in length but may occur only at ends of panel. (Examples of permissible combinations: 3 router patches and 3 shims, 2 router patches and 4 shims, 1 router patch and 5 shims, or 6 shims.) Suitable synthetic fillers may be used to fill 1/32" wide checks, splits up to 1/16" x 2", and chipped areas or other openings not exceeding 1/8" x 1/4".
A	Presents smooth surface. Admits—Pitch streaks blending with color of wood and averaging not more than 3/8" in width. —Sapwood. —Discolorations. Veneer shall be free from knots, knotholes, splits, pitch pockets and other open defects. If of more than one piece, veneer shall be well joined. Repairs shall be neatly made, parallel to grain, and limited to 18 in number in any 4' x 8' sheet, excluding shims; proportionate limits on other sizes.	Patches of "boat," "router," and "sled" type only, not exceeding 2-1/4" in width, and may be die-cut if edges are cut clean and sharp. Radius of ends of boat patches shall not exceed 1/8". • Multiple patching limited to 2 patches, neither of which may exceed 7" in length if either is wider than 1". • Shims admitted except over or around patches or as multiple repairs. Suitable synthetic fillers may be used to fill 1/32" wide checks, splits up to 1/16" x 2", and chipped areas or other openings not exceeding 1/8" x 1/4".
B	Presents solid surface. Admits—Knots up to 1" across the grain if both sound and tight. —Pitch streaks averaging not more than 1" in width. —Discolorations. —Slightly rough but not torn grain, minor sanding and patching defects, including sander skips not exceeding 5% of panel area. Veneer shall be free from open defects except for splits not wider than 1/32", vertical holes up to 1/16" in diameter if not exceeding an average of one per square foot in number, and horizontal or surface tunnels up to 1/16" in width and 1" in length not exceeding 12 in num-	ber in a 4' x 8' sheet (proportionately on other sizes). Repairs shall be neatly made and may consist of patches, plugs, synthetic plugs and shims. • Patches may be "boat," "router," and "sled" type not exceeding 3" in width individually when used in multiple repairs or 4" in width when used as single repairs. • Plugs may be "circular," "dog-bone," and "leaf-shaped," not exceeding 3" in width when used in multiple repairs or 4" in width when used as single repairs. • Synthetic plugs shall present a solid, level, hard surface not exceeding above dimensions. Suitable synthetic fillers may be used to fill small splits or openings up to 1/16" x 2", and chipped areas or other openings not exceeding 1/8" x 1/4".
C	Admits—Tight knots up to 1½" across the grain. —Knotholes not larger than 1" across the grain. Also an occasional knothole not more than 1½" measured across the grain, occurring in any section 12" along the grain in which the aggregate width of all knots and knotholes occurring wholly within the section does not exceed 6" in a 48" width, and proportionately for other widths. —Splits ½" by one-half panel length; 3/8" by any panel length if tapering to a point; 1/4" maximum where located within 1" of parallel panel edge. —Worm or borer holes up to 5/8" x 1½". —Open pitch pockets not wider than 1".	Repairs shall be neatly made and may consist of patches, plugs, and synthetic plugs. Patches ("boat," including die-cut) not exceeding 3" in width individually when used in multiple repairs or 4" in width when used as single repairs. Plugs may be circular, "dog-bone" and leaf-shaped. Synthetic plugs shall present a solid, level, hard surface not exceeding above dimensions.
C (plugged)	Admits—Knotholes, worm or borer holes, and other open defects up to 1/4" x 1/2". —Sound tight knots up to 1½" across the grain. —Splits up to 1/8" wide.	—Ruptured and torn grain. —Pitch pockets if solid and tight. —Plugs, patches and shims.
D	D veneer used only in Interior type plywood and may contain plugs, patches, shims, worm or borer holes. Backs: Admits tight knots not larger than 2½" measured across the grain and knotholes up to 2½" in maximum dimension. An occasional tight knot larger than 2½" but not larger than 3" measured across the grain or knothole larger than 2½" but not larger than 3" maximum dimension, occurring in any section 12" along the grain in which the aggregate width of all knots and knotholes occurring wholly within the section does not exceed 10" in a 48" width and proportionately for other widths. Inner Plys: Permits tight knots. Knotholes limited as for backs. —In sanded panels, knotholes not larger than 2½" maximum dimension in veneer thicker than 1/8".	—Knotholes not exceeding 3½" maximum dimension in center ply of 5-ply STANDARD and C-D Plugged grades. All Plys: Pitch pockets not exceeding 2½" measured across the grain. Splits up to 1" except in backs only not more than one exceeding ½"; not exceeding 1/4" maximum width where located within 1" of parallel panel edge; splits must taper to a point. White pocket in inner plys and backs, not exceeding three of the following characteristics in any combination in any area 24" wide by 12" long. (a) 6" width heavy white pocket. (b) 12" width light white pocket. (c) One knot or knothole or repair 1½" to 2½", or two knots or knotholes or repairs 1" to 1½".

By permission, American Plywood Association

TABLE 21.

Classification of Species

Group 1	Group 2	Group 3	Group 4	Group 5
Birch	Cedar, Port Orford	Alder, Red	Aspen	Fir, Balsam
Sweet	Douglas Fir 2**	Cedar, Alaska	Bigtooth	Poplar, Balsam
Yellow	Fir	Pine	Quaking	
Douglas Fir 1*	California Red	Jack	Birch, Paper	
Larch, Western	Grand	Lodgepole	Cedar	
Maple, Sugar	Noble	Ponderosa	Incense	
Pine, Caribbean	Pacific Silver	Spruce	Western Red	
Pine, Southern	White	Redwood	Fir, Subalpine	
Loblolly	Hemlock, Western	Spruce	Hemlock, Eastern	
Longleaf	Lauan	Black	Pine	
Shortleaf	Almon	Red	Eastern White	
Slash	Bagtikan	White	Sugar	
Tanoak	Red Lauan		Poplar, Western***	
	Tangile		Spruce, Engelmann	
	White Lauan			
	Maple, Black			
	Mengkulang			
	Meranti			
	Pine			
	Pond			
	Red			
	Western White			
	Spruce, Sitka			
	Sweetgum			
	Tamarack			

*Douglas Fir 1 - Washington, Oregon, California, Idaho, Montana, Wyoming, British Columbia, Alberta.
**Douglas Fir 2 - Nevada, Utah, Colorado, Arizona, New Mexico
***Black Cottonwood

By permission, American Plywood Association

TABLE 22.

Guide to Identification Index on Engineered Grades[1]

Thickness (inch)	STANDARD (C-D) INT-DFPA [2] C-C EXT-DFPA			STRUCTURAL I C-D INT-DFPA [3] STR. I C-C EXT	STRUCTURAL II C-D INT-DFPA [3]	
	Group 1	Group 2 or 3 [4]	Group 4 [5]	Group 1 only	Group 1	Group 2 or 3 [4]
5/16	20/0	16/0	12/0	20/0	20/0	16/0
3/8	24/0	20/0	16/0	24/0	24/0	20/0
1/2	32/16	24/0	24/0	32/16	32/16	24/0
5/8	42/20	32/16	30/12	42/20	42/20	32/16
3/4	48/24	42/20	36/16	48/24	48/24	42/20
7/8	----	48/24	42/20	----	----	48/24

Notes:

1. Identification Index numbers shown in the table appear in DFPA grade-trademarks on STANDARD C-D, C-C EXT, STRUCTURAL I C-C and C-D and STRUCTURAL II C-D grades. They refer to maximum recommended spacing of supports in inches when panels are used for roof decking and subflooring with face grain across supports. The left hand number shows spacing for roof supports. The right hand number shows spacing for floor supports. Numbers are based on panel thickness and species make-up detailed in Product Standard PS 1. Under each grade, the table identifies the species classification of the veneer used for outer plys.
2. Also available with exterior or intermediate glue. (Check dealer for availability of intermediate glue in your area.)
3. Manufactured with exterior glue only.
4. Panels made with Group 2 outer plys may carry the Identification Index numbers shown for Group 1 panels when they conform to special thickness and construction requirements detailed in PS 1.
5. Panels made with Group 4 outer plys may carry the Identification Index numbers shown for Group 3 panels when they conform to special thickness and construction requirements detailed in PS 1.

By permission, American Plywood Association

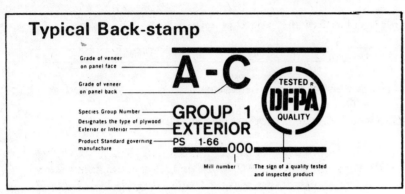

© Copyright 1966 American Plywood Association.

FIGURE 15. – Grade mark of the American Plywood Association (By permission, A.P.A.)

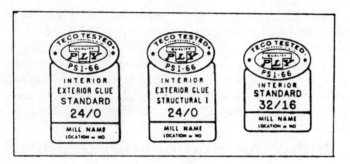

FIGURE 16. – Grade marks of the Timber Engineering Company (samples) (By permission TECO)

Structural I is made with Group 1 species in all plies. Structural II may have Group 1, 2 or 3 species. As a consequence Structural I has higher strength properties than Structural II. This will be mentioned further in Chapter 7.

Several types of Structural I plywood are:

Structural I A-A (Group 1 species, A grade veneer face and back, D or better core.)

Structural I A-C (Group 1 species, A face, C back, D or better core.)

Structural I C-C (Group 1 species, C grade face and back, D or better core.)

Structural I (without face or back designation is C face, D back and core and Group 1 species.)

Structural II is made only with C grade veneer faces and D or better back and core. With Group 1 face and back and Groups 2 or 3 core it carries stresses associated with Group 2. With Group 2 face and back veneers of an oversize thickness and Group 2 or 3 core it also carries stresses associated with Group 1. With Group 2 and/or Group 3 veneers of the normal   thicknesses specified, it carries Group 3 stresses and is used on shorter spans as indicated in Table 22 and Table 25.

It is likely at this point that the matter of plywood grades appears very complicated. This is true and it is one of the consequences of the great variety of species that the industry must handle to utilize the forest resource with a minimum of waste. The manufacturers have been very conscious of the need to keep grades simple so plywood can be easily used by designers. To that end they have devised systems of marking, quality inspection, and surveillance of the use of grade marks. If the user will become familiar with the marking system, place his trust in the integrity of the quality inspection agencies, and insist upon grade marked plywood, he need not worry about species mixes in the plywood products he specifies. The practical simplicity of the grade marking system will become more evident in Chapter 7.

Grade Marks

Figures 15 and 16 illustrate typical grade marks of two principal plywood quality control agencies. The American Plywood Association uses the letters DFPA while the Timber Engineering Company uses the letters TECO. Another quality control agency grade mark is PTL for Pittsburgh Testing Laboratories, and others may occur from time to time. The important feature of any grade mark to insure conformance of the plywood to industry standards is the inclusion of PS1-66.

Grades for General Construction

On the whole, plywood is used for roof and wall sheathing and for subflooring and decking more than any other purpose. The "Standard" grade represents the real bulk of softwood production. Faces are C grade veneer and back and core is D grade. Standard, like Structural I and II, cannot be marked as an Exterior use product although it is often made with the same waterproof adhesive found in marine plywood. It is therefore marked "Interior," with "Exterior Glue" footnoted to the grade stamp as shown in Table 19.

Standard CD, as it is traditionally called, generally is bonded with an Interior or Intermediate glue. The term "Intermediate" is used to describe an adhesive that is much more water-resistant than some of the natural glues formerly used for softwood plywood, which had very little water resistance. Intermediate glue bonded Standard panels are suitable where moderate delays occur in providing the weather protection that is intended, such as moderate construction delays. With Exterior glues durability is assured if protracted delays are encountered. A protracted delay might be three months in a very humid, rainy region.

Identification Index Numbers appear on some of the grade marks in the engineered grades of Table 19. These signify the maximum spacing of supports on which the plywood should be used. The left-hand number is the roof support spacing. The right-hand number is the support spacing for subflooring. These numbers are related both to the grade and the thickness of the plywood, as well as its construction, so the same grade in different thicknesses would have different Indentification Indices, as illustrated in Table 22. Index numbers do not apply to wall sheathing, inasmuch as deflection requirements are less crucial. For walls, straightness, racking resistance and nailing properties for attached siding or shingles are primary considerations.

The spans indices are accepted by most major building codes. Local interpretation may vary so you should familiarize yourself with local codes. Span indices are discussed at further length in Chapter 16.

Concrete Form Plywood

A number of plywood constructions are offered for concrete forming. Concrete form plywood thickness is chosen to minimize the deflection between supports to avoid bulging of the forms. An example of the simplest type of concrete form product is American Plywood Association's B-B Plyform, described in Table 19. It is 5-ply construction, manufactured in 5/8" and 3/4" thickness in two strength and stiffness classes.

Concrete Form Plywood Class I has Group 1, B-grade faces and backs; Group 1 or Group 2 crossbands of C-grade; with a center of C-grade of any species group. It is 50 percent stiffer than Plyform Class II.

Concrete Form Plywood, Class II construction requires Group 1 or Group 2 faces, with species of any group for crossbands and centers. Group 3 may be used for face and back if it is made from veneer that is 1/8" thick as it goes into the press, and if the inner plies are limited of Group 3 or stronger species.

Concrete Form Plywood is sanded smooth and coated at the mill with a release oil to ease removal of the forms and their cleaning for reuse. It is a high-quality product and is usually reused, often ten times or more. It is reoiled after use, sometimes after each use, often less frequently. This is Exterior plywood with edges sealed to prevent moisture penetration into the end grain.

Numerous proprietary concrete form products are offered by various manufacturers. These are usually designed to maximize the reusability, to reduce form cleaning labor, and to improve surface smoothness and release properties. Various oil-exuding surface coatings, polyethylene wax and overlaid fiber surfaces are used. Some coatings are hot roll coated to the plywood in sufficient thickness that sanding can be omitted and the use of lower grade face veneer with attendant economy, made possible.

Other Plywood Products

Hardwood plywood for utilitarian as well as decorative purposes is manufactured very extensively using both native North American species and imported woods. In Europe and Asia softwood plywood has not occupied the position in the building industry that it has in North America. It is receiving increasing acceptance in those countries, however, and is being manufactured more extensively in the Scandinavian countries and is exported from the U.S.A. and Canada. Hardwood plywood is widely used in Europe and Asia and is imported into the North American countries.

The species classification table (Table 21) includes numerous hardwoods, both native and imported, which appear as decorative faces as well as in the core of some ostensibly softwood plywood products. As long as PS1-66 is a part of the grade mark label, this practice is approved.

CHAPTER 7

DESIGN PROPERTIES OF SOFTWOOD PLYWOOD

Designing with plywood presents no unusual difficulties. The proper choice of strength properties and section properties is the key to structural design computations for plywood. The American Plywood Association publication "Plywood Design Specification" provides all the information required for designs based on plywood produced under PS 1-66. (See page 50, Chapter 6.) Similar information is available from the Council of the Forest Industries of British Columbia, covering Canadian softwood plywood. This chapter draws particularly upon the information in the APA "Plywood Design Specifications."

Section Properties

Plywood manufacturers require some latitude in the way they assemble various thicknesses of veneer together to form panels. This is necessary for the economical recovery and use of all the different grades of veneer in a log. In high speed plywood mills the time required to peel a 20-inch log to veneer is usually 15 to 30 seconds. During this short period of time it is not feasible to stop the process to examine the veneer quality or to make adjustments to the thickness of the peeled veneer. Since a log may contain two or more levels of wood quality, it may produce several grades of veneer. The mill needs to have some place for each of these grades.

If each plywood construction had equal veneer thickness in all layers, the veneer thickness would need to be different for each of the 3-ply sizes, for each of the 5-ply sizes, and for each of the 7-ply sizes. Veneer of a particular thickness would have very limited use under these circumstances. PS 1-66 specifies minimum veneer thicknesses for the various layers in plywood construction.

As an example, the minimum thickness of face and back veneers in 1/2" rough 3-ply panels is 1/8". The cross-band for a panel of this thickness would need to be 1/4" thick. It would be permissible for a producer to manufacture this panel with three 1/6" veneers, and this is commonly done by many mills. The user might not know which of these constructions he would receive on an order. The properties information in Tables 23 and 24 are based on 1/8" face and back veneers for design in the parallel-to-face-grain direction, and on 1/6" veneer for design in the direction across the face grain. This practice results in safe design regardless of which construction the user receives. Note the information on 1/2" rough 3-ply construction in Table 26.

The published section properties used for designing with plywood are the minimum ones that could be found in any panel of the thickness and grade that could be produced under PS 1-66.

If all veneer layers were of the same species group, one table of plywood section properties, such as Table 23, would suffice. However, a mixing of species groups within a plywood grade is often done. Different groups, with their different elastic moduli, require a transformation of veneer layer widths in developing the section properties. Section properties for plywood with inner plies of different species groups than outer plies are found in Table 24. The section properties in these two tables are for plywood sections one foot wide, except the "effective thickness for shear" in colums 3 and 4, which is for shear-through-the-thickness calculations.

While there is a certain inefficiency in the need to assume the minimum section properties for both the parallel and perpendicular-to-face grain directions when they cannot possibly co-exist, the need for a simple system of assuredly safe section properties adapted to the great variety of plywood construction variables justifies that inefficiency.

Allowable Stresses for Plywood

Table 25, taken from "Plywood Design Specification," gives the allowable stresses for softwood plywood. With the exception of the two types of shear properties all of the allowable stresses in Table 25 are counterparts of lumber design properties.

Table 23. Effective Section Properties for Plywood (12" widths)

All plys from same species group.

(Includes following grades: Structural I and II, Marine Exterior, all grades using Group 4 stresses.)

		All properties adjusted to account for reduced effectiveness of plys with grain perpendicular to applied stress									
		Effective Thickness for Shear		Properties for Stress Applied Parallel with Face Grain				Properties for Stress Applied Perpendicular with Face Grain			
1 Thickness (in.)	2 Approx. Weight (psf)	3 All Grades Using Exterior Glue (in.)	4 All Grades Using Interior Glue (in.)	5 Area for Tension and Compression (in.2)	6 Moment of Inertia I (in.4)	7 Effective Section Modulus KS (in.3)	8 Rolling Shear Constant I/Q (in.)	9 Area for Tension and Compression (in.2)	10 Moment of Inertia I (in.4)	11 Effective Section Modulus KS (in.3)	12 Rolling Shear Constant I/Q (in.)
Unsanded Panels											
5/16 U	1.0	0.318	0.300	2.400	0.026	0.147	0.216	1.200	0.002	0.032	—
3/8 U	1.1	0.375	0.375	2.400	0.048	0.215	0.286	1.500	0.003	0.049	—
1/2 U*	1.5	0.574	0.500	3.600	0.100	0.339	0.410	2.400	0.029	0.183	0.215
5/8 U	1.8	0.662	0.625	4.586	0.175	0.477	0.546	3.000	0.056	0.286	0.269
3/4 U	2.2	0.750	0.750	4.600	0.266	0.603	0.663	4.500	0.132	0.509	0.348
13/16 U	2.4	0.794	0.813	4.605	0.319	0.668	0.722	4.500	0.182	0.628	0.403
7/8 U	2.6	0.949	0.875	6.900	0.474	0.922	0.594	4.500	0.207	0.643	0.507
1 U	3.0	1.037	1.000	5.354	0.574	0.976	0.728	6.639	0.391	1.020	0.589
1-1/8 U	3.3	1.125	1.125	6.840	0.815	1.231	0.776	5.250	0.502	1.122	0.729
Sanded Panels**											
1/4 S	0.8	0.276	0.240	1.680	0.013	0.091	0.179	1.200	0.001	0.027	—
3/8 S	1.1	0.375	0.375	1.680	0.040	0.182	0.308	2.100	0.007	0.079	—
1/2 S	1.5	0.574	0.500	3.120	0.081	0.277	0.438	2.400	0.029	0.183	0.215
5/8 S	1.8	0.662	0.625	3.135	0.135	0.367	0.557	2.914	0.076	0.345	0.316
3/4 S	2.2	0.750	0.750	3.876	0.207	0.470	0.691	4.400	0.168	0.597	0.394
7/8 S	2.6	0.949	0.875	3.994	0.329	0.639	0.637	5.786	0.279	0.811	0.535
1 S	3.0	1.037	1.000	5.520	0.498	0.846	0.673	6.646	0.454	1.119	0.636
1-1/8 S	3.3	1.125	1.125	5.978	0.664	1.003	0.746	6.660	0.650	1.385	0.753

*for 1/2" 3-ply use the following:

1/2 U	1.5	0.463	0.500	3.000	0.110	0.373	0.387	2.000	0.008	0.088	—

**includes Touch-Sanded

By permission, American Plywood Assn.

Table 24. Effective Section Properties for Plywood (12" widths)

Face plys of different species group from inner plys.

(All grades not in Table 23)

		All properties adjusted to account for reduced effectiveness of plys with grain perpendicular to applied stress									
		Effective Thickness for Shear		Properties for Stress Applied Parallel with Face Grain				Properties for Stress Applied Perpendicular with Face Grain			
1 Thickness (in.)	2 Approx. Weight (psf)	3 All Grades Using Exterior Glue (in.)	4 All Grades Using Interior Glue (in.)	5 Area for Tension and Compression (in.2)	6 Moment of Inertia I (in.4)	7 Effective Section Modulus KS (in.3)	8 Rolling Shear Constant I/Q (in.)	9 Area for Tension and Compression (in.2)	10 Moment of Inertia I (in.4)	11 Effective Section Modulus KS (in.3)	12 Rolling Shear Constant I/Q (in.)
Unsanded Panels											
5/16 U	1.0	0.286	0.270	2.400	0.026	0.147	0.216	0.600	0.001	0.024	—
3/8 U	1.1	0.323	0.323	2.400	0.047	0.215	0.286	0.750	0.002	0.038	—
1/2 U*	1.5	0.471	0.410	3.000	0.099	0.336	0.409	1.200	0.016	0.115	0.215
5/8 U	1.8	0.527	0.498	3.493	0.171	0.466	0.539	1.500	0.031	0.180	0.269
3/4 U	2.2	0.585	0.585	3.500	0.261	0.591	0.659	2.250	0.070	0.316	0.347
13/16 U	2.4	0.615	0.629	3.502	0.313	0.655	0.720	2.250	0.096	0.388	0.401
7/8 U	2.6	0.730	0.673	4.650	0.418	0.813	0.662	2.250	0.110	0.397	0.502
1 U	3.0	0.788	0.760	3.876	0.531	0.903	0.800	3.320	0.204	0.625	0.585
1-1/8 U	3.3	0.848	0.848	4.620	0.724	1.093	0.869	2.625	0.262	0.688	0.722
Sanded Panels**											
1/4 S	0.8	0.241	0.210	1.680	0.013	0.091	0.179	0.600	0.001	0.019	—
3/8 S	1.1	0.305	0.305	1.680	0.040	0.181	0.309	1.050	0.004	0.053	—
1/2 S	1.5	0.450	0.392	2.400	0.080	0.271	0.436	1.200	0.016	0.115	0.215
5/8 S	1.8	0.508	0.480	2.407	0.133	0.360	0.557	1.457	0.040	0.214	0.315
3/4 S	2.2	0.567	0.567	2.778	0.201	0.456	0.687	2.200	0.088	0.366	0.393
7/8 S	2.6	0.711	0.655	2.837	0.301	0.585	0.704	2.893	0.145	0.496	0.531
1 S	3.0	0.769	0.742	3.600	0.431	0.733	0.763	3.323	0.234	0.682	0.632
1-1/8 S***	3.3	0.825	0.825	3.829	0.566	0.855	0.849	3.307	0.334	0.843	0.748

*for 1/2" 3-ply use the following:

1/2 U	1.5	0.393	0.424	3.000	0.109	0.372	0.387	1.000	0.006	0.067	—

**includes Touch-Sanded

***for 2-4-1 use the following:

1-1/8 2-4-1	3.3	0.832	0.832	5.360	0.655	1.000	0.746	4.894	0.322	0.844	0.642

By permission, American Plywood Assn.

Table 25. Allowable Stresses for Plywood

Dry Location   **Normal Load Basis, psi**   **Conforming to U. S. Product Standard PS 1**

Type of Stress	Species Group	EXTERIOR A-A, A-C, C-C', and comparable grades of Overlaid plywood. STRUCTURAL I A-A, STRUCTURAL I A-C, STRUCTURAL I C-C, and Marine (Use Group 1 stresses)	EXTERIOR A-B, B-B, B-C C-C (Plugged). Plyform Class I[1] Plyform Class II[1] and comparable grades of Overlaid plywood. STRUCTURAL I C-D (Use Group 1 stresses). STRUCTURAL II C-D STANDARD SHEATHING (Exterior Glue)[1] ALL INTERIOR GRADES WITH EXTERIOR GLUE	All other grades of Interior including STANDARD SHEATHING[1]
Extreme fiber in bending, Tension Face grain parallel or perpendicular to span (at 45° to face grain use 1/6)	1 / 2, 3 / 4	2,000 / 1,400 / 1,200	1,650 / 1,200 / 1,000	1,650 / 1,200 / 1,000
Compression Parallel or perpendicular to face grain (at 45° to face grain use 1/3)	1 / 2, 3 / 4	1,650 / 1,200 / 1,000	1,550 / 1,100 / 950	1,550 / 1,100 / 950
Bearing (on face)	1 / 2, 3 / 4	340 / 220 / 160	340 / 220 / 160	340 / 220 / 160
Shear in plane perpendicular to plys[2] Parallel or perpendicular to face grain (at 45° increase 100%)	1 / 2, 3 / 4	250 / 185 / 175	250 / 185 / 175	230 / 170 / 160
Shear, rolling, in plane of plys[3] Parallel or perpendicular to face grain (at 45° increase 1/3)	All	53	53	48
Modulus of Elasticity in bending Face grain parallel or perpendicular to span	1 / 2 / 3 / 4	1,800,000 / 1,500,000 / 1,200,000 / 900,000		

(1) Exterior C-C, Structural II and Standard Sheathing: The combination of Identification-Index designation and panel thickness determine the minimum species group and, therefore, the stress permitted, as follows:

5/16 - 20/0, 3/8 - 24/0, 1/2 - 32/16, 5/8 - 42/20, 3/4 - 48/24 — Use Group 2 working stresses.

All other combinations of C-C and Standard — Use Group 4 working stresses. Other combinations of Structural II — Use Group 3 working stresses.

For Plyform Class I — Use Group 1 stresses. For Plyform Class II — Use Group 3 stresses.

For 2-4-1 — Use Group 1 stresses.

(2) Shear-through the thickness stresses are based on the most common structural applications where the plywood is attached to framing around its boundary. Where the plywood is attached to framing at only two sides — as in the heel joint of a truss — multiply the allowable shear-through-the-thickness values by 89% where framing is parallel to face grain and 75% where it is perpendicular.

(3) For Marine and STRUC I grades use 75 psi. For STRUC II use 56 psi.

Wet or Damp Location

Where moisture content is 16% or more, multiply the dry location values by the following factors:

For all grades of Exterior and Interior plywood with exterior glue,

Extreme fiber in bending — 75%	Modulus of Elasticity — 89%
Tension — 69%	Shear — 84%
Compression — 61%	Bearing — 67%

For all other grades of Interior,

Extreme fiber in bending — 69%	Modulus of Elasticity — 80%
Tension — 69%	Shear — 84%
Compression — 61%	Bearing — 67%

PLYWD PROPERTIES

Table 26. Plywood Panel Constructions Used in Calculating Section Properties

Other constructions in common use produce higher Section Property values

Plywood Thickness (inches)	No. of Plys	Veneer Thickness (inches)					
		For properties parallel to face grain			For properties perpendicular to face grain		
		Faces	Centers	Crossbands	Faces	Centers	Crossbands
Rough Panels							
5/16 R	3	1/10 0.100	— —	1 @ 1/10 0.100	1/10 0.100	— —	1 @ 1/10 0.100
3/8 R	3	1/10 0.100	— —	1 @ 3/16 0.175	1/8 0.125	— —	1 @ 1/8 0.125
1/2 R*	3*	1/8 0.125	— —	1 @ 1/4 0.250	1/6 0.167	— —	1 @ 1/6 0.167
1/2 R	5	1/10 0.100	1 @ 1/10 0.100	2 @ 1/10 0.100	1/10 0.100	1 @ 1/10 0.100	2 @ 1/10 0.100
5/8 R	5	1/10 0.100	1 @ 3/16 0.182	2 @ 1/8 0.121	1/8 0.125	1 @ 1/8 0.125	2 @ 1/8 0.125
3/4 R	5	1/10 0.100	1 @ 3/16 0.183	2 @ 3/16 0.183	1/8 0.125	1 @ 1/8 0.125	2 @ 3/16 0.188
13/16 R	5	1/10 0.100	1 @ 3/16 0.184	2 @ 7/32 0.214	1/8 0.125	1 @ 3/16 0.188	2 @ 3/16 0.188
7/8 R	7	1/10 0.100	2 @ 3/16 0.188	3 @ 1/10 0.100	1/8 0.125	2 @ 1/8 0.125	3 @ 1/8 0.125
1 R	7	1/10 0.100	2 @ 1/8 0.123	3 @ 3/16 0.185	1/8 0.125	2 @ 1/10 0.098	3 @ 3/16 0.184
1-1/8 R	7	1/10 0.100	2 @ 3/16 0.185	3 @ 3/16 0.185	1/8 0.125	2 @ 7/32 0.219	3 @ 1/6 0.146
Sanded Panels**							
1/4 S	3	1/10 0.070	— —	1 @ 1/10 0.100	1/10 0.070	— —	1 @ 1/10 0.100
3/8 S	3	1/10 0.070	— —	1 @ 7/32 0.235	1/8 0.100	— —	1 @ 3/16 0.175
1/2 S	5	1/10 0.070	1 @ 1/8 0.120	2 @ 1/8 0.120	1/8 0.100	1 @ 1/10 0.100	2 @ 1/10 0.100
5/8 S	5	1/10 0.070	1 @ 1/8 0.121	2 @ 3/16 0.182	1/8 0.100	1 @ 3/16 0.182	2 @ 1/8 0.121
3/4 S	5	1/10 0.070	1 @ 3/16 0.183	2 @ 7/32 0.214	1/8 0.100	1 @ 3/16 0.183	2 @ 3/16 0.183
7/8 S	7	1/10 0.070	2 @ 1/10 0.096	3 @ 3/16 0.181	1/8 0.100	2 @ 1/10 0.096	3 @ 1/6 0.161
1 S	7	1/10 0.070	2 @ 1/6 0.160	3 @ 3/16 0.180	1/8 0.100	2 @ 1/8 0.123	3 @ 3/16 0.185
1-1/8 S***	7	1/10 0.070	2 @ 3/16 0.179	3 @ 7/32 0.219	1/8 0.100	2 @ 3/16 0.185	3 @ 3/16 0.185

*Allowed in Standard sheathing grades only
**Includes Touch-Sanded
***for 1-1/8 2-4-1 use the following:

1-1/8 2-4-1	7	1/10 0.070	2 @ 3/16 0.179	3 @ 7/32 0.219	3/16 0.158	2 @ 1/8 0.125	3 @ 3/16 0.187

By permission, American Plywood Association

Figure 17 depicts principal types of plywood loading and the commonly used design formulae for simple plywood structures. The anisotropic nature of plywood can lead to analysis as orthotropic multilayered plate models for precise design, but such treatment cannot be justified in the usual engineering budget for timber structures.

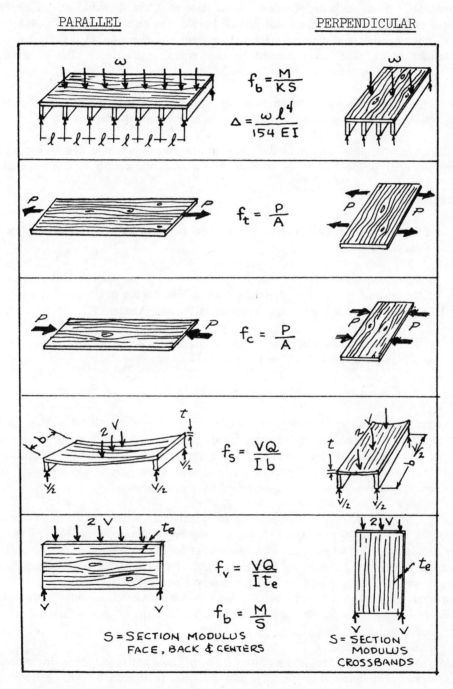

Figure 17. Relationships of Principal Stress to Plywood Face Grain

Extreme fiber in bending (F_b) is selected from Table 25 on the basis of plywood grade and species group of the face veneer. This allowable stress is used for either principal face grain direction with respect to span direction. The directional difference in performance is taken into account in the Section Modulus properties for the two directions in Tables 23 and 24, the KS column. Do not substitute I/C for KS or errors will be incurred.

Tension (F_t). When designing plywood for use in tension, the allowable stresses are selected from Table 25 on the basis of face ply species group and plywood grade. The plies which are effective in sustaining tension stress differ for the two directions with reference to face grain. Consideration of the effective plies (those parallel to load direction) and of the lower strength species group in the inner plies of some constructions, is incorporated into the section property data of Tables 23 and 24.

In certain designs where the tension load might be at a 45-degree angle to the face grain 1/6 F_t is used with the *full cross-sectional area* of all plies, if all plies are of the same species group.

In cases where all plies are not of the same species group, panel thickness is reduced by calculating the effect of a hypothetically reduced inner ply thickness by the ratio of inner ply to face ply elastic modulus.

The procedure is:

1. Determine an actual construction of panel (as from Table 26) and calculate total thickness of material for each species group.

2. Determine adjusted thickness of inner plies by multiplying their actual thickness by the modulus of elasticity of the inner plies divided by the modulus of elasticity of the face plies. Assume lowest species group permitted in Product Standard PS 1-66. (See Chapter 6.)

3. Add this adjusted thickness to the actual thickness of the face plies, arriving at an effective thickness somewhat less than the actual thickness.

4. Apply stresses for the species group of the face plies to this new adjusted thickness.

Compression (F_c) is the direct counterpart of F_c parallel to grain in lumber. Only the veneers with grain parallel to load direction are included in the area values given in Tables 23 and 24. In cases where direction of compressive stress is at 45 degrees to face grain direction 1/3 F_c is used in conjunction with the *full cross-sectional area of all plies,* when all plies of the same species group. A species group adjustment to this area, for dissimilar species groups on basis of E, as described for tension is sometimes necessary.

Bearing Compression ($F_{c⊥}$) perpendicular to the panel faces is used in the same way for plywood as for lumber. Allowable values are given in Table 25 and are selected for design on the basis of face ply species group. The designer should note that when extra-thick face veneers of Group 2 species are used in Group 1 panels, and of Group 4 species in Group 3 panels, per footnotes 4 and 5 of Table 22, allowable bearing stress for the actual species group of the panel face should be used for design. Since the choice is usually out of the control of the designer, inasmuch as the two alternates are usually regarded as interchangeable in the market, it would be prudent to design bearing areas on the basis of the Group 2, or Group 4 species. Bearing is not always a crucial aspect of plywood design.

Shear stress in plywood designs does differ from the usual horizontal shear stress (shear parallel-to-grain) concepts for lumber. This arises from the markedly different performance resulting from cross-lamination of veneers.

Rolling Shear in Plane of Plies (F_s). When plywood is loaded perpendicular to the panel faces, in flexure, the plies with grain perpendicular to the direction of the span are the weakest aspect of the construction with respect to shear stress resistance. The wood fibers in these plies roll at stresses below the shear parallel to grain strength normally accorded solid lumber. The presence of checks in the veneer, which form during the cutting process, and usually open when the peeled veneer layer is flattened in the pressing operation, are partly responsible for this condition, even though many of these "lathe checks" as they are called are filled with adhesive. This is illustrated in Figure 18.

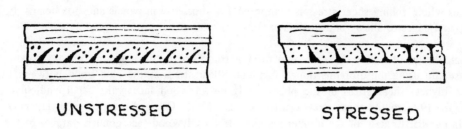

Figure 18. Rolling Shear in Crossband

The formula for shear stress design is:

$$f_s = \frac{VQ}{bI}$$

V = Vertical shear load, pounds.

b = Width of panel, inches (width of web for stressed skin glued panels).

f_s = Rolling shear stress, psi.

I = Moment of inertia of section perpendicular to the span, in^4

Q = Statical moment of the area of the plies with grain parallel to the stress direction, which are outside of the ply containing the neutral axis, in^3

Values of I/Q are given in columns 8 and 12 of Tables 23 and 24. I/Q is called the "rolling shear constant." To illustrate:

For ½" 3-ply from Table 23, parallel to grain.

I = 0.110 (actually 0.1094 if calculated)
Q = 0.125 x 12 x .187 = 0.281
I/Q = 0.1094/0.281 = 0.387

For 1/2" 5-ply from Table 23, parallel-to-face grain

I = 0.100 (actually 0.097 if calculated.)
Q = 0.1 x 12 x 0.2 = 0.24
I/Q = 0.097/0.24 = 0.410

For 1" 7-ply from Table 23, parallel-to-face grain

I = 0.574 (actually 0.564, if calculated)
Q = 0.1 x 12 x 0.45 + 0.125 x 12 x .155 = 0.772
I/Q = 0.564/0.772 = 0.728

Of course it is not necessary to carry out the kinds of calculations illustrated above, because the necessary I/Q values are in Tables 23 and 24.

The allowable values F_s are found in Table 25. These are appropriate to all flexural conditions where the neutral axis is at the center of the panel.

In cases where rolling shear stress is computed for stressed-skin panels and box-beams, F_s is reduced by 50 percent at panel edges to allow for stress concentrations.

The calculation of rolling shear stress in the innermost rolling shear region of a plywood-lumber building component is set up using the aforementioned formula. Shear stress at the glue bond between the lumber and plywood is the highest shear stress in the plywood. If the plywood face grain is perpendicular to the lumber grain, as in Figure 19A, rolling shear stress can be calculated with Q based on the veneer layers outboard of this plane with grain parallel to grain of the lumber member. If the plywood face grain is parallel to the lumber grain, as in Figure 19B, rolling shear stress can be calculated with Q based on those veneer plies with grain parallel to lumber grain, which are outboard of the crossband nearest the neutral axis.

In reality the shear load is spread over a region within the plywood that extends beyond the width of the lumber, and more so as it approaches the extreme faces of the component. Rolling shear stresses were developed with some dependence on this spread of the stress. Consequently, if the rolling shear region is at a panel edge, this spreading of stress can extend in only one direction and the 50 percent reduction in F_s is made in view of the concentration that must occur.

The allowable rolling shear stress for plywood is about one-half of the shear parallel to grain allowable stress for lumber.[1] Table 27 helps illustrate why the rolling shear is usually the critical shear stress in a stressed-skin panel. The shear stress level increases as the location becomes closer to the neutral axis. This increase is not usually great enough to exceed the shear parallel to grain allowable stress for lumber, unless web depth becomes large.

Table 27 illustrates this effect. For two sizes of lumber webs, and an assumed 12"-web spacing in a stressed skin panel made with 5/8" 5-ply Structural I skins, values of Q/I have been tabulated at four distances from, and at, the neutral axis. The allowable shear loads, V, from the formula:

$$F_s = \frac{VQ}{bI} \qquad V = \frac{F_s\, bI}{Q}$$

have also been tabulated, using F_s = 75 psi for Structural I plywood and F_s = 1.66 x 95 = 158 psi for webs without severe end checking. It is evident that the most limiting loads, V, for the 6 3/4" deep panel, are dictated by the stress at the innermost crossband of the plywood, i.e., the inside face of the middle ply (which is congruent with the outer face of the crossband closest to the neutral axis). For deeper panels, such as the 12 1/2" deep design, stress at the web neutral axis becomes limiting.

If the lumber-web-to-plywood-skin joint is at the edge of a plywood sheet, the value of F_s for plywood would need to be reduced to 37.5 psi, in which case the plywood crossband nearest to the neutral axis would limit the load V for the 12 1/2" panel to 1915 lbs. (3830 ÷ 2 = 1915) and it would become limiting. However, usually the load tributary to the edge web is lower than that carried by a central web in a panel.

This discussion of rolling shear is included to provide a little deeper insight into the significance of this property for design. It comes to our attention again in Chapters 16 and 17.

---

1. No.1 Douglas fir J & P, Table 3A, F_v = 95 x 1.66 = 158 psi
   Structural 1 plywood, F_s = 75 psi

A - PLYWOOD FACE GRAIN PERPENDICULAR TO GRAIN OF LUMBER WEB.

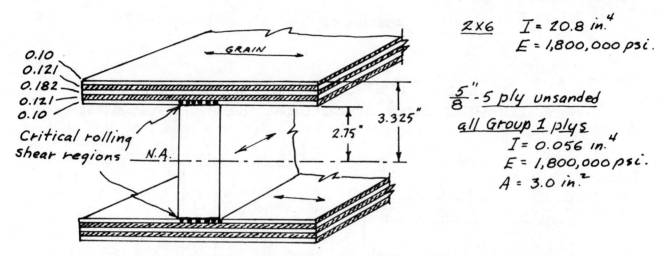

GRAIN

0.10
0.121
0.182
0.121
0.10

Critical rolling shear regions

N.A.

3.325"

2.75"

2×6 $I = 20.8$ in.^{4}
$E = 1,800,000$ psi.

$\frac{5}{8}$" - 5 ply unsanded
all Group 1 plys
  $I = 0.056$ in.^{4}
  $E = 1,800,000$ psi.
  $A = 3.0$ in.^{2}

Q = Statical Moment of crossbands about neutral axis.
$= 12 \times 0.121 [(2.75 + 0.1605) + (2.75 + 0.4635)]$
$= 8.9$ in.^{3}

I = Moment of Inertia of lumber web and two plywood flanges about the neutral axis.
$= 20.8 + 2(0.056 + 3.0 \times 3.0625^2) = 77.112$ in.^{4}

b = width of contact area between flange & web.

B - PLYWOOD FACE GRAIN PARALLEL TO GRAIN OF LUMBER WEB.

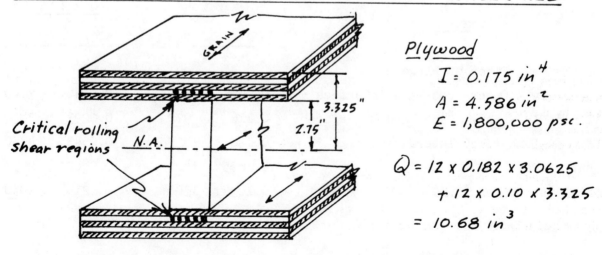

GRAIN

Critical rolling shear regions

N.A.

3.325"

2.75"

Plywood
  $I = 0.175$ in.^{4}
  $A = 4.586$ in.^{2}
  $E = 1,800,000$ psi.

$Q = 12 \times 0.182 \times 3.0625$
$+ 12 \times 0.10 \times 3.325$
$= 10.68$ in.^{3}

$I = 20.8 + 2(0.175 + 4.586 \times 3.0625^2) = 107.55$ in.^{4}
b = width of contact area between flange & web.

FIGURE 19. - I and Q for lumber-plywood component
(an example)

Table 27. Location of Critical Shear Region

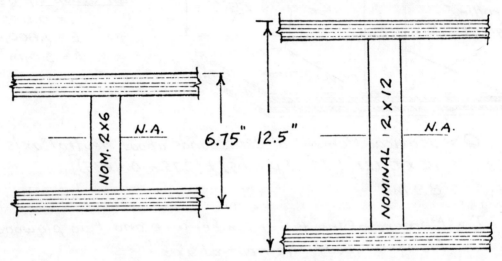

PLYWOOD: ⅝" STRUCTURAL 1 F_s = 75 psi
LUMBER: NO.1 STRUCTURAL J&P F_s = 158 psi

PLYWOOD FACE GRAIN
PARALLEL TO GRAIN
OF LUMBER WEB

Location	Panel with 2 x 6 Webs		Panel with 2 x 12 Webs	
	Q/I	V	Q/I	V
At Extreme Fiber of Plywood	0	oo	0	oo
Outer Ply - Outer Crossband Interface	0.0625	1800	0.0148	7600
Middle Ply - Inner Crossband Interface	0.116	970	0.0293	3830
Plywood-Lumber Web Interface	0.130	1825	0.0543	4350
Quarter-Depth of Web	0.1695	1400	0.0882	2690
Mid-Depth of Web (N.A.)	0.1835	1300	0.1219	1950

Table 25 provides for a 33 percent increase in F_s when the angle of face grain to direction of principal stress is 45 degrees. If each ply was of the same species group they would all have the same effective strength and stiffness at this angle to the grain. The elastic modulus as an angle of 45 degrees to grain is about 25 percent of the parallel to grain angle. Applications where this is important are infrequent, but do come up from time to time.

Shear in plane perpendicular to plies, F_v. When plywood is subject to shear though its thickness a considerably higher value of allowable shear stress governs designs. Structures in which plywood serves as the webs of bending members, such as plywood box beams, folded plates, or diaphragms, are subject to this type of shear stress. Allowable values are given in Table 25 and are selected on the basis of face-ply species group. The usual shear equation:

$$F_v = \frac{VQ}{bI} = \frac{3V}{2bh}$$

is used for these computations. The value of bh is obtained using the height, h, of the web member, and an effective thickness, b, from columns 3 and 4 of Tables 23 and 24. *Do not use I/Q from Columns 8 or 12.*

The allowable stresses, F_v, apply for face grain either parallel or perpendicular to direction of principal stress. In instances where face grain is at 45 degrees to direction of principal stress, F_v may be doubled. This is an important consideration which may prove useful in designing for maximum performance in shear of box-beam web members.

Elastic modulus, E. The values of elastic modulus in Table 25 are suitable for use in flexural calculations for plywood panels loaded perpendicular to the faces. This is an effective modulus of elasticity including an allowance for shear deflection. A discussion of shear deflection is given in Appendix D. The deflection of members in flexure relates to two wood properties. Basically, the elastic modulus of the wood fibers in tension and compression, determines the amount of lengthening of fibers below the neutral axis, and shortening of fibers above the neutral axis. In addition the tendency of the fiber layers to slide on one another, or deform elastically in this fashion, depends on the shear modulus of wood, a property not often published or used in design, but generally in the range of 10 to 20 percent of the elastic modulus in tension and compression.

For plywood the shear modulus in the cross plies is extremely low, and the published effective E values for plywood have been reduced ten percent to provide for this shear slip contribution to total deflection, adequate for most sheathing plywood applications

In certain cases, however, where short spans are involved (span to thickness ratios from 15 to 20 or lower), deflections computed using the tabulated modulus of elasticity will underestimate the total actual deflection. In such cases the shear deflection should be calculated separately and added to the bending deflection.

Bending deflection is calculated in the usual way using modulus of elasticity at 1.1 times the values given in Table 25, and I from Table 23 or 24.

Shear deflection is approximated using the following formula *for a uniformly loaded 5-ply panel:*

$$\Delta_s = \frac{w \; C \; h^2 \; \ell^2}{1270 \; E_e \; I}$$

where Δ_s = shear deflection, inches
w = uniform load, lbs per square foot
h = panel thickness, inches
ℓ = clear span between supports, inches
E_e = modulus of elasticity from Table 25
I = moment of inertia, from Tables 23 or 24
C = constant, equal to 120 for panels applied with face grain parallel to direction of principal stress, and 60 panels with face grain perpendicular to direction of principal stress

Other formulas for 3-ply and 7-ply panels would be needed for designs using that type of plywood. Such design procedures are the topic of more advanced courses on wood structural design.

Stressed skin panels and box beams have such low shear stresses in the flanges that shear deflection in the flanges may be ignored. For these assemblies, therefore, the usual modulus of elasticity may be increased 10 percent for flange material, to restore the portion of the deflection which is ordinarily caused by shear.

Duration of Load

The allowable design properties of Table 25 are all for "normal" load duration. As with lumber allowable stresses, adjustment for other durations of maximum load follow Figure 10 with no adjustment for E.

These increases are not cumulative. The resulting structural sections shall not be smaller than required for a longer duration of a lesser load. The increases apply to mechanical fasteners and glued or nailed-glued joints.

Duration of load factors are treated at length in Chapter 3, beginning on page 27.

Adjustments for Moisture Conditions in Service

Commercial softwood plywood is manufactured at a moisture content suitable for dry-use conditions. No allowances for "installed green, seasoned in service" of the type required for some lumber and heavy timber are necessary. The values in Table 25 are for dry-use conditions.

If equilibrium moisture content in service will be 16 percent or higher, as in applications directly exposed to weather, modify the dry location of use values as described in the footnotes to Table 25.

Exterior plywood must be used if moisture content is ever likely to exceed 18 percent.

Adjustments for Chemical Treatment

The allowable stresses of Table 25 apply without any adjustment to plywood that is pressure-impregnated with preservative chemicals except any arising out of moisture in use conditions previously mentioned. This assumes the treatments used are approved processes of the American Wood Preservers Association Specification C-9. Other processes may affect strength and stiffness, and the designer should consult the company which furnishes such other treatments.

Surface and dip preservation treatments do not require that wood strength or stiffness be adjusted.

Allowable stresses for plywood pressure-impregnated with fire-retardant chemicals in accordance with AWPA Specification C-27, shall be reduced 1/6th; modulus of elasticity shall be reduced 1/10th.

CHAPTER 8

DESIGN CRITERIA FOR WOOD STRUCTURES

The selection of design criteria is an exercise of experience, knowledge and judgment that is a primary responsibility of the designer. The fact that building codes, agencies such as the Federal Housing Administration (FHA), and some clients define criteria does not absolve the designer of this duty. Codes and government agencies characterize their criteria as minimum performance requirements. Often these recommendations are designed to insure a minimum level of performance for designs executed by builders who may not be qualified to prepare an adequate engineering design.

Departures from code recommendations are generally in the form of more restrictive requirements imposed by the designer or local authorities, to achieve a level of quality better fitted to the project at hand. In certain circumstances a relaxation of minimum criteria is justifiable, when competent design and fabricating skills are available. Codes have provisions for evaluating departures from their standards, and in instances where sizable economies will result without violating the performance principle of the code, (usually structural integrity) a designer ought to consider obtaining approval for his concept. Were it not for this flexibility in the more well-administered codes, innovation and progress would be impossible.

It is not possible to set forth recommendations about criteria that are absolute. Each designer, as he gains experience, will observe structures in service, study climatological information, and develop his knowledge about clients' needs and idiosyncrasies, and acquire skill at making proper criteria decisions.

Historically, workable criteria standards have developed and have acquired broad acceptance. Codes are the embodiment of such historical knowledge. To that extent it is possible to give the new designer a starting point. That will be the purpose of this chapter.

In general, performance standards are independent of the material to be used. Practically, the act of codification sets down slightly different yardsticks of performance. The writers of our major building codes endeavor to set down relatively simple criteria aimed at uniform performance in service, irrespective of the material used. Only the criteria needed for designing wood structures will be discussed here. Many of these are identical to those for concrete and steel, but in some instances (very few, actually) they will be peculiar to wood structures.

LOAD CRITERIA

Our primary interest is in load and deflection criteria. Load criteria fall into the general categories of dead load and live load. Live load may be separated into several types on the basis of load duration.

Dead load is defined in the Uniform Building Code (UBC) as the weight of the structure and all permanently affixed equipment, machines and fixtures either installed initially, or anticipated for future installation.

It is generally assumed that the designer can estimate dead load prior to undertaking the design, and will recheck the dead load when the design is executed, making appropriate adjustments at that time. Codes will usually offer no dead load deflection criteria, which will be mentioned in sections to follow. An instance where dead load recommendations are established is in the Minimum Property Standards of FHA. (See Table 28.) This is a form of client recommendation as FHA is a mortgage insuring agency concerned with their interest in quality, and the value of the housing mortgages they insure.

Weights of construction materials are given in Table 29.

CRITERIA

Table 28. Minimum Design Criteria for Residential Housing.

	Dead Load	Live Load	Live Load Deflection
Floor Joists[1]			
Rooms used for sleeping areas and attics	10	30	$\ell/360$[2]
Rooms for all other uses	10	40	$\ell/360$[2]
Ceiling Joists			
Supporting floors in habitable rooms	same	as for	floor joists
Limited attic space (no stair access)	10	20	$\ell/360$
No attic storage (3 in 12 slope or less)	10	10	$\ell/360$
Low Slope Rafters (3 in 12 slope or less)			
Supporting a finished ceiling			
(normal roof loading)	15	20	$\ell/360$
(heavy roof loading)	15	30	$\ell/360$
Not supporting finished ceiling			
(normal roof loading)	10	20	$\ell/240$
(heavy roof loading)	10	30	$\ell/240$
High Slope Rafters (over 3 in 12 slope)			
Supporting a finished ceiling			
(normal roof loading)	15	20	$\ell/360$
(heavy roof loading)	15	30	$\ell/360$
Not supporting finished ceiling[3]			
Roof covering 5 psf and over			
(normal roof loading)	15	15	$\ell/180$
(heavy roof loading)	15	25	$\ell/180$
Roof covering below 5 psf			
(normal roof loading)	7	15	$\ell/180$
(heavy roof loading)	7	25	$\ell/180$

[1] For two span continuous floor joists, the members are designed for deflection with one span at full live load and one at 50% live load.

[2] $\ell/360$ up to 15 ft. span, decreasing proportionally to $\ell/480$ at 24 ft. span.

[3] The spans are measured parallel to the slope, the deflections are measured perpendicular to the slope, for the component of load acting perpendicular to the slope. In all other classes, span is horizontal projection and loads and deflection are vertical.

Table 29. Weights of Construction Materials.

Material	Weight, psf
CEILINGS	
Acoustical fiber tile	1.0
Channel suspended system	1.0
Plaster and lath (see WALLS AND PARTITIONS)	
FLOORS	
Hardwood, 1 in. nominal	4.0
Plywood, per inch of thickness	3.0
Asphalt mastic, per inch of thickness	12.0
Cement finish, per inch of thickness	12.0
Ceramic or quarry tile, 3/4 in.	10.0
Concrete, per inch of thickness	
Lightweight	6.0 to 10.0
Reinforced	12.5
Stone	12.5
Cork tile, 1/16 in.	0.5
Flexicore, 6 in. slab	46.0
Linoleum, 1/4 in.	1.0
Terrazo finish, 1 1/2 in.	19.0
Vinyl tile, 1/8 in.	1.4
Timber decking	
ROOFS	
Lumber sheathing, 1 in. nominal	2.5
Plywood sheathing, per inch of thickness	3.0

Timber decking 15% MC	2 in nom.	3 in nom.	4 in nom.
Cedar, Alaska	4.0	6.6	9.3
western red	3.1	5.1	7.2
Hemlock, western	4.0	6.7	9.4
eastern	3.7	6.2	8.6
Fir, true	3.6	5.9	8.3
Douglas fir	4.3	7.1	10.0
Larch, western	4.6	7.7	10.8

Material	2 in nom.	3 in nom.	4 in nom.
ROOFS (continued)			
Pine, Southern	4.9	8.2	11.4
ponderosa	3.7	6.2	8.7
lodgepole	3.7	6.2	8.7
white	3.6	5.9	8.3
Spruce, Sitka	3.6	6.1	8.5
white	3.6	6.1	8.5
Engelmann	3.1	5.1	7.2

Material	Flat	Corrug. (1 1/2 & 2 1/2 in)	
Aluminum (includes laps)			
12 American or B&S ga	1.2		
14 or B&S ga	0.9	1.1	
16 or B&S ga	0.7	0.0.9	
18 or B&S ga	0.6	0.7	
20 or B&S ga	0.5	0.6	
22 or B&S ga		0.4	
20 or B&S ga			

Material	Flat	Corrug. (2 1/2 & 3 in.)	
Galvanized steel (includes laps)			
12 U.S. Std. ga	4.5	4.9	
14 U.S. Std. ga	3.3	3.6	
16 U.S. Std. ga	2.7	2.9	
18 U.S. Std. ga	2.2	2.4	
20 U.S. Std. ga	1.7	1.8	
22 U.S. Std. ga	1.4	1.5	
24 U.S. Std. ga	1.2	1.3	
26 U.S. Std. ga	0.9	1.0	

Material	Weight, psf
Concrete plank, per in. thickness	6.5
Insulrock	2.7
Petrical	2.7
Porex	2.7
Poured gypsum	6.5
Tectum	2.0
Vermiculite concrete	2.6

(continued on following page)

Table 29. (Continued)

Material	Weight, psf	Material	Weight, psf
Asbestos, corrugated		WALLS AND PARTITIONS	
1/4 in.	3.0	Masonry, per 4 inches	
Felt, 3 ply	1.5	of thickness	
Felt, 3 ply with gravel	5.5	Brick	38.0
Felt, 5 ply	2.5	Concrete block	30.0
Felt, 5 ply with gravel	6.5	Cinder concrete block	20.0
Insulation, per inch of		Hollow clay tile,	
thickness		load bearing	23.0
Expanded polystyrene	0.2	Hollow clay tile,	
Fiberglas, rigid	1.5	nonbearing	18.0
Loose	0.5	Hollow gypsum block	13.0
Roll roofing	1.0	Limestone	55.0
Shingles		Terra-cotta tile	25.0
Asphalt, approx. 1/4"	2.0	Stone	55.0
Book tile, 2"	12.0	Plaster, 1 in.	8.0
Book tile, 3"	20.0	Plaster, 1 in., on wood	
Cement asbestos,		lath	10.0
approx. 3/8 in.	4.0	Plaster, 1 in., on	
Clay tile (for mortar		metal lath	8.5
add 10 lb)	9.0 to 14.0	Porcelain-enameled	
Ludowici	10.0	steel	3.0
Roman	12.0	Stucco, 7/8 in.	10.0
Slate, 1/4"	10.0	Windows, glass, frame,	
Spanish	19.0	and sash	8.0
Wood, 1".	3.0		
WALLS AND PARTITIONS			
Wood paneling, 1 in.	2.5		
Wood studs, 2 x 4			
12 in. o.c.	2.1		
16 in. o.c.	1.7		
24 in. o.c.	1.3		
Glass block, 4 in.	18.0		
Glass, plate, 1/4 in.	3.3		
Glazed tile	18.0		
Marble or marble			
wainscoting	15.0		

From "Timber Construction Manual" by permission of AITC. (Weights of timber decking changed to conform to current lumber size standards.)

Live loads, according to the UBC, are all loads other than dead loads, and include snow, wind, seismic and impact type loads. Some structural engineers do not consider snow, wind, seismic and impact loads to be live loads, which they define as the weight superimposed by occupancy. This seems to be a matter of personal habit and is only mentioned to note that some difference in the concept exists. It does not appear a matter for real consequence.

Floor Live Loads

Minimum uniformly distributed live loads for floors are listed in Table 30. These unit loads are treated as normal duration loads in the context discussed in preceding chapters. Similar tables are published in building codes, often listing other occupancies and uses, and sometimes with different load values for some of these occupancies and uses. The designer should familiarize himself with codes used in the regions where his projects are located.

In addition to designing floors for uniformly distributed loads, concentrated load criteria are recommended in the AITC Timber Construction Manual, and the UBC. These state that certain types of floors must safely bear, in addition to the dead load, concentrated loads are given in Table 31. These are also treated as normal duration loads.

The representation of floor loads as uniformly distributed is more a convenience than a reality. Furnishings and occupants are almost never uniformly distributed. In the case of residential structures the FHA recommendations produce floors with dynamic characteristics (response to moving occupants) which satisfy residents for the most part. They are intended to be used to design fairly conventional wood-framed floors. A steel floor system, or a plywood stressed-skin floor system designed to the same criteria of load and deflection might prove to behave quite differently from a wood-framed system designed to the same criteria of load and deflection might prove to behave quite differently from a wood-framed system constructed with nailed connections and simple spans. This arises out of differences in mass and damping properties.

Because of the growing effort at innovative design, the introduction of new and different materials and improved and more efficient lumber and plywood systems, the dynamic requirements for satisfactory floors are the subject of rather intensive research. The objective is to set forth some performance standards based on dynamic response to moving live loads. When this is accomplished, criteria for floors that are more truly performance-oriented will be the basis for design.

Since uniformly distributed loading is not truly representative of real service conditions for floors, the UBC permits floor live loads to be reduced on any member supporting more than 150 square feet of surface area. The reduction is 0.08 percent per square foot.

For recommended live loads less than 100 PSF the reduction must not exceed 60 percent (40 percent for passenger car garages) or the value of R where:

$$R = 23.1 \left[\frac{\text{Live Load} + \text{Dead Load}}{\text{Live Load}} \right]$$

For live loads exceeding 100 PSF the same reduction may be taken but must not exceed 20 percent.

Example: A building has a timber deck floor supported by laminated beams spanning 24 feet and located 10 feet apart. The floor area per beam is 240 square feet. The calculated reduction of live load on the basis of 0.08% per sq. foot is 19.2%.

If the dead load is 20 PSF and the live load is 50 PSF, R = 23.1 x 1.4 = 32.3%.

Table 30. Minimum Uniformly Distributed Floor Live Loads[1]

Occupancy or Use	Live Load, psf	Occupancy or Use	Live Load, psf
Apartments (see Residential)		Residential	
Armories and drill rooms	150	Multifamily houses	
Assembly halls and other		Private apartments	40
places of assembly:		Public rooms	100
Fixed seats	60	Corridors	60
Movable seats	100	Dwellings	
Balconies (exterior)	100	First floors	40
Bowling alleys, poolrooms,		Second floors and	
and similar recreational		habitable attics	30
areas	75	Uninhabitable attics	20
Corridors		Hotels	
First floor	100	Guest rooms	40
Other floors, same as		Public rooms	100
occupancy served except		Corridors serving	
as indicated		public rooms	100
Dance halls	100	Public corridors	60
Dining rooms and restaurants	100	Private corridors	40
Dwellings (see Residential)		Reviewing stands and bleachers	100
Garages (passenger cars)	100	Schools	
Floors should be designed		Classrooms	40
to carry 150% of the maxi-		Corridors	100
mum wheel load anywhere		Sidewalks, vehicular	
on the floor		driveways, and yards	
Grandstands (see Reviewing		subject to trucking	250
stands)		Skating rinks	100
Gymnasiums, main floors		Stairs, fire escapes, and	
and balconies	100	exitways	100
Hospitals		Storage warehouses, light	125
Operating rooms	60	Storage warehouses, heavy	250
Private rooms	40	Stores	
Wards	40	Retail	
Hotels (see Residential)		First floors, rooms	100
Libraries		Upper floors	75
Reading rooms	60	Wholesale	125
Stack rooms	150	Theaters	
Manufacturing	125	Aisles, corridors	
Marquees	75	and lobbies	100
Office Buildings			
Offices	80	Orchestra floors	60
Lobbies	100	Balconies	60
Penal instiutions		Stage floors	150
Cell blocks	40		
Corridors	100		

[1]

From the Timber Construction Manual by permission of AITC.

Table 31. Concentrated Live Loads

Location	Load, Lbs.[1]
Office floors (on a 2.5 sq. ft. area)	2000
Garages, passenger car (on a 2.5 sq. ft. area)	1.5 x max. wheel load
Structures where loaded trucks will be used	maximum wheel load
Stair treads (on a 2.5 sq. ft. area)	300
Finish light floor construction (on a 1 sq. in. area)	200
Elevator machine room grating (on a 4 sq. in. area)	300

1. Located to produce maximum stress. By permission of ICBO.

The calculated live load reduction of 19.2% is less than either 32.3% or 60% so it may be taken, making the design live load 50(1.0 - 0.192) = 40.4 PSF. *These reductions do not apply to places of public assembly.*

The UBC imposes the logical requirement that where structural members supporting floors are continuous over three or more supports, loading conditions that would cause maximum shear and bending moments be investigated. Where uniform floor loads are involved this may be limited to full dead load on all spans with full live load on adjacent spans, and also on alternate spans.

Roof Live Loads

Design live loads for roofs are particularly dependent upon the designer's knowledge of weather conditions as they affect snow loads and wind loads. Building codes offer minimum roof live loads for design. Table 32 from the UBC is an example.

Live loads are assumed to act vertically (excepting lateral wind and earthquake forces) on the horizontal projection of the roof.

In many instances an unbalanced live load condition may impose more stress on a member than a balanced load. Examples would be beams continuous over three or more supports, and certain overhang conditions. A UBC suggestion is that for uniform roof loads consideration of full dead loading on all spans and live load on alternate spans may be an adequate investigation. In the case of arches and trusses partial loading may reverse the stresses in some portions and increase the size requirements over those resulting from a balanced load stress analysis. The designer should give attention to these conditions.

Where water can accumulate on flat roofs due to dead load elastic deflection, dead load creep, and live load elastic deflection, the structure should be sized to support the accumulated water load, or ponding. Criteria for ponding are described under deflection criteria.

Roofs that serve as roof gardens, sun decks, or promenades should meet the requirements of floor live loads as well as roof live loads.

Table 32.   UBC Roof Live Loads[1] - PSF

Roof Slope	Tributary Loaded Area in Square Feet for any Structural Member		
	0 to 200	201 to 600	over 600
Flat or rise less than 4 inches per foot. Arch or dome with rise less than 1/8 of span.	20	16	12
Rise 4 inches per foot to less than 12 inches per foot. Arch or dome with rise 1/8 to less than 3/8 of span.	16	14	12
Rise 12 inches per foot and greater Arch or dome with rise 3/8 of span or more.	12	12	12

1.   Does not provide for snow loads.   Duration of load is "normal."

By permission of ICBO.

The duration of load for roof live loads is quite variable, and usually of less cumulative duration than the normal load condition assumed for floor live loads.

Snow Loads

Snow loads are a form of roof live loads that requires the designer's consideration. Snow loads may be full or unbalanced depending on the geometry of the roof. Portions with different pitches will retain different snow loads. Curved roofs may shed snow in some areas and not in others. The roof surface smoothness will affect snow shedding, with metal roofs shedding at different pitches than roofs with rougher surfaces.

Insulation, as it affects heat loss through roofs, has a great influence on snow retention. Overhangs tend to accumulate snow and ice because of the unheated lower surface. Sometimes electric resistance heaters are placed at overhangs to prevent ice dams and water accumulation.

Valleys formed by dormers and angularly arranged gable roofs will produce pockets for the localized accumulation of snow.

The Uniform Building Code does not attempt to recommend snow loads, but assigns the task to the local building code authorities, which is wise considering the variable nature of terrain and climate in many regions. It is not unusual for design snow loads to vary as much as threefold in a given county in mountainous regions. The local building official must establish snow loads on the basis of climatological information from the weather bureau, his own observations, and the information gleaned from long-time residents of the area in question.

UBC does recommend a snow load reduction practice related to pitch of the roof. Snow loads in excess of 20 PSF may be reduced by S/40 minus 1/2 for each degree of pitch exceeding 20 degrees. S is the total snow load PSF.

Example: Snow load for design is 45 PSF. For a roof pitch of 30 degrees this may be reduced by

$$\left(\frac{45}{40} - \frac{1}{2}\right) \quad \left(30 - 20\right) \quad = 6.25 \text{ PSF}$$

The design snow load becomes 38.75 PSF.

Figure 20 is a U.S. Weather Bureau chart showing maximum ground level snow loads in the United States. Figure 21 is a similar chart for Canada. These can be a general guide, but owing to the scale of the maps, are only useful in regions with uniform land elevations, such as the Great Plains.

Snow weight varies a great deal, depending upon the amount of melting and compaction that occurs during its period of accumulation. The deepest snow is not always the heaviest snow. The most dangerous conditions often occur in the spring when rain falls on roofs covered with well-frozen snow, at which time the snow may retain an equal added load of water. This is a short time condition, usually of a few hours or a day at a time.

With respect to the density of snow, D. W. Boyd of the National Research Council of Canada, who has developed snow load data, has these comments. Fresh snow has a specific gravity of 0.1. Old snow ranges from 0.2 to 0.4, even more. The average density at the time of maximum snow load, measured over a 30-year period in Canada, appears to be about 0.2. A convenient figure to remember is that 1 inch of snow corresponds to a pressure of about 1 PSF. Rain weighs 5.2 lbs. per inch, and snow can absorb and hold about its own weight of rain. These data may be helpful in examining or setting up special criteria for jobs in remote areas.

Snow load duration has been studied extensively. A period of "2 months" for the cumulative duration of the maximum snow load is generally used. Certainly snow remains on roofs for far longer periods, but not at maximum load intensity. It has been determined that over a period of 100 years, two months is a very adequate cumulative maximum snow load life.

Snow loads are calculated as acting on the horizontal projection of the roof structure.

Wind Loads

Wind produces loads on walls as well as roofs which take the form of both pressure and suctions. The size of these loads and their distribution over various parts of a building is related to wind direction, building shape, the location of openings, as well as wind intensity. The AITC Timber Construction Manual contains an excellent section on wind loads for design that will permit the designer to make a very detailed study for any particular structure.

A more simplified set of general wind load recommendations is contained in the UBC and are presented here.

Table 33 along with chart, Figure 22, enable the designer to establish minimum wind loads in the continental United States. Similar data are produced in other countries where building codes are used. For other areas the designer would need to obtain historical information on wind intensities and derive the related pressures.

Buildings and structures should be designed to withstand minimum horizontal and uplift forces obtained by using Table 33 and Figure 22 together with the interpretations which follow. For structures other than

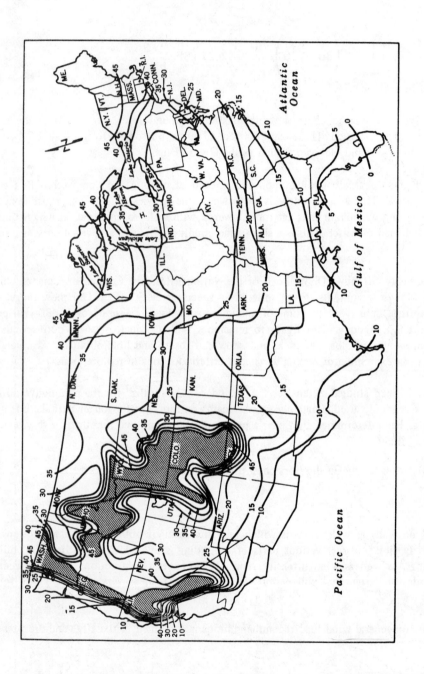

Figure 20. Greatest Snow Load on the Ground at Any One Time, PSF. This chart is based on records furnished by the Weather Bureau, U.S. Department of Commerce, entitled "Greatest Snow Depth on Ground at Any One Time," covering a period of time from 1871 to 1944. Snow loads within the hatched areas are to be determined by local investigations and in no case shall be less than 45 psf.

By permission of AITC.

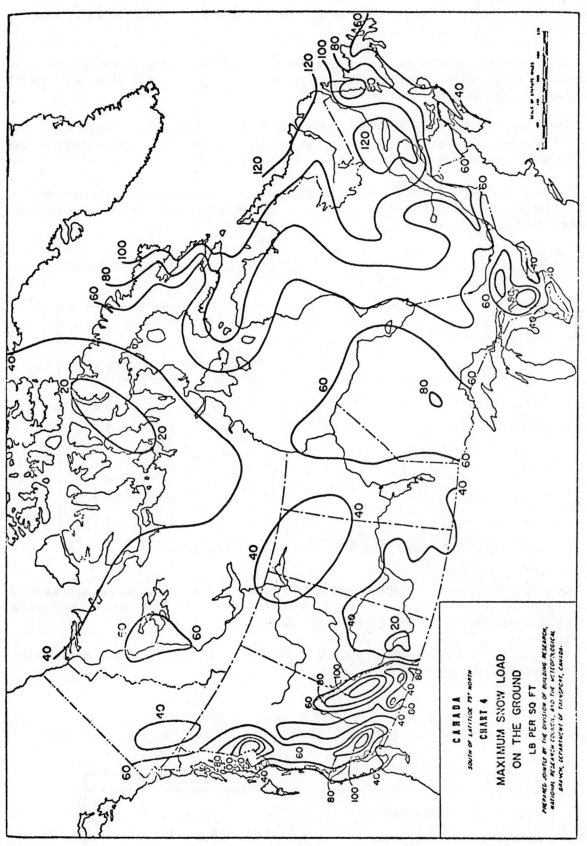

Figure 21. Snow Load Map for Canada

Courtesy of National Research Council, Canada.

rectangular and of conventional flat, pitched or arched roofs, a detailed development of wind loads should be made.

Horizontal Wind Forces are the pressures given in Table 33 and are applied to the vertical projection of the structure in any and all directions of the compass. For structures in a height zone of 10 feet or less use 2/3 of the values in the first line of the table.

Uplift Wind Forces on the roofs of enclosed buildings or other structures are three-fourths of the values in Table 33. They act upward in a direction at right angles to the roof surface. An enclosed building has a wall around the entire perimeter, with all openings closed by doors and glazed windows.

Roofs of unenclosed buildings, roof overhangs, architectural projections, eaves, canopies, cornices, marquees, or similar structures open on one or more sides are designed to withstand upward forces of 1.25 times the values in Table 33, over the entire roof area.

Table 33. Wind Pressures for Various Height Zones Above Ground

Height Zones (in feet)	Wind-Pressure Map Areas[1] (PSF)						
	20	25	30	35	40	45	50
Less than 30	15	20	25	25	30	35	40
30 to 49	20	25	30	35	40	45	50
50 to 99	25	30	40	45	50	55	60
100 to 499	30	40	45	55	60	70	75
500 to 1199	35	45	55	60	70	80	90
1200 and over	40	50	60	70	80	90	100

1. Does not provide for tornadoes.   By permission of ICBO.

Downward Wind Forces. Roofs sloping more than 30 degrees are designed for forces acting inward and perpendicular to the roof surface, shown in Table 33, applied to the windward slope only. The force on the other slope is the uplift for that height zone as previously described, and acting outward.

Chimneys, tanks and solid towers are designed for minimum wind pressures for the height zone which prevails multiplied by factors from Table 34.

Table 34. Multiplying Factors for Wind
Pressures - Chimneys, Tanks, and Solid Towers

Horizontal Cross Section	Factor
Square or rectangular	1.00
Hexagonal or octagonal	0.80
Round or elliptical	0.60

By permission ICBO.

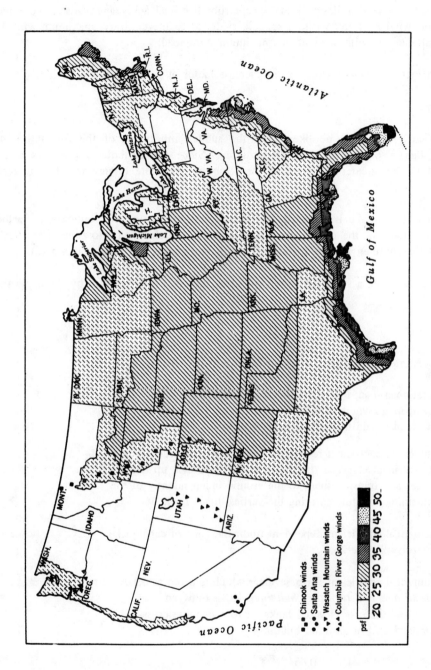

Figure 22. Wind Pressure Map of the United States. Based on recommendations contained in American Standard Building Code Requirements for Minimum Design Loads in Buildings and Other Structures, A 58.1-1955 by American Standards Association, Inc.

By permission of ICBO.

Open-frame towers, of trussed construction, are designed using shape factors in Table 35. These pressures apply to the total normal projected area of all elements of one face.

The overturning moment calculated from wind forces must not exceed two-thirds of the dead load resisting moment, which may include the weight of earth superimposed over footings.

In determining stresses, all vertical design loads except roof live load and crane loads are considered to be acting simultaneously with wind pressure. Without specific evidence to the contrary, maximum wind load is thought of as occurring simultaneously with one-half the maximum snow load.

Duration of load for wind is one-day with a stress increase factor of 1.333 for wood.

Earthquake Loads

The effect of an earthquake may be likened to the sudden movement of the foundation of the structure, resisted by the inertia of the mass of the structure. Since the earthquake produces a definite acceleration of the foundation, the greater the mass of the structure the more intense will be the reactions produced in the structure.

The intensity of the earthquake is reflected in the acceleration rate of the foundation. Earthquake intensities for regions in many parts of the world have been measured, and classified into zones. Figure 23 is an earthquake intensity map of the continental United States. (UBC includes maps of Hawaii and Alaska).

The lateral load for designing a structure to withstand earthquakes is determined by the application of the formula:

$$V = ZKCW$$

where V =   total lateral load, or shear at the base, lbs.

            W =   total dead load, lbs., except in storage and warehouse occupancies where W is taken to include 25% of the floor live load in addition to the total dead load.

            K =   numerical coefficient related to the type of construction as it may involve special structure or bracing to pick up lateral forces and transmit them to the ground independently of the remaining structure carrying the vertical load, Table 36.

            Z =   numerical coefficient dependent upon the zone of earthquake intensity. Figure 23.

            C =   numerical coefficient for base shear which is taken as 0.10 *for all one- and two-story buildings*. KC is between 0.12 and 0.25 for elevated tanks on four or more cross-braced legs. For all other buildings:

$$C = 0.05/\sqrt[3]{T}$$

where T =   the fundamental period of vibration of the structure in the direction under consideration, seconds.

Table 35. Shape Factors for Open-Frame and Trussed Towers[1]

Type of Exposure	Factor
Wind normal to one face of tower--	
Four-cornered, flat or angular sections	2.20^2
Three-cornered, flat or angular sections	2.00^2
Wind on corner, four-cornered tower, flat or angular sections	2.40^2
Wind parallel to one face of three-cornered tower, flat or angular sections	1.50
Factors for towers with cylindrical elements are two-thirds of those for similar towers with flat or angular sections:	
Wind on individual members--	
Cylindrical members	
Two inches or less in diameter	1.00
Over two inches in diameter	0.80
Flat or angular sections	1.30

1. The shape factors are applied to the wind pressures of Table 33 and are additional to the 1.3 shape factor already included in those wind pressures.

2. The AITC Timber Construction Manual, further refines the factors to account for the ratio of actual face area of the structure to the area of a solid face tower of the same gross outline.

By permission of ICBO.

T may be established experimentally by various means, for the particular structure or similar structures. However, in the absence of such infomration, T = 0.10N in all buildings that have a moment-resisting space frame which resists 100% of the required lateral forces and which frame is not enclosed by or adjoined by more rigid elements which would tend to prevent the frame from resisting lateral forces. (N = number of stories) In all other cases T = 0.05H/$\sqrt{D}$; where H = height of main portion of the structure above the base (feet); and D = dimension of the structures in a direction parallel to the applied forces, feet.

This illustrates how lateral forces are determined. They must be distributed over the height of the structure using methods described in the UBC and also in the AITC Timber Construction Manual. As that process is rather extensive and advanced for a textbook of this kind, and since it is applicable to buildings of any construction material, it is not taken up in further detail here.

Most wood buildings fall into the one- and two-story height category, which somewhat simplifies the procedure of determining V, such that:

$$V = Z (1.33) (0.10) W = 0.133 Z W$$

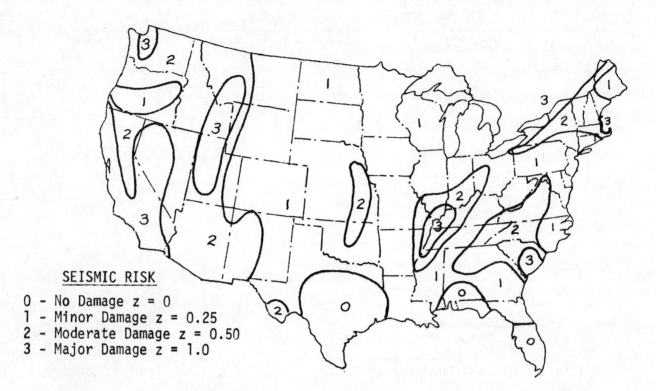

SEISMIC RISK
0 - No Damage z = 0
1 - Minor Damage z = 0.25
2 - Moderate Damage z = 0.50
3 - Major Damage z = 1.0

Figure 23.   Zones of Approximately Equal Seismic Probability.   Recommended
by the International Conference of Building Officials.

By permission of ICBO.

This simplification is based on the proposition that the wood building will have lateral force resisting shear walls, with roof and floor systems designed or checked for structural integrity as horizontal diaphragms. This is called a "box system."

The duration of load for wood for earthquake load durations is taken as one day, cumulative over the life of the structure, for which the allowable stresses may be increased 33 1/3%, the same conditions generally allowed for wind loads. Wind and earthquake loads are not usually considered as acting simultaneously.

Moving Loads

Criteria for moving loads are determined by the designer. He may use the recommendations of the American Association of State Highway Officials (AASHO) or the American Railway Engineering Association (AREA) or the criteria laid down by particular political jurisdications. In fact, he will probably be constrained to meet the requirements of one of these groups in the design of any highway or railroad structures.

"Standard Specifications for Highway Bridges" (AASHO) bases design of wood highway bridges on normal duration of load.

AREA specifications assume all railway bridges and trestles will be designed for long-time loading, using 90% of the allowable stresses as normally published.

For information on load criteria for crane beams the reader is referred to the "Timber Design and Construction Handbook" by the Timber Engineering Company (F.W. Dodge Corp. publication) or to the Timber Construction Manual by AITC.

Table 36.   Horizontal Force Factor "K" for Structures

Type or Arrangement of Resisting Elements	K
All building framing systems except as classified below.	1.00
Buildings with a box system.	1.33
Buildings with a complete horizontal bracing system capable of resisting all lateral forces, including a moment-resisting space frame that will independently carry 25% of the required lateral force. (See latest UBC.)	0.80
Buildings with a moment-resisting space frame that will carry 100% of the required lateral force when acting independently of any other more rigid elements. (See latest UBC.)	0.67
Elevated tanks and contents supported with four or more cross-braced columns and not supported by a building.	3.00
Structures other than buildings, and parts and portions of buildings or other structures covered specifically in the UBC. (See latest UBC.)	2.00

By permission ICBO.

Impact Loads

There are no recognized impact load criteria of a generally recommended nature. Each impact load condition requires special investigation and impact loads can become quite complex. However, a few impact conditions can be described to illustrate that the static weight of a load can magnify itself under impact conditions.

A very simple experiment can be performed to show how easy it is for an impact load to cause a stress that is double the value it would produce statically. Place a thin piece of wood about 1/4" thick by 2 inches wide and six feet long on two supports spaced about 66 inches apart. Let one support be a thin-edged solid piece and the other a roller which prevents any support friction in the system. This is illustrated in Figure 24a.

Measure the space under the midspan, then place a weight of 3 to 5 lbs. on the center of the span and measure the space under the deflected piece of wood. Subtract the smaller from the larger to obtain the static deflection.

Using this static deflection, make a small block cut to such a height that if it is placed under the piece of wood at the mid-point of the span, the clearance to the unloaded piece of wood will be *two* static deflections. See Figure 24b.

Now suspend the weight by a string from some convenient overhead support so the weight just touches the top of the thin piece of wood but does not actually deflect it any. If you now cut the string with a pair of scissors, or a sharp knife, the sudden application of the weight will make the wood deflect until it touches the block. See Figure 24c. This will occur very rapidly and will be hard to see. If you put an ink drop on the block before you cut the string, you can tell it has just touched the ink. There are various ways to check this, but if the experiment is carefully done this is what happens.

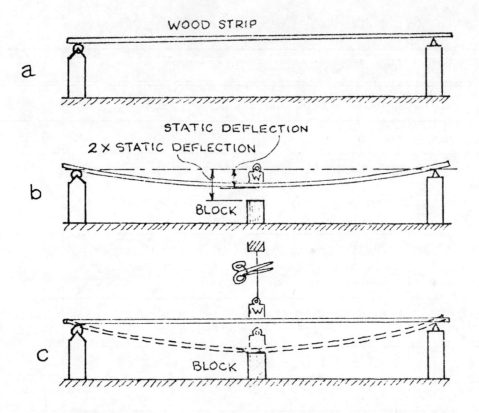

Figure 24.   An Experiment in Impact Loading

The weighted strip of wood will oscillate a few times and come to rest at the static deflection.

This simply shows that a suddenly applied load, dropped from a distance of zero, causes a deflection that is twice the amount it would cause if very slowly applied. If it causes twice the deflection dynamically than it did statically, it stresses the piece of wood twice as much.

There are many ordinary-use situations that cause impact loads very much like this. A man stepping from one scaffold plank to another at the same level is an example. An automobile moving across the planks of a bridge that are not connected by tongues and grooves is another.

In Chapter 3, (Figure 10) it was mentioned that wood can sustain very short-time loads, that cause twice the normal allowable stress. The types of loads mentioned above cause twice the stress they would cause statically. So pieces designed statically to support the load W in Figure 21, will also support it under the type of impact load just described, for quite a few repetitions before it would fail.

The above experiment merely substantiates a well-known relationship for the effect of falling objects upon elastic bodies which is

$$y' = y \left(1 + \sqrt{1 + \frac{2h}{y}} \right)$$

where y' =   deflection due to impact of a weight, inches

        y =   static deflection caused by the weight, inches

        h =   height of free fall in inches.

If h = 0, as in the experiment: y' = 2y. This is what is observed. For other values of h the formula yields various values of y' as given in Table 37.

It is evident that the amount of deflection magnification grows as the height of the fall increases, but at a diminishing rate. A 48-inch fall only causes about twice as much deflection as a 12-inch fall (for 0.25-inch static deflection.

Also note that for equal ratios of height of fall to static deflection, the magnification due to impact is a constant. For a ratio of 48 (i.e., 12/.25, 24/0.5, 48/1.0) the value of y'/y = 10.88. Other magnifications are effective for other ratios.

Table 37. Effect of Height of Free Fall
on Dynamic Magnification of Deflection

Height of Fall Inches	y'/y For Various Static Deflections (y)				
	0.25"	0.50"	1.0"	2.0"	4.0"
0	2.0	2.0	2.0	2.0	2.0
12	10.88	8.0	6.0	4.6	3.65
24	14.92	10.88	8.0	6.0	4.6
48	20.68	14.92	10.88	8.0	6.0

By permission of ICBO.

Since stresses are proportional to deflections, the dynamic or impact stress due to a given weight on a given member will be related to the static stress in the same ratio as the dynamic and static deflections.

The foregoing suggests that an impact load condition requires a fairly thorough analysis, and that all impact loads cannot be treated alike. The statement in NDS which says, "Allowable unit stresses for normal loading conditions may be used without regard to impact if the stress induced by impact does not exceed the allowable unit stress for normal loading" is a very safe statement. However, it is impossible to disregard an impact load and still determine what stress it will induce in a member. The statement does not readily dispose of the impact problem. Actually the above statement limits the allowable stress caused by an impact load to the normal load stress, not twice the normal stress as suggested by the allowable stress duration of load adjustment of a 100 percent increase that is generally published. NDS appears to be somewhat ambiguous on this point.

DEFLECTION CRITERIA

Limits are placed on deflection for a number of reasons, all connected with the satisfaction of the occupant or user.

Brittle finishes such as gypsum board, plaster, terrazzo, and roofing compounds, may crack if deflection exceeds certain limits. Limitations on deflection are a means of controlling the vibrational properties of floor structures. Excessive sag in roofs interferes with roof drainage, and in floors allows stored chinaware and household goods to rattle and produce noise. Beams can interfere with the operation of doors and windows should the sag exceed prescribed limits. In certain instances the sag of beams under dead load can be visibly unattractive and denote a shoddy quality of construction or design. Deflection limits, then, arise out of requirements for structural performance, aesthetics, and function.

The deflection limits for *light-frame housing* are given in Table 28. These are limits on live load deflection. Dead load deflection does not affect plaster cracking or interfere with function, ordinarily. It can, of course, interfere with roof drainage and be unsightly if it is large enough. Deflection of flat roofs is more likely to be a problem, than of pitched roofs.

In Table 28 the *floor joist* criteria of $\ell/360$ on live load is primarily to produce walking comfort and freedom from vibrational annoyance. Ceiling deflection is limited to $\ell/360$ to prevent plaster cracking. Low slope rafters often support plaster ceiling finish and are limited to $\ell/360$. In instances where a roof will not carry a brittle ceiling finish the designer might reasonably consider permitting a deflection of $\ell/240$ instead of $\ell/360$.

Deflection criteria for *rafters* that do not support a finished ceiling are $\ell/240$ at slopes of 3 in 12 and less, and $\ell/180$ for steeper slopes. These criteria are based upon considerations of drainage and aesthetics.

In these FHA criteria no special allowance is computed for creep under long-time dead load. Probably more housing is built to meet these criteria than any others in the United States.

The UBC criteria follows the rule that for roof structures supporting plaster, *live load deflection* may be $\ell/360$ and *live load plus dead load creep* shall not exceed $\ell/240$. UBC accepts the general concept that creep is one-half of dead load elastic deflection for seasoned lumber, and equal to dead load elastic deflection for unseasoned lumber. The discussion in Chapter 3 suggests that creep deformation is greater than these amounts. That discussion assumes a somewhat higher dead load to total load ratio, hence higher permanent stress, than occurs in practice most of the time. It also assumes the stress level exists throughout the member, rather than graduating from a zero to a maximum. Much creep research has been done on beams loaded to create a uniform moment along the length. For these reasons, the practice followed by designers regards creep to be at these lower levels in actual service. For floors with or without plaster ceiling below, UBC sets the same criteria just mentioned for roofs. Designs must satisfy each of these permissible deflection criteria as maxima. The FHA and UBC criteria for deflection of roofs with plaster, and for floors are compatible. UBC does not stipulate any deflection criteria for roof rafters without plaster. See Table 38.

Table 38. Maximum Allowable Deflection for
Structural Members by UBC

Type of Member	Seasoned or Unseasoned	Seasoned	Unseasoned
	Live Load	Live Load + $\dfrac{\text{Dead Load}}{2}$	Live Load + Dead Load
Roof Member Supporting Plaster, or Floor Member	$\ell/360$	$\ell/240$	$\ell/240$

By permission of ICBO.

The recommendations of the AITC for industrial, commercial and institutional structures are in Table 39. These AITC figures provide a little more guidance than those of the UBC, and are no less restrictive for the two types of members the UBC limits.

Roof beams and decking are designed on the basis of live load deflection only, unless dead load exceeds 50 percent of live load. In the latter case dead plus live load governs.

Floor beams are limited to the same live load deflections as those imposed by UBC and FHA, the AITC criteria being slightly more restrictive for seasoned lumber.

Deformation due to dead load creep is in addition to the dead plus live load elastic deflection limit in **Table 39** with the following exceptions:

Table 39. Maximum Allowable Deflection for Sawn
Structural Members per AITC

Use Classification	Live[1] Load Only	Dead and Live Load
Roof Beams:		
Industrial	$\ell/180$	$\ell/120$
Commercial and Institutional		
Without plaster ceiling	$\ell/240$	$\ell/180$
With plaster ceiling	$\ell/360$	$\ell/240$
Floor Beams [2]	$\ell/360$	$\ell/240$
Highway Bridge Stringers	$\ell/200$ to $\ell/300$	---
Railway Bridges	$\ell/300$ to $\ell/400$	---

1. Live load = all load except dead load.
2. May be more restrictive for structures subject to machinery vibrations; these values are for human occupancy.

(a)   For flat or low pitched roofs where drainage problems may result.

(b)   Wherever clearance under a member if functionally critical (over doors, glass, non-bearing walls).

Laminated timber may be manufactured with camber which enables the designer to produce the same structural performance with a somewhat smaller beam. To illustrate; the actual total deflections permitted sawn timber, equal or exceed the dead load plus live load deflections in Table 39. By cambering to produce a level glued laminated member under dead load elastic deflection plus creep, the live load deflection can be equal to the values in column 3, Table 39 and still not exceed the criteria.

Beams for flat roofs are often cambered to have an average pitch of 1/4-inch per foot in addition to dead load deflection and creep. This is to provide for drainage.

Camber applies to any of the fabricated specialty products, i.e., glue-laminated beams, wood trusses, composite wood and metal trusses, and plywood-lumber box beams. Camber suited to each of these structural systems will be discussed in the appropriate chapter.

The deflection criteria for walls is not often defined. The UBC requires that non-bearing interior walls be designed for a maximum deflection of $\ell/240$ for brittle finishes, and $\ell/120$ for flexible finishes with a load of 5 PSF applied perpendicular to the wall. No limitations are set by the UBC for load-bearing walls, but similar deflection allowances seem appropriate, based on the 5 PSF lateral load and the eccentric load moment due to the wall-bearing load.

Wall deflections under earthquake conditions are considered in the recommended lateral forces for design of the UBC section on seismic design. They are not usually specified in numerical dimensions. Wood diaphragms, for example, when designed by the procedures approved by the codes, will not deflect excessively. These criteria are fairly complex and to a large degree based on empirical data.

Elastic Modulus for Deflection

For all types of framed structures and decking where transverse distribution of load between parallel members is achieved, the deflection is computed on the basis of the average modulus of elasticity (E). For laminated timber the published value of E for the grade of beam is used for design irrespective of the existence of transverse distribution elements. For special applications of lumber where maximum deflection is highly critical from a functional point of view, a 50 percent reduction in E would provide a high degree of assurance that the calculated deflection would not be in error. See page 45, Chapter 5. The use of machine-stress-rated lumber would provide the same assurance of deflection limit at about a 20 percent reduction in average E value. The use of such reduced E values is extremely rare.

CHAPTER 9

DESIGN OF BENDING MEMBERS

Wood bending member design is quite similar to steel or reinforced concrete bending member design. Design differences arise from material property differences. In this chapter significant aspects of these differences as they affect wood flexural members will be summarized.

It is recommended that designers obtain a copy of the "National Design Specification for Stress Grade Lumber and Its Fastenings" (NDS) for reference use. This document is revised and re-issued every two or three years because technology advances for structural design with wood are evolving fairly rapidly in the face of competitive pressures and the need for efficient material economy.

For bending member design, consideration is given to:

(a)   deflection under the service loads
(b)   bending stress under the maximum controlling load for design
(c)   shear stress at the neutral axis and at flange-web connections
(d)   compression stress at points of bearing.

DEFLECTION

Criteria for deflection, discussed in Chapter 8, are usually expressed as a fraction of the span. In almost all circumstances where lumber and timbers are used for their intended purpose, the conventional deflection formulas found in general engineering handbooks are applicable. Some of these are found in Appendix C.

For simple spans and the end-spans of beams continuous over several supports, the span is measured from the mid-point of the required bearing area. For members continuous over supports the span is measured to the center of the support.

Elastic modulus (E) is not time-dependent, so no duration of load adjustments apply to deflection calculations. In portions of this chapter which follow adjustment factors for depth effect, shape and form of beam cross-section, and curvature factors will be explained. *These adjustments do not apply to deflection calculations.*

The deflection of bending members is influenced by their span-to-depth ratio. This effect is not peculiar to wood, but occurs for all materials. However, the effect is more pronounced for wood. The formula for deflection of a uniformly loaded simple span beam given in textbooks on strength and mechanics of materials, using energy methods is:

$$\Delta = \frac{5}{384} \cdot \frac{w\ell^4}{EI} + \frac{K}{AG} \cdot \frac{w\ell^2}{8}$$

For rectangular beams K = 6/5, for round beams 10/9, with other values for other shapes. The first element of this formula is the deflection due to the longitudinal extension of the material on the tension side of the member, and the longitudinal compression of the material on the compression side of the member. If all cross-sections of an unstressed beam remained plane when placed under load, this first element would be the only essential element of the deflection formula. That condition is not a real one, since plane sections become curved, due to the fact that horizontal shear stress varies from a maximum at the neutral axis and near the ends of a uniformly loaded simple beam, to zero at the extreme fibers. The resulting curvature of sections taken through a beam is illustrated in Figure 25b.

BEAMS

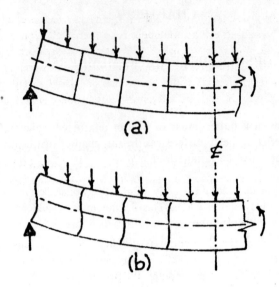

Figure 25

(a) Assumed condition that plane sections remain plane.
(b) Actual condition that plane sections become curved.

The second element of the deflection formula represents the added deflection due to horizontal shear, or shear in planes parallel to the neutral axis. In this element of the formula, A is the area and G is the modulus of rigidity, or shear modulus as it is often called.

$$\frac{5\ w\ell^4}{384\ EI} = \text{deflection due to extension and compression of the longitudinal fibers.}$$

$$\frac{Kw\ell^2}{8\ AG} = \text{deflection due to shear between parallel layers of fiber.}$$

The formula for deflection of a simple rectangular beam just presented can be written in another way to illustrate why the shear deflection is more significant in design with wood than with steel.

$$\Delta = \frac{5\ w\ell^4}{384\ EI}\left[1 + 0.96\left(\frac{h}{\ell}\right)^2\ \frac{E}{G}\right]$$

For steel the shear modulus (G) is about 38 percent of the elastic modulus (E), making E/G = 2.6 For wood the ratio is in the range of 10 to 16. By substituting 2.6 for steel and 14 for wood, into the above formula, it is evident that for a span-to-depth ratio (ℓ/h) of 20 the shear deflection is 0.576 percent of Δ for steel and 3.36 percent of Δ for wood. Of course steel beams are rarely of rectangular cross-section so a smaller shape factor is involved, and furthermore allowable loads on steel beams are not generally limited by considerations of deflection, but rather extreme fiber stress, or allowable web shear.

The elastic modulus values for wood, as published for design use, are about 94 percent of the true values. This is done because most wood structural members for which deflection is a critical factor, have an ℓ/h ratio of 15 to 25. When wood members have smaller ℓ/h ratios the designer may expect the conventional deflection formulas to underestimate deflection. In critical design situations use of the preceding, more exact, formula may be justified. Also, in research and testing work these conditions require attention if precise results are wanted. However, for the majority of designs the shear deformation is not considered, so the redced E compensates for the error.

When rectangular wood members are used in the flat attitude, as plank for example, an increase in elastic modulus is justifiable, although seldom actually used. In the case of wood decking, the increase is included in the published E for design use. In the unusual circumstance where decking would be loaded parallel to the wide face, a decrease in E would be appropriate. Again, this is rarely considered as the effect is small and not usually critical.

Since engineers and architects may encounter the application of this span-to-depth effect in the development of new products, or the consideration of performance data offered by proponents of new products, this explanation seems worthwhile. Further detail is found in Appendix D.

Another consideration related to deflection of wood decks is the influence of end-joints on deflection. That topic is covered in the chapter on wood decking design.

In using deflection formulas for wood, $\frac{\ell}{240}$ or some other fraction of the span is usually substituted for Δ.

BENDING STRENGTH

The required strength of a member is based on the total load, not merely the live load often used in choosing member sizes to meet deflection criteria as described in Chapter 8.

For most frame building design, total load is dead load plus live load for normal duration, but snow and wind loads are frequently great enough to control design.

The conventional formulas for bending stress are used in designing with stress-rated lumber. The general form is:

$$f_b = M \frac{c}{I} = M/S \leq F_b$$

f_b = actual unit stress for extreme fiber in bending, psi

F_b = allowable unit stress for extreme fiber in bending, psi

I = moment of inertia, inches^4

c = distance from neutral axis to extreme fiber, inches

S = section modulus, inches^3

M = maximum bending moment, inch-pounds

Bending moment is related to the load and support conditions. Formulas may be derived or obtained from Appendix C, or other engineering references. For a simple beam, supported at each end and uniformly loaded:

$$M = \frac{w\ell^2}{8}$$

where w = uniform load in pounds per inch

ℓ = span in inches

The bending formula for this load and support condition is:

$$f_b = \frac{w\ell^2}{8\,S} \leq F_b$$

The design of wood bending members using stress-rated joists, plank, beams, stringers, posts, timber and decking of rectangular cross-section *does not require any modification of this formula if used in the attitude for which the material was graded.* With the exception of decking and scaffold plank, these commodity products are all graded with the intent that bending load will be applied parallel to their largest cross-sectional dimension. For decking and scaffold plank, load is normally perpendicular to the wide face.

Depth Effect Factor

The depth of a member does have an effect on bending strength, but the grading rules have been designed in such a fashion that the limitations arising from depth effect, are countered by compensating limitations on allowable size of knots and other strength related properties. Thus the depth effect if included in the development of size-related grade descriptions (or machine calibration in the case of machine stress-rated lumber) to provide prescribed strength properties independent of size, for stress-graded lumber.

This practice of incorporating the effect of depth on allowable bending stress into the grading process was introduced in U. S. grade rules written and published in 1970.* Lumber graded under older U.S. grade rules, and rules still in use in other countries require the introduction of a depth factor (C_d) in the bending formula for beams greater than 12 inches deep. For this reason, and also because depth factor adjustments are still necessary for glued-laminated beams more than 12 inches deep, an explanation of depth factor is given here. An understanding of depth factor is also important for anyone likely to be concerned with research and testing of wood members in bending.

Research engineers working with wood in the 1920's noted that wood members of identical quality displayed reduced apparent unit bending strength, as the depth was increased. They observed that this effect became more pronounced as wood quality was reduced. Several relationships were developed for use with wood of various quality levels, and as recently as 1968 a new relationship for laminated timber was introduced into practice.

The bending strength reduction factor for lumber in the stress grades normally produced is:

$$C_d = 0.81 \left(\frac{h^2+143}{h^2+88} \right)$$

h = depth in inches

---

* For depths 12-inches and less.

This relationship is plotted in Figure 26. Notice that for depths less than 12 inches C_d is greater than 1.0; and is less than 1.0 at depths exceeding 12 inches. Rules embody certain liberalizations of allowable defects for pieces less than 12 inches deep so the depth factor is not used to increase allowable bending stress at depths below 12 inches. It is applied to sizes exceeding 12 inches to reduce F_b

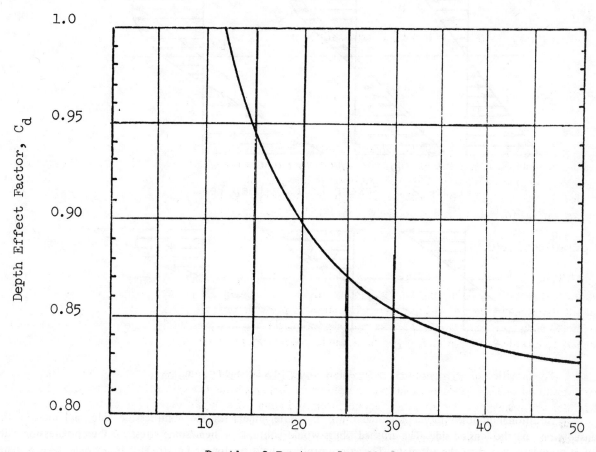

Figure 26. Depth Effect Factor.

There are numerous theories to explain why deep bending members display a lower extreme fiber stress at ultimate than do shallow members. The Newlin-Trayer explanation is most frequently cited. It seems to fit the observations as well as any, and is not highly complex.

The average ultimate strength of dry clear wood in compression parallel to the grain is less than the average ultimate in tension parallel to the grain. In the case of seasoned western larch, for example, ultimate compression averages about 7600 psi, with tension at about 13,000 psi, for clear seasoned material.

A clear, or high quality beam would exhibit a fairly linear distribution of stress[1] from the compression to the tension faces up to an extreme fiber stress approaching the compression ultimate, as depicted in Figures 27a and 28a.

---

[1]This linear assumption is not precise, inasmuch as the outermost fibers will be stressed beyond the proportional limit, when centrally located fibers are not. The assumption does not affect the validity of the explanation.

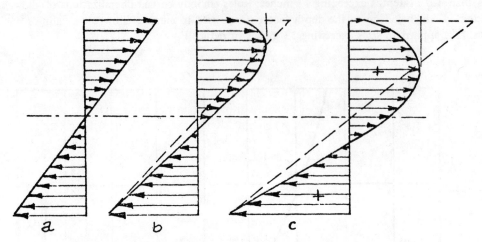

Figure 27.   Stress Profile-Deep Beam

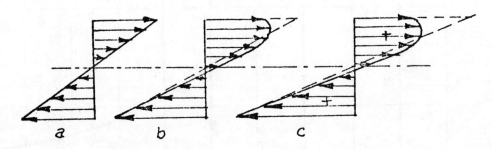

Figure 28.   Stress Profile-Shallow Beam

Additional imposed moment would crush the outer fibers on the compression side, and increase the tensile stress on the tension side. The crushed fibers would continue to bear some stress on the compression side, but it would be less than the ultimate. The stress profile would no longer be straight, but would take a shape somewhat as shown in figure 27b. Some of the compression fibers nearer the neutral axis which were not stressed to the compression ultimate, have now become more highly stressed than would have been the case had the extreme compression fibers not crushed (the dashed profile). The moment of forces on all compressively stressed fibers must equal the moment of forces on all tensile stressed fibers, so the neutral axis must move downward from its earlier position.

The normal mode of bending failure for high quality wood beams is the development of a compressive crushing ridge on the top at some load short of ultimate, with continuing increase in load until a tensile failure occurs on the lower surface of the beam. Therefore, the neutral axis probably continues to move downward as the compression fibers at progressively lower levels assume those portions of the load that these fibers would have carried in a material with equal tensile and compression strength (Figure 27c). At the same time the extreme fibers on the tension face accept ever greater stress until they reach their ultimate and fail.

[The ultimate bending strength, or modulus of rupture as it is usually called, is a hypothetical strength property determined by calculating a stress for the maximum bending moment and the section modulus, with the neutral axis assumed to be at the mid-point of beam depth. This value, obviously, is less than the ultimate tensile strength of wood, and greater than the ultimate compression stress parallel to the grain.]

For a beam of smaller depth than the one shown in Figure 27, the slope of the linear stress profile will be steeper and fibers in the proximity of those which first began to yield to crushing will be less highly stressed. That is to say, at the transition level between compression fibers which have been stressed to their ultimate, and those not yet at that point, one will find nearby fibers with greater reserve to assume added load than in the case of a deeper member.

Also, the actual distance from the compressive face to the transition level is smaller for the shallower member than the deeper one, at the same percentage of ultimate load. Since the physical size of the fibers (tubular columns) is the same in each beam, the surface fibers near the compression face of the shallow beam receive more support against compressive buckling than is true for a deeper beam. Even though partially crushed, these fibers near the compressive face of shallow beams contribute proportionately more to the moment resistance than do the fibers above the transition zone of a deeper beam. Figure 28 has been drawn to illustrate the shallow beam conditions just described. Note that for loadings depicted by b and c of both Figure 27 and 28 the fibers at the compressive face are carrying greater stress for the shallow beam, hence contributing more to load resisting moment.

It is not easy to advance this theory with mathematical exactitude, owing to the difficulty in measuring the stress distribution in the overloaded parts of the compression side.

The presence of knots, sloping grain, or other defects near the compression or tension faces often cause the mode of failure to be different than that described here for high quality wood pieces. If knots are present and located in such a way that the effective strength of the wood on the tension side is below that on the compression side, the beam will fail on the tension side before fibers on the compression side reach their ultimate strength. In such cases, no initial formation of a pressure ridge on the compression side will occur, and no doubt the application of depth factor is not justified.

In actual service there is just as much probability that the member will be placed in a structure with its most serious face defects on the compression side, as on the tension side, thus further impairing compression strength and accentuating the depth factor. For that reason it is necessary to always apply depth factor, either in the production of grading rules or the design of beams.

As mentioned before, for stress-grades of lumber and timbers *the depth effect has been incorporated into the grading process.* For glued-laminated beams this has not been done and depth effect is a part of the design process. This is brought out in the chapter on glued-laminated members.

Form Factor for Box and I-Sections

The foregoing discussion of depth effect factor applies to beams of rectangular cross-section. In cases of other section shapes different adjustments are employed.

The form factor is a variation of the depth effect factor which gives considerations to the variation in amount of wood in the member at various levels with respect to the neutral axis.

The general expression of form factor is:

$$C_f = 0.81 \left[1 + \left(\frac{h^2 + 143}{h^2 + 88} - 1 \right) C_y \right]$$

h = depth of beam, inches

$C_y = P^2 (6 - 8p + 3p^2)(1-q) + q$

p = ratio of depth of compression flange to full depth of beam

q = ratio of thickness of web or webs to full width of beam.

You will note that the above formula for C_f includes the depth effect factor, which is seen more clearly if written:

$$C_f = 0.81 \ C_y \left(\frac{h^2 + 143}{h^2 + 88} \right) + 0.81 \ (1 - C_y)$$

If p and q are equal to 1.0 as for solid rectangular beams, this expression reduces to the depth effect factor, C_d

It is applied to bending strength calculations in the formula:

$$f_b = \frac{M}{C_f S} \ \leq \ F_b$$

Form Factor for Circular Sections or Diagonally Loaded Square Sections

The most common form of round beams is the pole, which is used principally as a bending member in electric utility and communications service, and various uses as spars.

Research has revealed that round beams exhibit a higher extreme fiber stress at failure, than square beams of the same depth. This is explained by the "support theory" advanced to resolve depth effect for rectangular beams. The area of a slice of the section at the extreme fiber of a round section is adjacent to and backed up by a slice of yet larger area. There are not only less highly stressed fibers adjacent to the extremes in a round section, but more of them.

As it develops, the effect is an 18 percent *increase* in apparent unit bending strength for round sections. The bending strength formula is:

$$f_b = \frac{M}{1.18 \ S} \ \leq \ F_b \qquad \text{for a round beam}$$

as compared to:

$$f_b = \frac{M}{S} \ \leq \ F_b \qquad \text{for a square beam of the same depth.}$$

The depth effect factor must also be applied to round beams over 12 inches in diameter such that:

$$f_b = \frac{M}{1.18 \ C_d S} \ \leq \ F_b$$

The figure 1.18 is a form factor C_f for round shape of cross section.

In the case of a square beam with the neutral axis on a diagonal, it has been determined that $C_f = 1.414$ so that:

$$f_b = \frac{M}{1.414\ S} \leqq F_b$$

If the beam is more than 12 inches on a side, a depth factor computed on the basis of beam width must be applied:

$$f_b = \frac{M}{1.414\ C_d S} \leqq F_b$$

The likelihood of using a square beam in this position is rather remote, but the effect is noted here for whatever use it may have. Perhaps most significant is the fact that in both of these cases (the round and the square beam) form factors greater than 1.0 have been determined. The fact that both beam sections increase in width toward the neutral axis, with the extreme fiber in the one with the larger C_f backed up by a proportionally larger area of wood substance, is another illustration of the "support theory" of depth effect. See Figure 29.

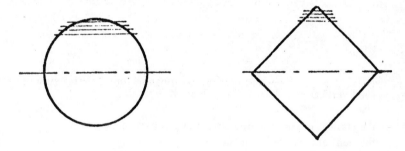

Figure 29

Curvature Factors

Several considerations related to the curvature of glued-laminated wood beams affect the application of the usualy bending formula. These will be described in the chapter on glued-laminated timber.

SHEAR STRENGTH

Compared to steel, the shear strength of wood parallel to the grain is in much smaller proportion to tension, compression and bending strength properties. To illustrate, the properties of a structural grade of steel and one of wood are contrasted in the following Table 40.

Shear strength of wood is only about 13 percent of its bending strength, whereas in a common grade of steel it is 66 percent of that material's bending strength. For this reason it is particularly important to check all wood designs for shear stress. Shear perpendicular to the grain of wood is very high. It is practically impossible to produce a vertical shear failure in a wood member, because the failure develops at right angles to that axis, in the parallel-to-grain plane.

Table 40. Properties of Structural Steel and Douglas Fir Wood

Property	36,000 psi Yield Structural Steel	No. 1 Douglas Fir Joist and Plank
F_t	22,000 psi	1000 psi
F_c	22,000 psi	1400 psi
F_b	24,000 psi	1500 psi
F_v	14,500 psi	190 psi
F_c (Bearing)	24,000 psi	385 psi
E	29×10^6 psi	1.8×10^6 psi

The basic shear formula for wood is:

$$f_v = \frac{VQ}{Ib} \leqq F_v$$

V = total vertical end shear or end reaction, pounds

Q = the statical moment of the area shown above or below the neutral axis, in.^{3}; or outside the shear plane.

I = moment of inertia, in.^{4}

b = width of the member at the shear plane, inches.

h = depth of the member, inches

For a rectangular member this becomes:

$$f_v = \frac{3\,V}{2\,bh} \leqq F_v$$

Duration of load adjustments, as they would affect controlling load and allowable F_v are considered in design for shear. The allowable shear stress for normal load duration, as published in the tables (Appendix A), takes into account the possible presence of seasoning defects that often occur. As noted in Table 16, the published values of F_v may be generously increased if end split is minor, still leaving considerable reserve for seasoning checks elsewhere in the member.

The determination of a proper value of total vertical shear, V, is an important design step. Several considerations deserve attention at this juncture:

1. Take into account any relief to the beam end shear resulting from the distribution of load to adjacent parallel beams by flooring or other members. Common practices in this regard are described in further detail on page 109.

2. Neglect all loads within a distance from the supports equal to the depth of the beam. As an example, for a uniformly distributed load, w pounds per unit length: $\frac{w}{2}(\ell - 2h)$

   For a moving point load, maximum $P\left(\frac{\ell - h}{\ell}\right)$

3. With a moving load, or a series of connected moving loads such as a vehicle, place the largest load a distance from the support equal to the depth of the beam, keeping others in their normal spatial relation to it.

4. Treat all other loads in the usual manner. For several types of load, concentrated, uniformly distributed, and moving, obtain maximum V for each and summarize them for total maximum value of V.

If the shear stress for a beam problem involving concentrated loads exceeds the allowable shear stress when treated by the foregoing procedure, the reaction due to the concentrated loads may be more accurately determined by the following formula:

$$V' = \frac{10\,P}{9} \cdot \frac{\ell - x}{\ell} \cdot \frac{(x/h)^2}{[2 + (x/h)^2]}$$

V' = modified end reaction, or end shear in pounds

x = distance in inches from reaction to load

P = concentrated load in pounds

The modified end reaction is inserted into customary shear formula as follows:

$$f_v = \frac{3\,V'}{2\,bh} \leq F_v$$

F_v is adjusted for any appropriate duration of load condition.

In using the equation for V', it is helpful to have some understanding of how V' is affected by the choice of a distance x from load to support. The development of the equation if too lengthy for inclusion in this text, but is described in a paper by J. A. Newlin, in the Proceedings of the American Railway Engineering Association, 1934, Volume 35, entitled, "Shear in Checked Beams."

In using the equation for the modified end shear reaction, the designer has to decide on a value of the distance x, from the support which will produce the maximum value of V'. A series of trials can be made to bracket the maximum value. This can be quickly done by use of a graph such as Figure 30.

This graph was made so the straight broken lines are the end shears for various distances of a concentrated load from a support, with x in terms of h plotted on the horizontal axis. Each of the lines is for a different beam length, i.e., 10h, 20h, and 30h. These lengths fairly well encompass the sizes of beams used in structures. From these broken lines, at x/h = 1.0, you can obtain V at x = h, as recommended in the foregoing

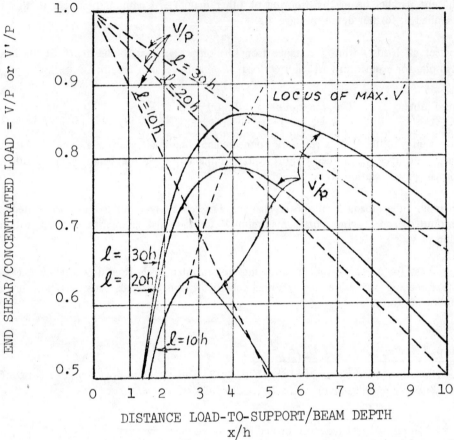

Figure 30. Modified end shear as a function of
load-to-support distance.

procedures 2 and 3. These are the points V/P = 0.966, V/P = 0.95 and V/P = 0.9 for ℓ = 30h, 20h and 10h, respectively.

The solid curves represent the equation for modified end shear, for three values of ℓ = 30h, 20h and 10h. The maximum values of V' fall on the locus of the maxima of these curves. A designer can easily interpolate along the curved locus to estimate x/h for maximum V' at any anticipated ratio of ℓ/h. Using this graph, the need for trial and error computations to find V' maximum is practically eliminated.

Example No. 1: A 15-1/4" deep beam is 30 feet long and carries a moving concentrated load of 5,000 lbs. What is the value of end shear for use in the design formula?

$$\frac{\ell}{h} = \frac{30 \times 12}{15.25} = 23.3$$

Interpolating between the 20h and 30h curves on the locus, find x/h = 3.8 and V'/P = 0.82.

$$V' = 0.82 \times 5000 = \underline{4100} \text{ pounds}$$

This modified value is considerably less than the value of end shear obtained by procedure 2 or 3, i.e., at

$$x = h : V = 5000 \left(\frac{360 - 15.25}{360} \right) = 4790 \text{ lbs.}$$

Example No. 2: Suppose in the preceding example, another concentrated load of 2,000 pounds, 12 feet from the load of 5,000 pounds was present. Find end shear for the two loads combined.

The contribution of the 5,000 pound load has been calculated at 4,100 pounds. The 2,000 pound load will be at a distance:

$$x = 3.8 \times \frac{15.25}{12} + 12 = 16.83 \text{ feet from support}$$

$$x/h = \frac{16.83 \times 12}{15.25} = 13.24$$

At $x/h = 13.24$, the graph in Figure 27 suggests that for $\ell = 23.3$ h, the curve for V' will be above the line for V. *Whenever V' exceeds V at a given value of x, use the smaller value V, for end shear.*

$$V = 2000 \left(\frac{30 - 16.83}{30} \right) = 877 \text{ pounds}$$

The combined end shear for the two loads is 4100 + 877 = 4977 lbs.

A general rule for finding the value of V is at x = 3h, or at the quarter point of the span, whichever is closer to the support. You can see from example no. 1 above that this would give V'/P = 0.79 or about 4.0 percent less than the value obtained by use of Figure 30. This general rule is mentioned in NDS, and the foregoing discussion will explain its origin.

Because end split becomes less consequential in the light of the two beam theory on which the preceding modified end shear formula is based, NDS recommends the following increased values of F_v be used:

Douglar fir	145 psi
Eastern Hemlock	110
Western Hemlock	120
Western Larch	145

Southern Pine	175
Norway Pine	130
Redwood	110
Eastern Spruce	130

BEARING STRENGTH

It is necessary to compute the stress in compression perpendicular to grain at points of concentrated load and at the support points of beams. $F_{c\perp}$ is the property (from tables in Appendix A) used in conjunction with bearing area to determine allowable bearing load. The duration of load factors apply to $F_{c\perp}$, with moisture content adjustments given in Table 15 for service conditions.

The curvature of a loaded beam may concentrate the bearing pressure toward one end of the bearing surface. The elastic modulus of wood perpendicular to grain is very low, 5 to 10 percent of E, and the surfaces will conform to the curvature well enough that no special consideration need be given to concentration of bearing stress at a particular place on the bearing area.

For bearings less than 6-inches in length and not closer than 3-inches from the end of a beam, the bearing allowable stress can be increased according to the relationship:

$$\frac{\ell + 0.375}{\ell} \qquad \begin{array}{l}\text{Where } \ell = \text{length of bearing surface parallel} \\ \text{to grain (See Figure 31)}\end{array}$$

This increase is based on the fact that the surface fibers for short bearing surface lengths act as suspension cables in tension and thus reduce the compressive load on other fibers near the surface of the wood.

Tapered Beams

Tapered beams require special design methods which are not included in this text. Procedures for tapered beam design are given in the AITC "Timber Construction Manual." Tapered round beams or poles, will be mentioned in Chapter 21.

Curved Beams

Curved beams are generally glued-laminated beams and will be discussed in Chapter 15.

COMBINED LOADING OF BEAMS

Structural members are often subject to a combination of bending and axial tension or compression loading. Such members must be designed so:

$$\frac{P/A}{F_t} + \frac{M/S}{F_b} \leq 1$$

$$\frac{P/A}{F'_c} + \frac{M/S}{F_b} \leq 1$$

P = axial load, pounds

F'_c = allowable compressive stress, psi
(This will be discussed under columns Chapter 10.)

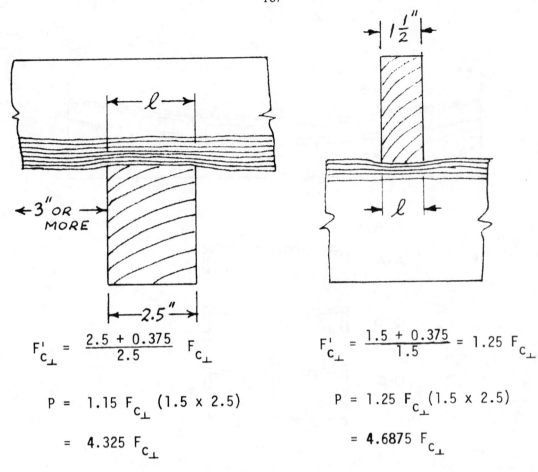

$$F'_{c_\perp} = \frac{2.5 + 0.375}{2.5} F_{c_\perp}$$

$$P = 1.15\, F_{c_\perp}\, (1.5 \times 2.5)$$

$$= 4.325\, F_{c_\perp}$$

$$F'_{c_\perp} = \frac{1.5 + 0.375}{1.5} = 1.25\, F_{c_\perp}$$

$$P = 1.25\, F_{c_\perp}\, (1.5 \times 2.5)$$

$$= 4.6875\, F_{c_\perp}$$

Figure 31. Stress increase for bearing area less than 6" long parallel to grain

Depth effect factor, C_d, is applied to F_b in these formulas when used for glued-laminated beam design.

LATERAL DISTRIBUTION OF CONCENTRATED LOAD

Structures that carry the load on a deck supported on parallel beams will distribute the load among several parallel beams. While the distribution is subject to analysis, it becomes very involved. Even a superficial examination of the variables involved attests to this complexity.

Consider three parallel beams spanned by a plank deck, Figure 32. The greatest deflection from a load at the middle of the central beam is at that location. The deck boards transmit reactions to the outside beams, causing them to deflect. The size of these reactions depends on the thickness and elastic modulus of the deck, and the spacing between beams, ℓ_o. The load that reaches the center beam is the center load, P, minus the reaction of each plank, upward on the center beam. Thus, the deflection of the center beam is a concentrated load deflection downward minus a non-uniformly distributed upward reaction of the deck planks. The actual deflection of the center beam under these superimposed loads is a function of the beam span, moment of inertia and elastic modulus. The upward reactions of the deck boards on the center beam are a function of their deflections, which are the difference between the center and side beam deflections at each station along the span of the beams.

With load, P, at midspan, the maximum bending moment in the central beam is the consequence of P downward and the upward reactions of all the planks upon the center beam.

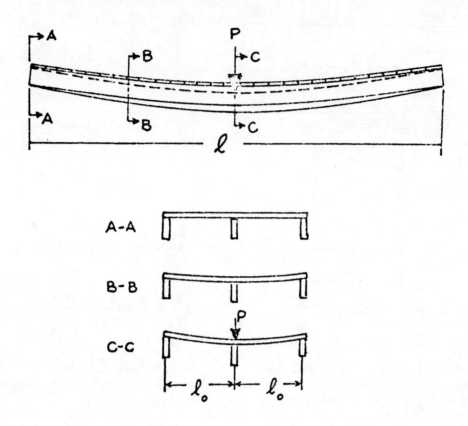

Figure 32. Lateral distribution of concentrated load on a deck.

It is also evident that at sections closer to the beam support points, the upward reaction of the bent deckboards grows less and less, since the boards at Sections BB and AA are deflected less. The division of load between the center and side beams is less at Section AA, than at CC.

The reactions at the ends of the supporting beams are the net summation of the loads imposed on them by the applied load, P, and the deck board reactions distributed along their length.

When plywood decks are used the analysis should also consider horizontal shear developed between deck and beams, i.e., T-beam action.

Load distribution problems of this type have been investigated sufficiently to provide some safe guidelines for design, although probably not truly efficient in the way they utilize material. Complex problems of this kind can be adapted to the data processing facilities now available. The opportunity to program them and obtain specific solutions to specific designs deserves considerably more attention than it has received.

In conventional frame building construction concentrated loads at midspan are distributed laterally for a considerable distance beyond just the adjacent parallel beams, but to the second and third beam removed from the one under the load. The beam most proximate to a concentrated load in nominal 2-inch, deck systems carries as little as 20 to 30 percent of the applied concentrated load.

In connection with bridge floors, the Standard Specifications for Highway Bridges, of the American Association of State Highway Officials, recommends the following practice for load distribution in bridge design for computing bending moment.

With a concentrated load at the center of the beam span, the distribution to the beams adjacent on each side by four types of deck may be estimated by the factors in Table 41.

Table 41. Lateral Distribution of a Concentrated Load at Midspan.

Kind of Deck	Load on Center Beam*
2-inch Wood	$\ell_D/4.0$
4-inch Wood	$\ell_D/4.5$
6-inch Wood	$\ell_D/5.0$
Structurally designed concrete	$\ell_D/6.0$

* ℓ_D = beam spacing in feet. If ℓ_D exceeds the denominator of the factor, use 100 percent. If load is not over a beam, distribute total beam load to two adjacent beams on the assumption that the deck acts as a simple span between these beams.

Example: A load of 1,000 pounds on a 2-inch wood deck supported by three or more parallel beams spaced 2.5 feet apart will be distributed as follows:

<u>To the center beam</u> $1000 \times \dfrac{2.5}{4} = 625$ pounds

<u>To each side beam</u> $\dfrac{1000 - 625}{2} = 187.5$ pounds

Maximum Bending Moment

$$M = \frac{P\ell}{4} = \frac{625\,\ell}{4} = 156.25\ell$$

The estimation of load distribution for shear would be based on the same load distribution given by the factors in Table 41 if the concentrated load is always at midspan. In the case of moving loads, the point of concentrated load for maximum shear is often taken as the quarter point of the span. The fraction of the load that goes to the center and side beams under these conditions is given in Table 42.

Example: If the 1,000 pound load in the previous example is a moving load, the maximum end reaction will occur when the load is near the quarter point of the span. For $\ell D/4.0 = 0.625$, use Table 42 and interpolate a value between 0.69 and 0.79 in column 2, corresponding to 0.625 in column 1. = 0.715.

Table 42. Load Distribution With Load at Quarter Point of Span

ℓ_D/K from Table 41	Distribution with Load Applied at Quarter Point of Span	
	Center Beam	Side Beam
1.0	1.0	0
0.9	.94	0.06
0.8	.87	0.13
0.7	.79	0.21
0.6	.69	0.31
0.5	.58	0.42
0.4	.44	0.56
0.33	.33	0.67

End reaction for design

$$V = 0.715 \ (1000) \ \frac{0.75\ell}{\ell} = 536 \text{ pounds}$$

$$\text{or} \quad V' = \frac{10}{9} \ (715) \ \frac{(.75) \ (x/h)^2}{2 + (x/h)^2} = \frac{593 \ (x/h)^2}{2 + (x/h)^2}$$

If x, distance to support, is $\ell/4$ and h, depth of beam is $\ell/20$, $x/h = 5$ and $V' = 550$ pounds.

EFFECT OF NOTCHES ON BEAM DESIGN

Notching reduces the cross sectional area of beams and affects both bending strength and, under certain circumstances, deflection. Not only do notches affect the section properties for design, but they create stress concentrations that affect allowable shear stress.

Notches at ends of beams on the lower face have no effect on bending strength or deflection. Square cornered notches, as shown in Figure 33, reduce F_v by the ratio h_e/h and the cross section for shear to bh_e.

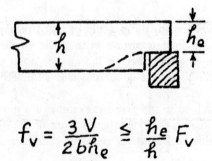

$$f_v = \frac{3V}{2bh_e} \leq \frac{h_e}{h} F_v$$

Figure 33. Beam notched on lower face

111

If the notch shown in Figure 33 is not square cornered, but has a very flat taper in the transition from depth h to depth h_e the full value of F_v may be used (see dotted line notch profile). The exact dimensions or slope for the taper when this full value is F_v is justified has not been defined. Any taper is an improvement on a square notch.

Notches in the top faces are not common, but if required, the shear stress calculation is modified whenever the notch extends inside the edge of the support. The formula for shear stress is:

$$F_v = \frac{3}{2}\ \frac{V}{bh'}$$

where h' is taken from the graph, Figure 34, corresponding to the values of h_e and e/h.

If e exceeds h, use h'= h_e

It is not recommended that notches be made in the central portion of a simple beam or near the point of maximum moment. If notches are necessary, they should be limited to a depth one-sixth the beam depth, and a width of one-third the beam depth. Bending moment at the notched secton must be calculated on the basis of actual distance from base of notch to unnotched side.

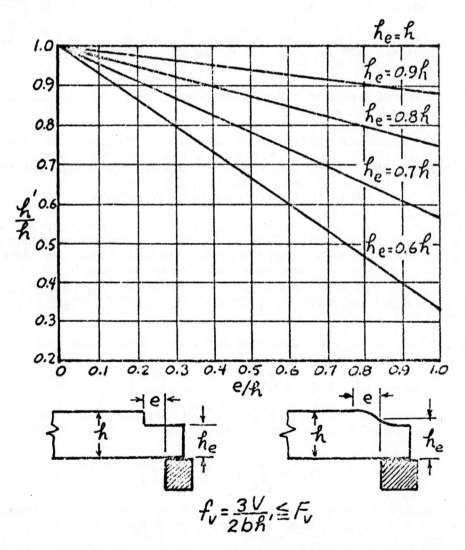

Figure 34. Shear stress in beam notched on top face

One notch in the beam at midspan has little effect on beam deflection. However, wide notches or numerous narrow notches will markedly reduce the stiffness of the member. Frequent notching is rarely necessary so methods of designing for this condition are not presented here. It is sufficient to note the above remarks.

LATERAL STABILITY OF BEAMS

Floor joists, when their depth to thickness ratio is 6 or more (nominal 2" joists of nominal 10" depth or larger) should be supported laterally by bridging installed at intervals of not more than 8 feet. Well connected joist to header construction, or end blocking can serve the function of bridging at ends of joists.

For solid sawn rectangular beams and roof joists, the following rules are generally used for lateral support requirements:

(a)   If ratio of depth to thickness is 2 or less, no lateral support is needed.

(b)   If ratio is more than 2, but not exceeding 3, the ends shall be held in position to prevent lateral rotation.

(c)   If ratio is more than 3, but not exceeding 4, the piece shall be held in line, as in the well-bolted chord member of a truss.

(d)   If ratio is more than 4, but does not exceed 5, one edge shall be held in line against lateral movement, as by connection to a plywood diaphragm or a diagonally braced wood decking diaphragm.

(e)   If the ratio is more than 5, but not exceeding 6, bridging at 8-foot intervals, as described above for floor joist, is required.

(f)   If a beam is subject to both flexure and compression, the ratio should not exceed 5, and one edge must be held in line, as by rafters or roof joists and diagonal braced sheathing. If the dead load is large enough in comparison to the compressive load, to produce tension in the lower surface of rafters, the ratio for the beam may be 6.

Design to Prevent Lateral Buckling

These rather general procedures have been used for many years, but recently a more rational procedure involving a consideration of the length as well as the breadth and depth of members has been established for wood members. Lateral buckling is, of course, also a function of length and elastic modulus. This new procedure is recommended by the American Institute for Timber Construction (AITC) for glued-laminated timber and should apply equally well to solid sawn beams. It is similar to the American Institute for Steel Construction (AISC) method for buckling of steel beams.

Beams of square section, or with breadth greater than depth, require no lateral support in pure bending.

Beams with the compression side supported against lateral movement do not require modification of F_b, inasmuch as the compression side cannot buckle.

When beam depth exceeds breadth, the beam must be secured against lateral rotation at points of bearing, and the allowable bending stress must be limited to those calculated by the formulae for short, intermediate and long beams.

Short Beams

When the slenderness factor, C_s, does not exceed 10, the full allowable unit stress in bending, F_b, adjusted for various conditions of load duration, moisture content in service, and depth effect factor is used for beam strength design.

$$C_s = \sqrt{\frac{\ell_e h}{b^2}}$$

where

C_s = slenderness factor

ℓ_e = effective length in inches, see Table 43

h = depth of beam, inches

b = breadth of beam, inches

Table 43. Effective Length of Glued Laminated Beams.

Type of Beam Span and Nature of Load	Value of Effective Length, ℓ_e
Single span beam, load concentrated at center	1.61ℓ*
Single span beam, uniformly distributed load	1.92ℓ
Single span beam, equal end moments	1.84ℓ
Cantilever beam, load concentrated at unsupported end	1.69ℓ
Cantilever beam, uniformly distributed load	1.06ℓ
Single span or cantilever beam, any load (conservative value)	1.92ℓ

*ℓ = unsupported length   **By permission of AITC.**

Intermediate Beams. Where C_s exceeds 10, but does not exceed C_k, the allowable bending stress, F'_b is:

$$F'_b = F_b \left[1 - \frac{1}{3} \left(\frac{C_s}{C_k} \right)^4 \right]$$

$$C_k = 0.775 \sqrt{E/F_b}$$

Long Beams. In cases where slenderness ratio exceeds C_k, but not greater than 50:

$$F'_b = 0.40 \ E/C_s^2$$

Unsupported Length. For beams with ends supported against lateral rotation, and the compression edge supported against lateral deflection throughout its entire length, the unsupported length, ℓ is zero.

If support at ends prevents lateral rotation but no restraint is provided for the compression edge, the full length of the member is the unsupported length, ℓ.

With support against lateral rotation and lateral displacement at the ends and at intermediate points along the length, the distance between points of lateral support is the unsupported length.

If, at the intermediate points, the restraint prevents lateral rotation but does not prevent lateral deflection (as with vertical bridging), the unsupported length is the full length between bearing points of the member.

The provision of adequate lateral support should be given careful attention by the designer to insure that the decking sway bracing, bridging or tie stringers are properly anchored and fixed.

DEFLECTION AND STRESS DUE TO PONDING

Conditions of service that allow water to accumulate on flat roofs requires special attention. Horizontal surfaces exposed to the weather should be avoided, but if they are necessary they should be pitched to drain. If this cannot be done, or if drain malfunction is conceivable, the structure should be designed to support the weight of water that will accumulate in addition to the dead and live load that controls the design.

Flat structures will progressively deflect as water accumulates until the level of impounded water rises to the point where it can overflow the pond. The structure should be capable of supporting the total weight on the structure under such a condition.

Structures designed for light loads and long spans are most likely to pond water loads great enough to produce failure. As a general guideline, structures that will deflect 1/2-inch under a 5 PSF uniformly distributed load are susceptible to failure by ponding.

A formula for determining the effect of ponding on the stress and deflection of a flat roof is:

$$C_p = \frac{1}{1 - (W'\ell^3/\pi^4 \ EI)}$$

C_p = factor for multiplying stresses and deflections under existing loads to determine stresses and deflections under existing loads plus ponding

W' = total load that a uniform depth of one inch of water would produce on the area supported by the member, lbs.

ℓ = span length of the member, inches

$$E \quad = \quad \text{elastic modulus of the member in psi}$$

$$I \quad = \quad \text{moment of inertia of the member in inches,}^4$$

This formula was developed and verified by engineers at the U. S. Forest Products Laboratory. It does not account for the added load of water due to any creep that exists in a structure prior to the application of the ponding condition. If dead load creep has occurred prior to ponding, an added weight of water will be present in the basin formed by the creep. This will increase the deflection at the overflow condition by an amount:

$$\Delta_c = \frac{w\ell^8}{34,103 \ E^2 I^2}$$

$\Delta_c \quad = \quad$ deflection caused by the water load in the creep basin, inches

$w \quad = \quad$ dead load in lbs. per lineal inch that would cause creep. This is usually taken as half the actual dead load for material that is seasoned and the full dead load for material installed unseasoned.

$\ell \quad = \quad$ length of the member in inches

$E \quad = \quad$ elastic modulus of the member in psi

$I \quad = \quad$ moment of inertia of the member in inches^4

The total deflection of a beam with ponding and creep would then be:

$$\left[\begin{array}{c} \text{Deflection by} \\ \text{existing load} \end{array} \right] C_p \quad + \quad \left[\begin{array}{c} \text{Deflection} \\ \text{due to} \\ \text{creep} \end{array} \right] + \Delta_c$$

The increase in stress caused by the extra water retained in the basin formed by the creep of an initially level beam is the stress caused by an added bending moment:

$$M_c^* = \frac{w\ell^6}{3040 \ EI}$$

And the total stress in a beam with ponding and creep would be:

$$\left[\begin{array}{c} \text{Stress due to existing} \\ \text{load before ponding} \end{array} \right] X \quad \left[C_p + \frac{M_c}{M_i} \right]$$

*For derivation of this formula, see Appendix E.

The increase in the reactions due to the weight of water in the basin formed by creep is:

$$R_c^* = \frac{w\ell^5}{554\ EI}$$

These relationships are all useful in computing the effects of creep on ponding conditions.

At this juncture, it is important to note that where both decking and supporting beams can deflect and are both susceptible to ponding and creep, the magnification factors are cumulative.

Example:

A flat-roofed structure consists of Douglas fir nominal 8" x 14" beams of No. 1 Beam & Stringer grade which are installed unseasoned. They span 24 feet and are spaced 8 feet apart. The beams support a 2-inch nominal, tongue and groove roof deck of Commercial grade Douglas fir and are installed seasoned with a random length continuous decking arrangement. (See Chapter 22.)

The total load is 45 PSF, of which 15 PSF is dead load and 30 PSF is snow load. It is necessary to build this deck virtually flat, so that any stoppage of the drains could cause ponding. This would be most severe when a mixture of rain and snow occurred on the roof (rain saturated snow).

There will be a ponding effect on both the decking and the beams, and since the beams support the decking the increased ponding load on the deck adds to the load on the beams.

First, calculate the midspan deflections and stresses on the decking and beams without ponding:

DECKING (12" actual width)

$$\Delta_i = w\ell^4/100\ EI$$

$$= \frac{(45/12)(96)^4}{100\ (1.7)\ 10^6(3.37)}$$

$$= 0.555\ \text{in.}$$

$$F_b = \frac{M}{0.667S}$$

$$M_i = \frac{w\ell^2}{10} = \frac{(45/12)96^2}{10}$$

$$= 3456\ \text{lbs.}$$

$$F_i = \frac{3456}{0.667(4.5)} = 1151\ \text{psi}$$

BEAM (support 8' deck)

$$\Delta_i = \frac{5}{384}\ \frac{w\ell^4}{EI}$$

$$= \frac{(45 \times 8/12)(288)^4}{1.6 \times 10^6 \times 1537.7}$$

$$= 1.095"$$

$$F_b = \frac{M}{S}$$

$$M_i = \frac{w\ell^2}{8} = \frac{(45 \times 8/12)(288)^2}{8}$$

$$= 311,040\ \text{in lbs.}$$

$$F_i = \frac{311,040}{(227.8)} = 1365\ \text{psi}$$

*For derivation of this formula, see Appendix E.

The magnification of load, stress and deflection for the decking are determined next:

$$W' = 5.2 \times 8 \times 1 = 41.6 \text{ lbs.}$$

$$I = 3.37 \text{ in}^4$$

$$E = 1.7 \times 10^6 \text{ psi}$$

$$\ell = 96 \text{ in.}$$

$$W'\ell^3/\pi^4 EI = {}^{41.6(96)^3}/\pi^4(1.7)(3.37)10^6 = 0.066''$$

$$C_p = \frac{1}{1 - 0.066} = 1.07$$

If dead load creep has occurred before ponding, an added deflection will be present:

$$\Delta_c = \frac{w\ell^8}{34,103 \ E^2 I^2} \quad \text{for a simple span}$$

Since the decking is a continuous span system, the actual deflection due to added water in the basin formed by the creep deformation of the (seasoned) decking will be:

$$\Delta_c \frac{384}{5} \times \frac{1}{100} = 0.768\Delta_c$$

$$= \frac{0.768 \ w\ell^8}{34,103 \ E^2 I^2} = 0.00246''$$

The total deflection of the deck will be:

$$\Delta_i C_p + \Delta_i \frac{15}{2 \times 45} + 0.768 \ \Delta_c$$

$$0.555 (1.07) + .0925 + .00246'' = 0.69$$

This is $\ell/139 < \ell/120$

The stress increase due to the added water in the basin will be:

$$1151 \left(C_p + \frac{M_c}{M_i} \right)$$

$$M_c = \frac{w\ell^6}{3040EI} = \frac{(15/24)(96)^6}{3040 \times 1.7 \times 3.37 \times 10^6} = 28.07 \text{ in lbs.}$$

This is for a simple span. To convert to random length continuous decking, multiply by 10/8 to obtain 35.08 in lbs.

$$M_i = 3456 \text{ in lbs.}$$

The increased stress will be:

$$1151 \left(1.07 + \frac{35.08}{3456} \right)$$

$$= 1151 \ (1.0801) = 1162.7 \text{ psi}$$

This does not exceed the allowable 1800 x 1.15 = 2070 psi.

The increased reaction of the deck on the beams will be:

$$R_i \left(C_p + \frac{R_c}{R_i} \right)$$

$$R_c = \frac{w\ell^5}{554EI} = \frac{(15/24)(96)^5}{554 \times 1.7 \times 10^6 \times 3.37} = 1.605 \text{ lbs.}$$

$$R_i = (45/12) \ \frac{96}{2} = 180 \text{ lbs.}$$

$$R = 180 \left(1.07 + \frac{1.605}{180} \right) = 180(1.0789) = 194.2 \text{ lbs/ft}$$

Design the beams to support the magnified deck load due to ponding and creep of 388.4 lbs/ft or w = 32.4 lbs/inch from the deck. This will change the values previously calculated for the beam without ponding in the direction of the beam span to:

$$\Delta_i = 1.095 \times \frac{388.4}{360} = 1.182 \text{ in.}$$

$$M_i = 311,040 \times \frac{388.4}{360} = 335,700 \text{ in. lbs.}$$

$$F_i' = 1365 \times \frac{388.4}{360} = 1473 \text{ psi}$$

Determine magnification of stress and deflection of the beam:

$$W' = 5.2 \times 24 \times 8 = 1,000 \text{ lbs.}$$

$$I = 1537.7 \text{ in}^4$$

$$E = 1.6 \times 10^6 \text{ psi}$$

$$\ell = 288 \text{ in.}$$

$$W'\ell^3/\pi^4 EI = \frac{1000\,(288)^3}{\pi^4(1.6)(1537.7)10^6} = 0.099$$

$$C_p = \frac{1}{1 - 0.099} = 1.11$$

If dead load creep in the (unseasoned) beam has occurred before ponding, an added deflection will be present:

$$\Delta_c = \frac{w\ell^8}{34,103E^2I^2} = \frac{(15 \times 8/12)(288)^8}{34,103(1.6)^2 10^{12}(1537.7)^2} = 0.0022''$$

The total beam deflection is:

$$\Delta_i C_p + \Delta_i \frac{DL}{TL} + \Delta_c$$

$$1.182(1.11) + 1.182 \frac{15 \times 8}{388.4} + 0.0022$$

$$1.313 + 0.364 + 0.0022 = 1.68''$$

This is $\ell/172 < \ell/120$

The stress increase due to the added water in the basin will be:

$$1473 \left(C_p + \frac{M_c}{M_i} \right)$$

$$M_c = \frac{w\ell^6}{3040EI} = \frac{(15 \times 8/12)(288)^6}{3040(1.6)(1537.7)10^6} = 768 \text{ in lbs.}$$

$$M_i = 335,700 \text{ in lbs.}$$

The increased stress will be:

$$1473 \left(1.11 \ + \ \frac{768}{335,700} \right)$$

1473 (1.11231) = 1655 psi

This does not exceed the allowable 1600 x 1.15 = 1840 psi.

The preceding example illustrates the rather complex chain of computations necessary to give complete consideration to creep. The problem will be greatly simplified if creep can be ignored. If circumstances justify this, the calculations would be:

C_p for decking = 1.07

C_p for beam = 1.11

Deflection of deck = 1.07(0.555) = 0.595"

Stress in deck = 1.07(1151) = 1236 psi

Deflection of beam = 1.07(1.11) 1.095 = 1.305"

Stress in beam = 1.07(1.11) 1365 = 1620 psi

CHAPTER 10

DESIGN OF LUMBER COMPRESSION MEMBERS

Simple Solid Members in Compression

Timber designers divide simple columns into two classes: short columns and long columns. *Short rectangular columns* have span-to-least dimension ratios less than:

$$\ell/d = \sqrt{\frac{0.3E}{F_c}}$$

Short columns with direct axial loads are designed to assure that unit compression stress does not exceed the allowable compression stress parallel to the grain, F_c

$$P/A \leqq F_c$$

F_c is subject to the usual duration of load and moisture content adjustments. In computing the limiting value of ℓ/d for short columns, duration of load factors may be applied to E. This is the only instance in timber design where duration of load is applied to elastic modulus. The practice should not suggest that elastic modulus if being accorded any special time-dependency, but merely that it is being used as a predictor of a compressive strength property.

For columns which are not rectangular, the limiting ℓ/r is $\sqrt{3.619E/F_c}$ where r is the least radius of gyration.

In most instances wood columns will be rectangular.

Long rectangular columns are those with ℓ/d exceeding $\sqrt{0.3E/F_c}$, but not greater than 50. Long columns are susceptible to instability and failure by buckling at stresses below F_c. They are designed to avoid exceeding an allowable compressive stress of:

$$F'_c = \frac{0.3E}{(\ell/d)^2} \geqq P/A$$

For columns that are not solid and/or rectangular, the more general equation is:

$$F'_c = \frac{3.619E}{(\ell/r)^2} \geqq P/A$$

where r is the radius of gyration. For rectangles, $r = d/\sqrt{12}$ and for circular sections $r = d/4$.

These are common formulas for computing F'_c. They assume the ends of the column are free to rotate, as with hinged or pin-connected ends. Actually, columns connections rarely allow free rotation at the ends. Usually they are subject to end-fixity of some degree. Even unfastened columns with square cut ends seated on flat surfaces show some degree of end-fixity. These formulas are used, even though they produce a conservative design, because the degree of end-fixity may be difficult to establish. In cases where the degree of end-fixity can be established the formula is modified by the insertion of an end-fixity factor U, such that:

COLUMNS

$$P/A \leq \frac{0.3UE}{(\ell/d)^2} \quad \text{or} \quad \frac{3.619UE}{(\ell/r)^2}$$

Values for U are given in Figure 35. They derive from the fact that for various degrees of fixity the effective length of the column, which is the distance between adjacent points of zero moment, is reduced.

In the British code of practice, values of U for columns with built-in ends (100% end-fixity) and built-in at one end and hinged at the other (Figures 35b and 35e) are 2.0 and 1.4. These reduced values have been recommended on the assumption that end-fixity cannot be reliably achieved. In the United States, designers do not usually impose this added limitation except in instances where they think it is justified.

The general long column formulas are, on a theoretical basis, conservative by a factor of 2.73. That is, the theoretically precise formula is: $P/A = F'_c = 9.9E/(\ell/r)^2$. By using the modified form, $3.619E/(\ell/r)^2$, provision is made for using an effective E equal to about 37 percent of the published value for average E. On the basis of the known variability of the elastic modulus property of about 20 percent of the average, the probability of designing a member that will not perform at the level predicted by these formulas is one in one-thousand. Inasmuch as design loads are also chosen on a conservative basis, and load sharing by distribution enters into most designs, the prospects of difficulty are very low indeed.

To summarize, short rectangular columns are designed on the basis of the allowable compression parallel to grain as published by the grading authorities (Appendix A) for values of effective length to least dimension (ℓ/d) up to $\sqrt{0.3E/F_c}$. At larger values of ℓ/d, columns are designated as long columns, and are designed on a modified compressive strength $F'_c = 0.3E/(\ell/d)^2$. These relationships for one particular species and grade of wood are illustrated in Figure 36. The maximum ℓ/d for solid rectangular columns is 50.

Example: A nominal 6-inch wide beam is to be supported by a nominal 6-inch wide x 16-ft. long column. The column will be No. 1 grade Douglas fir Post & Timber class material. The load is 12,000 lbs. The column size is to be determined, for normal load duration and dry use conditions.

Is this a short column?

ℓ/d = 16 x 12/5.5 = 34.9

E = 1,600,000 psi

F_c = 1,000 psi

Maximum ℓ/d for short columns is $\sqrt{0.3E/F_c}$ = 21.9

ℓ/d actually exceeds 21.9, so it is not a short column.

The design stress for this long column is:

$$F'_c = 0.3E/(\ell/d)^2 = \frac{0.3 \times 1,600,000}{(34.9)^2} = 394 \text{ psi}$$

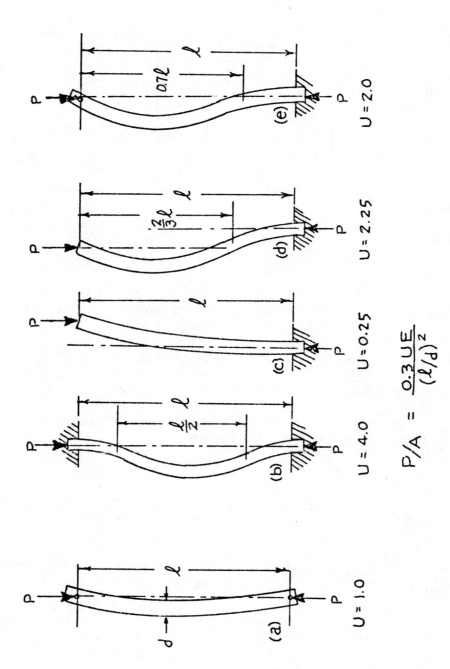

Figure 35. — End fixity factor for columns.

124

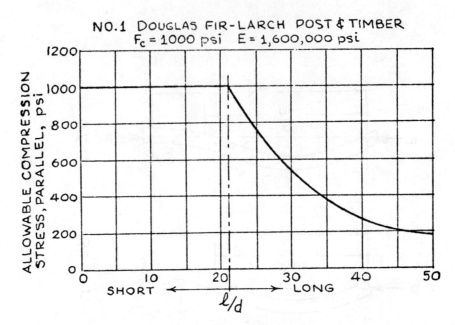

NO.1 DOUGLAS FIR-LARCH POST & TIMBER
$F_c = 1000$ psi $E = 1,600,000$ psi

Figure 36.   Allowable compression stress parallel to
grain for solid rectnagular columns with
ends free to rotate, U = 1.0.

Required column area = P/F'_c = 12,000/394 = 30.5 sq. in.

Minimum width = 30.5/5.5 = 5.55 inches

A nominal 6" x 6" piece has an area of 30.25 square inches. Sinces this is
within 1% of the required area, it may be used.

Combined Bending and Compression

Compression members often support lateral loads or eccentrically placed end loads that induce bending
moments which require consideration. The top chords of trusses and columns supporting equipment loads or wall
pressures are examples.

Members subject to axial compression and bending moment are designed to satisfy the following
equations:

For short members with $\ell/d \leq \sqrt{0.3E/F_c}$

$$\frac{M/S}{F_b} + \frac{P/A}{F_c} \leq 1$$

If the bending moment is the result of an eccentrically placed end load (Figure 37b) the value of M/S
for *short* columns is:

$$Pe/S = (P/A)(6e/d)$$

where e is the eccentric displacement, and A = bd
and $S = bd^2/6 = \frac{Ad}{6}$

And the short column formula may be written:

$$\frac{(P/A)(6e/d)}{F_b} + \frac{P/A}{F_c} \leqq 1$$

For eccentrically loaded *long* columns, the curvature of the member amplifies the induced moment, as a result of the additional eccentricity. In those cases the practice is to increase the induced moment by 25 percent, making:

$$M/S = (P/A)(7.5e/d)$$

and $\frac{(P/A)(7.5e/d)}{F_b - P/A} + \frac{P/A}{F'_c} \leqq 1$

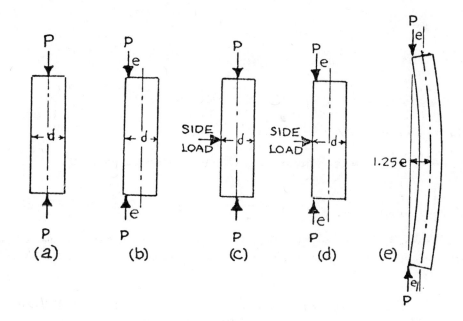

Figure 37. End loads, side loads and eccentrically placed end loads.

If bending moment is the result of an eccentrically placed *end load and a side load acting in combination*, (Figure 37d) then:

For a short member:

$$\frac{M/S + (P/A)(6e/d)}{F_b} + \frac{(P/A)}{F_c} \leqq 1$$

For a long member:

$$\frac{M/S + (P/A)(7.5e/d)}{F_b - P/A} + \frac{(P/A)}{F'_c} \leqq 1$$

A detailed development of these equations is found in U. S. Forest Products Laboratory Report No. 1782 by L. W. Wood.

Loads hung from brackets may be resolved into side loads and axial loads as shown in Figure 38. The following example illustrates the solution for a problem of this type.

Example: Determine the size of a column 12 ft. long and nominal 6 inches wide to support a direct axial load of 10,000 lbs. and an equipment load of 2,000 lbs. supported as shown in Figure 38, with a = 3 ft., b = 2 ft., and c = j = 1 ft. The material is No. 1 Douglas fir Post & Timber grade, for dry use conditions of normal duration.

$$E = 1,600,000 \text{ psi} \quad F_c = 1,000 \text{ psi} \quad F_b = 1,200 \text{ psi}$$

$$\ell/d = 144/5.5 = 26.2$$

$$\text{Maximum short column } \ell/d = \sqrt{\frac{0.3E}{F_c}} = \sqrt{\frac{0.3(1,600,000)}{1,000}} = 21.9$$

This is a long column.

$$F'_c = 0.3E/(\ell/d)^2 = \frac{0.3(1,600,000)}{(26.2)^2} = 700 \text{ psi}$$

The bending moment caused by the equipment is either

$$P_2 \frac{c \cdot a}{\ell} \quad \text{or} \quad \frac{P_2 \cdot c}{\ell}\left[\ell - (a+b)\right]$$

a = 3 ft.   b = 2 ft.   c = 1 ft.

$$P_2 \, c \, \frac{a}{\ell} = \frac{2000(1)(2)}{12} = 333 \text{ ft. lbs.}$$

$$\frac{P_2 c}{\ell}\left[\ell - (a+b)\right] = \frac{2000}{12}(12 - 5) = 1166 \text{ ft. lbs.}$$

Use M = 1166 ft. lbs. at the lower point of attachment.

$$\frac{M/S}{F_b - P/A} + \frac{P/A}{F'_c} \leqq 1$$

$$\frac{1166(12)/S}{1200 - 12000/A} + \frac{12000/A}{700} \leqq 1$$

Try a 6 x 6

$$S = 27.73 \text{ in.}^3 \qquad\qquad A = 30.25 \text{ sq. in.}$$

$$\frac{505}{803} + \frac{397}{700} = 0.628 + 0.568 = 1.196 \quad 6 \text{ x } 6 \text{ is } \underline{\text{TOO SMALL}}$$

Try a 6 x 8

$$S = 37.81 \text{ in.}^3 \qquad\qquad A = 41.25 \text{ sq. in.}$$

$$\frac{370}{908} + \frac{291}{700} = 0.407 + 0.416 = 0.823 \quad 6 \text{ x } 8 \text{ is } \underline{\text{ADEQUATE}}$$

127

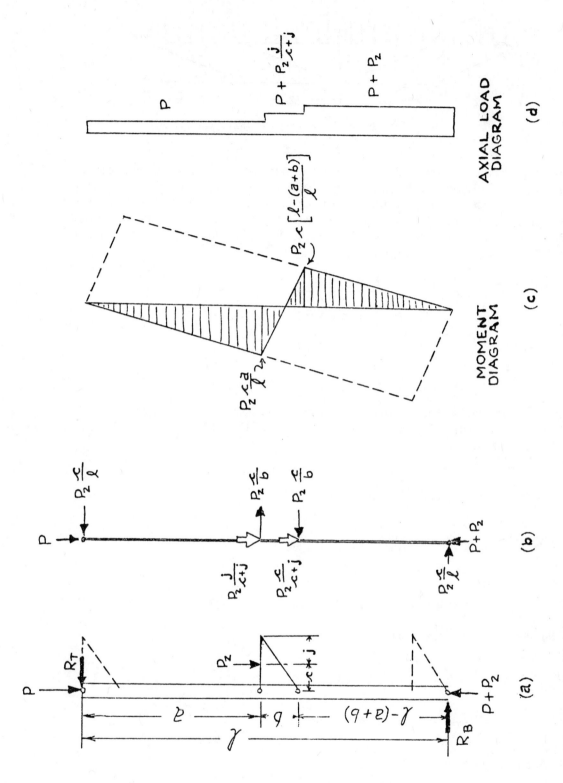

Figure 38. Moments and axial forces due to bracket load on a column.
(a) Column and bracket arrangement showing three of several possible bracket positions.
(b) Free Body force diagram for column with end load and bracket load.
(c) Moment diagram for bracket in center position; dashed lines for extreme positions.
(d) Axial load diagram for central bracket position.

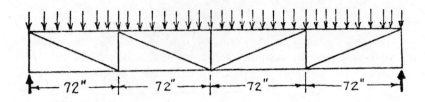

Figure 39

Example: The truss in Figure 39 carries a normal duration uniformly distributed load of 140 lbs per foot on the top chord. An analysis has shown that the compressive loading of the top chord is 4,500 lbs. maximum, and the maximum bending moment in the top chord is 3,900 inch lbs. Determine the required size of the top chord assuming the roof structure gives it adequate support against buckling in the horizontal direction and the chord member is set on edge. The wood is Hem-fir, No. 1, Structural Light Framing grade (2" x 4") or No. 1 Joist & Plank grade (2" x 6" or larger).

Hem-fir	No. 1 S.L.F.	No. 1 J&P
F_b	1,400 psi	1,200 psi
F_c	1,000 psi	1,000 psi
E	1,500,000 psi	1,500,000 psi

The top chord is continuous. The end-condition for the more heavily stressed central panels is somewhere between that of built-in ends and pin-connected ends. A value of U of 2.0 would be appropriate, so effective length is 0.7 x 72 = 50.2 in.

$$\ell/d = 50.2/3.5 = 14.4 \text{ for a 2" x 4" member}$$

$$\ell/d = \sqrt{\frac{0.3E}{F_c}} = \sqrt{\frac{0.3(1,500,000)}{1,000}} = 21.3$$

This is a short compression member.

Check for the adequacy of a 2" x 4" member.

$$\frac{M/S}{F_b} + \frac{P/A}{F_c} \leqq 1 \qquad \begin{array}{l} S = 3.06 \text{ in.}^3 \\ A = 5.25 \text{ sq. in.} \end{array}$$

$$\frac{3900/3.06}{1400} + \frac{4500/5.25}{1000} = 0.91 + 0.86 = 1.77 > 1$$
$$\text{2 x 4 is } \underline{\text{TOO SMALL}}$$

Check the adequacy for a 2" x 6".

$$\ell/d = 50.2/5.5 = 9.2 < 21.3 \text{ Short Member}$$

$$\begin{array}{l} S = 7.56 \text{ in.}^3 \\ A = 8.25 \text{ sq. in.} \end{array}$$

$$\frac{3900/7.56}{1200} + \frac{4500/8.25}{1000} = 0.43 + .545 = 0.975 < 1$$

So a 2" x 6" will be adequate.

NOTE: In this particular problem, a design involving the gluing of plywood roof sheathing to the top chord could produce an adequate design using 2 x 4 top chords. This possibility will be examined in Chapter 18.

Spaced Compression Members and Columns

Compression members consisting of two pieces separated by well-connected spacer blocks are quite common in timber designs. They are used both for vertical columns and for the chords, diagonals, or vertical struts of trusses.

The design of spaced compression members is a simple variation on the design of simple solid columns, with particular end-fixity conditions. Referring to Figure 40, two members separated by spacer blocks and connected by bolts in loose-fitting holes or by nails subject to slip would behave more or less like two simple columns, as indicated in Figure 40b.

If tight-fitting split-ring connectors or toothed rings of the type described in Chapter 13 are used in conjunction with bolts, the kind of performance illustrated in Figure 40c and d can be obtained.

End Condition A—Figure 40c describes a degree of end-fixity obtained when the connector (or center of gravity of a connector group) in each end block is centered at any location up to $\ell/20$ from the end. The design for this arrangement is carried out on the basis that:

$$F'_c = \frac{0.3(2.5)E}{(\ell/d)^2} = \frac{0.75E}{(\ell/d)^2} \geqq P/A$$

Of course, if $\ell/d \leqq \sqrt{0.75E/F_c}$ short column design theory would prevail, but this is not usually the case for spaced column applications. In the preceding formula for P/A, P and A may be either the total load on and total area of the two members; or they may be the load and area per column member. In either case, d is the thickness of one member. The members are equal in thickness.

The maximum allowable ℓ/d for spaced columns is 80. The maximum value of ℓ'/d (See Figure 40a) is 40.

End Block Shear—It is necessary to provide adequate shear strength in the connection between the end blocks and the members. The shear strength requirements at each of the faces between end block and column member may be obtained from Figure 41 by multiplying the area of the column member by the end-block constant for the appropriate species group as given in the following table.

Note that for the denser and stiffer species groups the end block constants and the required shear strength of the joint is higher than for the lower density groups. This follows from the fact that the F'_c values are larger for the denser species, with larger values of E. With the grade-related E-values now in use this procedure should probably be reorganized on the basis of E, rather than species groupings, but that work has not yet been completed.

Location and Size of Spacer & End Blocks—Spacer blocks located in the middle tenth of the column do not require connectors or shear restraint, but do require a bolt to tie the members together. If two or more spacer blocks are used, their greatest spacing must not exceed one-half the distance between the centers of end-block connectors (or connector groups), and they must have the same shear connection strength as the end blocks.

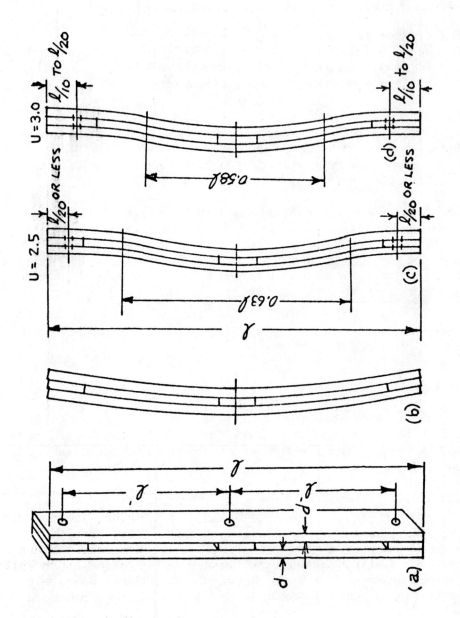

Figure 40. Spaced column. (c) End-fixity condition A (d) End-fixity condition B.

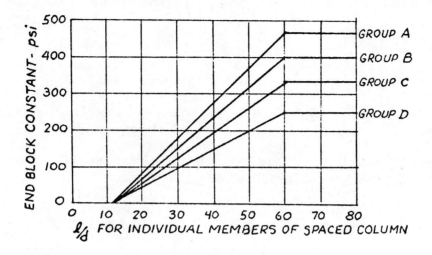

Figure 41. End block constants for spaced columns.

Table 44. Species Groups for End Block Constants for Timber Connectors

Group A	Group B	Group C	Group D
Ash, white Beech Birch Elm Hickory Maple Oak Pecan	Douglas fir Larch, western Pine, Southern yellow Sweetgum	Cedar, Alaska Cypress, Southern Douglas fir, South Hemlock, western Pine, Norway Redwood Spruce, red Spruce, Sitka Spruce, White Poplar, Yellow	Cedar, Western red Fir, True Hemlock, eastern Pine, Eastern White Pine, Lodgepole Pine, Ponderosa Pine, Sugar Pine, Western white Spruce, Englemann

Timber connectors have specific end and edge distance and spacing requirements which are explained in Chapter 13.

The thickness of end blocks and spacer blocks should be equal to the thickness of the individual members of the spaced column. End blocks should be thick enough to develop the required connector loads and of sufficient length and width to develop the required shear forces between members.

Spacer and end blocks one-half the thickness of the main members of the column may be used, provided their length is twice that required for blocks equal to the main member thickness.

For thicknesses from one-half to full main member thickness, specify length in proportion. Blocks thicker than main member thickness, do not improve the strength of the column.

Glued Blocks—If, instead of timber connectors, the end blocks are secured by gluing, the area of the block for shear parallel to the grain must be great enough so that $A_s F_v$ A (End Block Constant)

$$A_s \quad = \quad \text{length x width of end block}$$

$$A \quad = \quad \text{cross-sectional area of individual member}$$

$$F_v \quad = \quad \text{allowable shear stress, psi}$$

For glued construction, the blocks should be clear material, long enough to extend from the end of the member to $\ell/20$ plus 5 1/2 inches for end-fixity condition A and $\ell/10$ plus 5 1/2 inches for end-fixity condition B. Bolts of a size and quantity equal to that required for the timber connectors otherwise used, should be used in the glued joint to prevent failure in tension perpendicular to the grain.

The adhesive should be stronger than the wood itself and suited to the exposure conditions for intended service.

End Condition B—Figure 40d describes a degree of fixity obtained when the innermost connector from each end is centered at a location up to $\ell/10$ from the end. The design for this arrangement is carried out on the basis that:

$$F'_c \quad = \quad \frac{0.3(3)E}{(\ell/d)^2} \quad = \quad \frac{0.90E}{(\ell/d)^2} \quad \geq \quad P/A$$

As a part of the design of a spaced column, it is necessary to check the strength as a simple column in flexure in the wide direction of the members.

Example: A 3 1/8" x 12" laminated beam is to be supported by a spaced column at one end where the load on the column will be 3,000 lbs. (normal). The length of the column will be 12 feet. The species is Douglas fir for both beam and column members. The column members are to be nominal 3-inch lumber of No. 2 Joist and Plank grade. Design the spaced column for dry use.

To obtain the stiffest column, plan to use end-fixity condition B, so that:

$$F'_c = \frac{0.9E}{(\ell/d)^2}$$

$$\ell/d = 144/2.5 = 57.5 \qquad \begin{aligned} E &= 1,700,000 \text{ psi} \\ F_c &= 1,050 \text{ psi} \end{aligned}$$

$$F'_c = \frac{0.9(1,700,000)}{(57.5)^2} = 465 \text{ psi} < 1050 \text{ psi}$$

$$P/A = 3000/A = 465$$

$$A = 6.45 \text{ sq. in.}$$

This would indicate that two 3 x 4's at 8.75 sq. in. each would be more than adequate to do the job. However, such small members might buckle as simple columns in their wide direction, so the possibility should be examined. Check the capacity of a 4" x 3" as a simple column of length 0.9ℓ or = 130 inches.

$$\ell/d = 130/3.5 = 37.2$$

$$F'_c = \frac{0.3E}{(\ell/d)^2} = \frac{0.3(1,700,000)}{(37.2)^2} = 368 \text{ psi}$$

Capacity of one 4 x 3 is 8.75 x 368 = 3210 lbs.

These are more than adequate. A check will reveal that 3 x 3 pieces will be too small and also will not be wide enough for the smallest available size of split ring connector. Use two 3" x 4" members.

The shear requirements from Table 44 and Figure 41 are:

End block constant for Group B at an ℓ/d of 57.5 is 380.

Area of one member is 6.45 sq. in.

Shear requirement = 6.45 x 380 = 2450 lbs.

The beam, acting as one spacer block will carry connector load at 90 degrees to the grain direction. One 2 1/2" Split Ring connector, loaded at 90 degrees to grain in Group B wood on both faces of a block 3" or more thick will carry 1950 lbs. On one face of a 2 1/2" member, parallel to grain, it will carry 2750 lbs. (For split ring properties see Chapter 13.)

Use two 2 1/2" Split Rings in each shear face between beam and column members and one 2 1/2" Split Ring between lower end block and column members.

Spaced Compression Members in Trusses

Although this chapter has dealt primarily with column applications, these relationships apply to compression chords, and compression web members of trusses, and are very useful in achieving efficient designs.

The truss application must be carefully examined to determine the justification for end-fixity assumptions. While it is difficult to give precise general rules to follow, some guidelines are suggested.

In the compression chords of trusses, laterally supported panel points may define the ends for spaced columns. Portions of web or chord members will serve the function of end blocks. Spacer blocks may need to be added to the normal truss design on the compression side.

For vertical or diagonal web members the intersection with the lower chord, if it is in tension as is usually the case, may serve as an end block for a spaced column.

Built-Up Columns

Columns fabricated by mechanically laminating a series of wide-thin pieces together to form an approximately square member with cover plates over the exposed edges is an old practice that is described in many textbooks on timber design. The stiffness and strength of such columns is less than that of solid members of the same size, but considerably greater than the sum of the load capacities of the individual members treated as independently sharing the load. The exact capacity is highly dependent upon the number and size of nails, bolts, or other mechanical fasteners used to develop the shear between layers. It appears that well-fastened columns of this kind will perform at capacities above the average for the two conditions, i.e., solid versus unconnected laminae.

At the present time, some very interesting research on this type of member has been reported by Dr. J. R. Goodman of the College of Engineering at Colorado State, from which a rigorous design approach should follow. Meanwhile, other than to mention these possibilities, a design procedure will not be offered.

Glued built-up columns, using lumber of less than 19 percent moisture content, and bonded with casein or synthetic resin adhesives with good clamping pressure or well-bolted to produce good contact between surfaces should develop the strength of solid columns of the same size.

Round Columns

Round columns may be designed using the general formulas given at the beginning of this chapter. The radius of gyration, "r", will be one-quarter of the column diameter. The maximum ℓ/r for a round column will be 173 (equivalent to an $\ell/D = 43$; D = diameter).

A useful circumstance to note is that a round column will carry the same load as a square column of the same cross-sectional area. A square column that measures 0.886D on each face has the same area as a round column of diameter D.

Tapered Columns

A uniformly tapered column, either round or rectangular, may be designed on the basis of its dimensions at a point one-third of the length of the taper from the small end. For a rectangular column, d is the least dimension at this section.

CHAPTER 11

NAILS AND NAILED JOINTS

Nails are probably the most common and familiar form of mechanical fastenings. There are many types, sizes and forms of standard nails as well as a variety of special purpose nails. Growing international commerce is introducing a variety of nails manufactured to standards different than those to which the allowable loads given in the tables of this book apply.

Standard methods for testing nails to develop their allowable load characteristics are found in ASTM Standard D 1761, "Testing Metal Fasteners in Wood." This Standard may be used by the manufacturers and distributors of unfamiliar types of nails to produce the engineering data required for their design use. Such data are not always available, however, and unless the designer knows he can reliably infer the properties of non-standard nails from the generalized nail strength formulae presented in this chapter, he should specify only the familiar types of nails, whose properties are documented or readily calculated from basic theory.

Among the kinds of nails which have well-established allowable load properties one can find a variety of types at a variety of prices to suit special purposes. Often specialty nails, such as the grooved and hardened nails, have unique holding properties that justify their added cost.

In addition to nails, wire staples which are particularly suitable for power driving, have become important in the manufacture of wood products and in home building and structural system fabrication.

In general, nails give stronger joints when driven into the side grain of wood than into the end grain. Nails perform best when loaded laterally as compared to axial withdrawal, so nailed joints should be designed for lateral nail bearing if possible. Withdrawal load information is available and joints may be designed for that kind of loading if necessary.

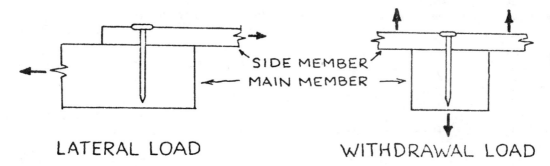

Figure 42

Table 45 gives sizes of common nails, spikes, threaded nails and box nails. Spikes are larger in diameter than common nails of the same length, but are made in longer sizes. Hardened nails cover the nail and spike length range. They are smaller in diameter than either common nails or spikes of the same length. Their performance with reference to lateral load resistance, size for size, is superior because they are formed from high-carbon steel wire and are annularly grooved, heat treated and tempered for strength. Box nails, you will note, have diameters equal to those of the next shorter standard common nail size. Box nails are preferred by many users because they have less tendency to split the wood and can penetrate more deeply than common nails of the same diameter.

Table 45. Nail and Spike Sizes

Pennyweight	Length inches	Diameter, inches			
		Common Nail	Box Nail	Hardened Nail	Spike
6d	2	0.113	--	0.120	--
8d	2 1/2	0.131	0.113	0.120	--
10d	3	0.148	0.131	0.135	0.192
12d	3 1/4	0.148	0.148	0.135	0.192
16d	3 1/2	0.162	0.148	0.148	0.207
20d	4	0.192	0.162	0.177	0.225
30d	4 1/2	0.207	0.192	0.177	0.244
40d	5	0.225	0.207	0.177	0.263
50d	5 1/2	0.244	0.225	0.177	0.283
60d	6	0.263	0.244	0.177	0.283
70d--5/16"	7	--	--	0.207	0.312
80d	8	--	--	0.207	--
3/8"	8 1/2	--	--	0.375	--
90d	9	--	--	0.207	--

By permission of NFPA.

WITHDRAWAL RESISTANCE

The resistance of a nail to direct withdrawal is a function of the specific gravity of the wood and the diameter and depth of penetration of the nail. For common wire nails and spikes driven into the side grain of *seasoned wood that will remain seasoned,* or *unseasoned wood that will remain unseasoned* in service, the allowable withdrawal load may be calculated from the formula:

$$P = 1380 \, G^{2.5} D$$

G = Specific gravity based on oven dry weight and volume.

D = Nail diameter in inches.

P = Allowable load in pounds per inch of penetration.

These allowable loads are based on one-fifth of the average ultimate load. The coefficient of variation of nail withdrawal properties is usually less than 30 percent of the average, so one may be confident that these nail strengths will be exceeded in practice about 199 times in 200. Joints consisting of two or more nails thus become completely reliable at these values for all practical purposes.

The specific gravities of common North American species used in construction are given in Table 46. Table 47 provides withdrawal values for common nails and spikes and for hardened threaded nails.

This general equation for nail withdrawal resistance appears to give the advantage in joint strength to the higher density species. The allowable loads are predicated on the assumption that nail spacing is great enough that splitting of the wood will not occur. As a rule the lower density species do not split so easily as the higher ones. This permits closer nail spacing in the lower density species, often permitting the design of joints equal to those in species of higher density via the use of more and larger nails per joint. This, of course, applies to laterally loaded nailed joints as well.

Table 46. Grouping of Species for Determining Allowable Loads for Lag
Screws, Nails, Spikes, Wood Screws, Drift Bolts

Group	Species of Wood	Specific Gravity* (G)
I	Ash, commercial white.	0.63
	Beech	.67
	Birch, sweet	.71
	Birch, yellow	.65
	Elm, rock.	.67
	Hickory, true.	.80
	Maple (hard), black	.60
	Maple (hard), sugar	.67
	Oak, commercial red.	.66
	Oak, commercial white.	.71
	Pecan	.73
II	Douglas fir	0.51
	Larch	.55
	Pine, southern	.55
III	Cedar, Alaska	0.47
	Cedar, Port Orford	.45
	Cypress, southern.	.49
	Hemlock, western	.47
	Pine, Norway	.47
	Redwood (old growth)	.44
	Sweet gum	.53
IV	Basswood	0.35
	Cedar, northern white	.32
	Cedar, southern white	.34
	Cedar, western red	.36
	Cottonwood, black	.34
	Fir, Balsam	.37
	Fir, commercial white	.40
	Hemlock, eastern	.44
	Pine, lodgepole	.44
	Pine, ponderosa	0.44
	Pine, sugar	.39
	Pine, eastern white	.39
	Pine, western white	.41
	Spruce, Engelman	.40
	Spruce, red, white, Sitka.	.42
	Yellow poplar	.45

*Based on weight and volume when oven-dry.

Table 47. NAILS and SPIKES—Allowable Withdrawal Loads—Normal Duration Allowable load in withdrawal, in pounds per inch of penetration of nail or spike into the member holding the point. Inserted perpendicular to grain in wood. d = pennyweight

Specific Gravity of Wood** d =	SIZE OF COMMON NAIL										SIZE OF THREADED NAIL*							SIZE OF COMMON SPIKE									
	6	8	10	12	16	20	30	40	50	60	30	40	50	60	70	80	90	10	12	16	20	30	40	50	60	5"/16	3"/8
.32	9	10	12	12	13	15	16	18	20	21	15	15	15	15	18	18	18	15	15	16	18	20	21	23	23	25	30
.34	10	12	14	14	15	18	19	21	23	24	18	18	18	18	21	21	21	18	18	19	21	23	24	26	26	29	35
.35	11	13	15	15	16	19	21	23	25	26	19	19	19	19	23	23	23	19	19	21	23	25	26	28	28	31	38
.36	12	14	16	16	17	21	22	24	26	28	21	21	21	21	24	24	24	21	21	22	24	26	28	30	30	34	40
.37	13	15	17	17	19	22	24	26	28	30	22	22	22	22	26	26	26	22	22	24	26	28	30	33	33	36	43
.38	14	16	18	18	20	24	25	28	30	32	24	24	24	24	28	28	28	24	24	25	28	30	32	35	35	38	46
.40	16	18	21	21	23	27	29	31	34	37	27	27	27	27	31	31	31	27	27	29	31	34	37	39	39	43	52
.41	17	20	22	22	24	29	31	33	36	39	29	29	29	29	33	33	33	29	29	31	33	36	39	42	42	46	56
.42	18	21	23	23	25	30	33	35	38	41	30	30	30	30	35	35	35	30	30	33	35	38	41	45	45	49	59
.43	19	22	25	25	27	32	35	38	41	44	32	32	32	32	38	38	38	32	32	35	38	41	44	48	48	52	63
.44	20	23	26	26	29	34	37	40	43	46	34	34	34	34	40	40	40	34	34	37	40	43	47	50	50	55	66
.45	21	25	28	28	30	36	39	42	46	49	36	36	36	36	42	42	42	36	36	39	42	46	49	53	53	59	70
.46	22	26	29	29	32	38	41	45	48	52	38	38	38	38	45	45	45	38	38	41	45	48	52	56	56	62	74
.47	24	27	31	31	34	40	43	47	51	55	40	40	40	40	47	47	47	40	40	43	47	51	55	59	59	65	78
.48	25	29	33	33	36	42	46	50	54	58	52	42	42	42	50	50	50	42	42	46	50	54	58	62	62	69	83
.51	29	34	38	38	42	49	53	58	63	68	49	49	49	49	58	58	58	49	49	53	58	63	68	73	73	80	96
.53	32	37	42	42	46	54	59	64	69	74	54	54	54	54	64	64	64	54	54	59	64	69	74	80	80	88	106
.59	42	48	55	55	60	71	76	83	90	97	71	71	71	71	83	83	83	71	71	76	83	90	97	104	104	115	138
.62	47	55	62	62	68	80	86	94	102	110	80	80	80	80	94	94	94	80	80	86	94	102	110	118	118	130	156
.64	51	59	67	67	73	87	93	102	110	119	87	87	87	87	102	102	102	87	87	93	102	110	119	128	128	141	169
.66	55	64	72	72	79	94	101	110	119	128	94	94	94	94	110	110	110	94	94	101	110	119	128	138	138	152	183
.67	57	66	75	75	82	97	105	114	124	133	97	97	97	997	114	114	114	97	97	105	114	124	133	143	143	158	190
.68	60	69	78	78	85	101	109	119	128	138	101	101	101	101	119	119	119	101	101	109	119	128	138	149	149	164	198
.71	65	76	86	86	94	111	120	130	142	152	111	111	111	111	130	130	130	111	111	120	130	142	152	164	164	181	218
.80	89	103	117	117	128	152	163	178	193	208	152	152	152	152	178	178	178	152	152	163	178	193	208	223	223	246	296

*Loads for threaded, hardened steel nails, in 6d to 20d sizes, are the same as for common nails.

**See Table 46 for species.

By permission of NFPA.

The withdrawal resistance of nails driven into end grain *is only half that obtained in side grain.* This will be touched upon under "Direction of Nailing."

Effect of Nail Surface on Withdrawal Resistance

The surface condition of the nail affects withdrawal resistance as does the type of head and point, the direction of driving, and whether the nail is clinched or unclinched. See page 148 for a discussion of clinching. The surface condition of nails can be modified by surface coatings, surface roughening, or shank deformation to improve withdrawal resistance. Residues of oil film applied during manufacture, and corrosion, can also affect nail withdrawal, but these factors are so variable their effect cannot be reliably evaluated.

Cement coatings are common, and in the low density species they may double the withdrawal resistance immediately after driving. This effect is not so evident in dense species because the coating is scraped off in driving. The increase in withdrawal resistance of cement-coated nails is not permanent and drops off in a month or so after driving. Cement-coated nails are useful for products of short service life, such as shipping containers, and should be useful for structures assembled by nail-pressure gluing methods.

Corrosion-resistant coatings improve joint life in a corrosive environment and in certain chemically treated wood products. They also prevent chemical staining in certain woods such as redwood and oak, and iron and rust staining rather generally. Such coatings have a tendency to improve rather than impair withdrawal resistance, but the effect is irregular and difficult to measure. Cyclic moisture change of the wood in a nailed joint also reduces any initial improvement in withdrawal strength. In any event the coatings do not impair the performance of the nails in any known way.

Chemically etched and sand blasted nails show effectively improved withdrawal resistance and are less affected by moisture cycling than are smooth shank nails.

Deformed-shank nails with shanks which are square, barbed, spirally or annularly grooved, etc., are commercially available. These nails offer some real advantages which the designer should consider. Allowable properties can be furnished by the manufacturers. Annular grooving is said to increase the withdrawal resistance and spiral grooving to raise the energy required to pull the nails. This suggests that although it takes a large force to initiate the withdrawal of annularly grooved nails, once begun the withdrawal proceeds with very little force. Such nails, though strong, would give little visible evidence of impending failure. Spirally grooved nails require the continued application of withdrawal force to extract them. They would be less likely to withdraw suddenly and without warning.

Deformed-shank nails carry somewhat higher maximum lateral loads than common wire nails, but both perform much alike at small joint distortions. Deformed-shank nails may fatigue more easily than smooth ones under conditions of vibration and load reversal, but these conditions are not often encountered in structures at the stress levels that cause failures.

LATERAL LOAD RESISTANCE

The allowable design load for common nails and spikes driven into the side grain of seasoned wood may be calculated from the formula:

$$P = K D^{1.5}$$

P   =   Allowable, lateral load in pounds per nail at rated penetration.

K   =   A constant related to the density of the wood.

D   =   Diameter of the nail.

In the case of lateral resistance, rather than introduce a specific gravity factor into the equation, it has been convenient to divide the common species of wood into groups arranged according to density and other mechanical properties that affect lateral load resistance. Values of K for the species groups in Table 46 are 2040 (Group I), 1650 (Group II), 1350 (Group III), and 1080 (Group IV). The lateral load computed by this formula is for nails that penetrated the main member 10 diameters for Group I, 11 diameters for Group II, 13 diameters for Group III and 14 diameters for Group IV.

Lateral loads for design, for standard common nails and spikes and for hardened threaded nails are listed in Table 48. The formula may be useful in estimating the lateral loads allowable for nail diameters not listed in Table 45.

This formula and the loads in Table 48 are based upon tests using specimens of nominal 1-inch (25/32") lumber, secured by the nail to a thicker block. These loads therefore are applicable to these nail types when the side member (piece containing the head end of the nail) is nominal one-inch thick and larger. The degree to which they apply to thinner lumber side members is not quantitatively known, but there are instances, which are discussed under "Nailed Joint in Plywood" where considerably thinner pieces of wood as side members have sustained the full rated lateral load of the nail. As a matter of information the distance along the grain to the end of the standard test specimen is 2 inches, and the distance across the grain to the edge is 1 inch.

At full rated penetration and load the lateral nail deflection is 0.015 inch laterally. This is sometimes useful when an estimate of nailed joint movement is wanted. In this range load versus deflection may be considered linear.

For nail penetrations less than those given above the nails will support reduced lateral load in the proportion of the actual penetration distance to the full load penetration—down to a minimum of one-third at one-third of rated penetration (Figure 43). No increase is allowed for penetrations above the full load amount, since lateral load capability is also a function of nail stiffness and action as a cantilever. Lateral load capacity is not improved by penetration beyond the full rated amount. Full load penetrations for the standard nail diameters for the four species groups are given in Table 49.

Nails in three-member joints can sustain increased lateral load under certain conditions. When nails fully penetrate all members of a three-member joint, their strength in double-shear is equal to from 1.33 to 1.66 times their strength in single-shear, depending upon the thickness of the main and side members. This is illustrated in Figure 44.

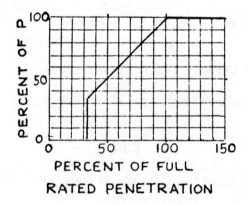

Figure 43

TABLE 48--NAILS AND SPIKES--Allowable Lateral Loads--Normal Duration

Allowable lateral loads (shear) in pounds for nails and spikes penetrating 10 diameters in Group I species, 11 diameters in Group II species, 13 diameters in Group III species and 14 diameters in Group IV species, into the member holding the point.

d = pennyweight

Species Group**	SIZE OF COMMON NAIL										SIZE OF THREADED NAIL*						
d =	6	8	10	12	16	20	30	40	50	60	30	40	50	60	70	80	90
Group I	78	97	116	116	132	171	191	218	249	276	171	171	171	171	218	218	218
Group II	63	78	94	94	107	139	154	176	202	223	139	139	139	139	176	176	176
Group III	51	64	77	77	88	113	126	144	165	182	113	113	113	113	144	144	144
Group IV	41	51	62	62	70	91	101	116	132	146	91	91	91	91	116	116	116

*Loads for threaded, hardened-steel nails in 6d to 20d sizes, are the same as for common nails.

Species Group**	SIZE OF COMMON SPIKE									
d =	10	12	16	20	30	40	50	60	5/16"	3/8"
Group I	171	171	191	218	249	276	306	306	357	469
Group II	139	139	155	176	202	223	248	248	289	380
Group III	113	113	126	144	165	182	202	202	236	310
Group IV	91	91	101	116	132	146	162	162	189	248

**For species in each group, see Table 46.

By permission of NFPA.

Table 49. Full Load Penetrations for Nails and Spikes

Diameter inches	Species Groups			
	I	II	III	IV
	10D	11D	13D	14D
	in.	in.	in.	in.
0.113	1.13	1.24	1.47	1.58
0.120	1.20	1.32	1.56	1.68
0.131	1.31	1.44	1.70	1.83
0.135	1.35	1.49	1.75	1.89
0.148	1.48	1.63	1.92	2.07
0.162	1.62	1.78	2.11	2.26
0.177	1.77	1.95	2.30	2.47
0.192	1.92	2.11	2.49	2.68
0.207	2.07	2.28	2.69	2.90
0.225	2.25	2.47	2.92	3.15
0.244	2.44	2.68	3.17	3.41
0.263	2.63	2.89	3.42	3.67
0.283	2.83	3.11	3.68	3.96
0.312	3.12	3.43	4.06	4.37
0.375	3.75	4.12	4.87	5.25

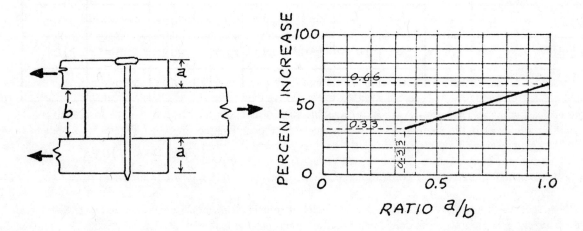

Figure 44

Example: A 12 penny common nail joining a 2-inch nominal (1.5") main member to two 1-inch nominal (3/4") side members of white fir (Group IV).

The single-shear load value for a 12 penny nail in white fir is 62 lbs. at full (14 diameters) penetration. Since the main member is less than 14 diameters the single-shear value is:

$$62 \times \frac{1.5}{14(0.135)} = 49.2 \text{ lbs.}$$

For double-shear with a/b = 1/2 the value is:

$$49.2 \left[1.333 + \frac{(0.5 - 0.333)}{(1.0 - 0.333)} 0.333\right] = 49.2(1.416) = 69.6 \text{ lbs.}$$

For nails up to 12 penny common, used in double-shear, fully penetrating three members plus three nail diameters *and clinched,* the double-shear value may be twice the single-shear value based on a penetration equal to the thickness of the main member. The minimum side member thickness in this case must be 3/8-inch. In other words, clinched nails in double-shear are treated as two nails in single-shear with penetration equal to the main member thickness.

Example: A 12 penny common nail joining a 2-inch nominal (1.5") main member to two 5/8-inch side members, would protrude 1/2-inch or 3.7 nail diameters. If this is clinched the double-shear value will be twice the single-shear value for 1.5" penetration. For white fir, this value will be:

$$2 \left[62 \times \frac{1.5}{14(0.135)}\right] = 2 \times 49.2 = 98.4 \text{ lbs.}$$

Values of K for lateral resistance are based upon proportional limit strengths of nailed joints. Nails, when loaded laterally, assume load increasingly with deformation and as long as this remains within the elastic range it is generally acceptable. From the viewpoint of actual failure these allowable lateral loads are about one-fifth of the average ultimate stregnths for softwoods and one-ninth for hardwoods. As in the case of withdrawal resistance, one may be confident that lateral load strengths will exceed these in 199 out of 200 instances. For multiple nail joints the possibility of joint failure at the design loading becomes insignificant, in the order of 1 in 2000 for a two-nailed joint, and even less if more nails are involved.

For nails in side grain the direction of the lateral load with respect to grain direction has no significant effect on lateral load resistance and no adjustments are made on that basis. However, when nails load a member across the grain, care should be taken to provide adequate edge distance in the direction of the load. This would be particularly important if the joint had few nails, and less important if the joint had a number of nail rows parallel to the grain. For nails up to 16 penny we have experience to the effect that a loaded edge distance of 1-inch minimum is necessary. This is a rather crude guideline, as obviously the spacing would be affected by nail penetration, nail diameter, and spacing along the grain. Some research in this area would be useful.

"Nail spacing should be sufficient to prevent unusual splitting," is about the extent of the guidance one can obtain from the common sources. Unless nail holes are prebored the nailing process is, to a degree, a splitting process. "Unusual splitting" therefore means splitting in excess of that normal to the nailing process in the area very local to the nail shank.

Rules for minimum nail spacing vary considerably and generally the designer is left to his own devices to determine what the proper spacing should be. Minimum spacing would depend on the density and moisture content of wood as well as the anatomical characteristics that affect split resistance, such as straight versus interlocked grain, and tangential versus radial grain orientation with reference to the nail axis. For these reasons any general spacing rules one could give can sometimes be safely violated. Spacing practices that have been used successfully are given in Table 50.

The diameters of *prebored holes* should be 90 percent of the nail diameter for Group I species and 70 percent for Groups II, III, and IV woods. Spacing of nails in plywood is discussed under "Nailed Joints in Plywood."

When *metal gusset or splice plates* are nailed to wood members the lateral load resistance in side grain can be increased by a factor of 1.25. The plates must be designed to carry the bearing load of the nails and have closely fitted drilled holes.

Nails driven into the end grain of wood have less lateral resistance than they have in side grain. Allowable lateral loads for nails in end grain are 2/3 of those in Table 48, suitably adjusted for moisture content.

Nail spacing is also a function of load resistance requirements. Plywood and lumber structural elements such as box beams, rigid frames, folded plates, vaulted panels and roof diaphragms all require specific nailing requirements which can be calculated as described in other sections of this book. These nailing requirements will dictate spacing and determine optimum combinations of nail size and spacing and the need for preboring of holes. See table 51.

Factors Affecting Allowable Nail Loads

Duration of Load—Nail performance is a wood property as much as it is a nail property, and to the extent that wood properties are affected by time, the performance of nailed joints are also affected by time. The duration of load factors which are generally applicable to wood should be applied to the lateral and withdrawal holding properties of wood for nails. In the case of diaphragms loaded by seismic forces nail values are increased 30 percent in addition to the duration of load adjustment for wind and earthquake. The duration of load adjustment factors are:

Permanently applied load	0.90
Normal—ten-year cumulative	1.00
Two months cumulative, aor snow	1.15
Seven-day cumulative	1.25
Wind or earthquake	1.33
Impact	2.00

Moisture Content—It was mentioned on page 136 that withdrawal resistance of nails driven into unseasoned wood which remains unseasoned in service is about the same as that for nails driven into seasoned wood that remains seasoned in service. In the case of lateral resistance to load, allowable loading in green or unseasoned wood is reduced to 75 percent of that for seasoned wood. Lateral resistance relates to proportional limit strength properties to a greater degree than does withdrawal resistance, and proportional limit of nailed joints are more affected by moisture content.

The effect of seasoning on joints nailed in the unseasoned condition is to reduce withdrawal resistance to 25 percent of the value given in Table 47. Lateral resistance under these conditions is reduced to 75 percent of the values given in Table 48, and in addition if the structure is subject to continuous cycling from green to dry, lateral nail strengths are often reduced to 25 percent of Table 48 values.

The concept that nailed structures fabricated green and seasoned in place will tighten and become stronger is not borne out by experience.

Table 50. Minimum Nail Spacings in Nail Diameters for Lumber

	No Prebored Holes	Prebored Holes
End distance	20	10
Edge distance	5	5
Perpendicular-to-grain spacing	10	3
Parallel-to-grain spacing	20	10

Table 51. Nail Spacing Guide

Nail Diameter	No Prebored Holes			Prebored Holes[1]		
	// and End	Edge	⊥	// and End	Edge	⊥
0.113	2.26	0.56	1.13	1.13	0.56	0.34
0.120	2.40	0.60	1.20	1.20	0.60	0.36
0.131	2.62	0.66	1.31	1.31	0.66	0.39
0.135	2.70	0.68	1.35	1.35	0.68	0.41
0.148	2.96	0.74	1.48	1.48	0.74	0.44
0.162	3.24	0.81	1.62	1.62	0.81	0.49
0.177	3.54	0.89	1.77	1.77	0.89	0.53
0.192	3.84	0.96	1.92	1.92	0.96	0.58
0.207	4.14	1.04	2.07	2.07	1.04	0.62
0.225	4.50	1.12	2.25	2.25	1.12	0.68
0.244	4.88	1.22	2.44	2.44	1.22	0.73
0.263	5.26	1.31	2.63	2.63	1.31	0.79
0.283	5.66	1.41	2.83	2.83	1.41	0.85
0.312	6.24	1.56	3.12	3.12	1.56	0.94
0.375	7.50	1.88	3.75	3.75	1.88	1.13

[1]The diameters of prebored nail holes are 90 percent of nail diameter for Group I species and 70 percent for Groups II, III, and IV woods.

Hardened, threaded nail performance in seasoned wood is an exception to these adjustments. No reductions are required for either withdrawal or lateral resistance of these nails under conditions of changing moisture content, which is a powerful argument for their use in engineered structures.

Direction of Nailing.—The rather large allowable load reductions for nails driven into end-grain were mentioned on pages 136 and 144. Allowable withdrawal loads for nails driven into end-grain (parallel to the L-axis of the wood) are 50 percent of those permitted in side-grain of seasoned and unseasoned wood. Allowable lateral loads for end-grain driven nails are reduced to 66 percent under like conditions of seasoning. (These end-grain reductions are cumulative with any moisture content adjustments required.)

Nails subject to lateral loading should be driven at 90 degrees to the loading direction whenever possible. For a configuration of the kind shown in Figure 45a, the nail should be perpendicular to the grain in the member receiving the point and sized for the horizontal component of the load, laterally. Figure 45b illustrates a condition where the vertical component of the load on the side member is a withdrawal load on the nail. The nail should be sized to resist that load as well as for lateral resistance to the horizontal component.

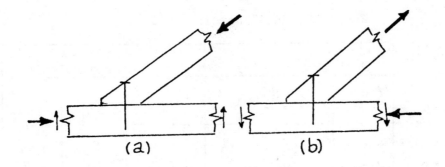

Figure 45. Angle joint (a) compression (b) tension

The courses of heavy roof decking are often fastened together by *slant-nailing* as shown in Figure 46. If the decking has well-fitted tongues and grooves the transfer of vertical force from one course to another is accomplished by the T & G joint. If decking is not well-seasoned, i.e., if it will shrink after installation, the T & G joint may disengage. In that case the nail must be designed to resist the withdrawal and lateral components of the transferred load. (Figure 46a)

The real purpose of slant-nailing decking, however, is to develop resistance to shear forces between the courses. These shear forces arise from wind and seismic loads applied laterally to the deck, or from components of vertical load that develop parallel to the surface of highly pitched roofs. Shear forces of this kind load the nails as shown in Figure 46c. Under these circumstances the nails are laterally loaded at 90 degrees to the grain axis, and will carry the full allowable lateral loads on the basis of their penetration measured along the nail axis.

Slant-nailing is also used to fasten joist and rafters to sills and plates in conventional structures of many types. While special metal anchorage hardware, such as the TECO Trip-L-Grips, are generally preferred, information on the performance of slant-nailed connections is available. Slant-nailed joints are generally superior to straight-nailed joints in resisting forces that pull directly away from the main member, the member containing the nail point. The withdrawal force per inch of penetration into the main member is reduced, and although the penetration into the main member may also be reduced, if the angle between the nail axis and the attached member (containing the head-end of the nail), does not exceed 30 degrees, the reduced withdrawal force will approximately balance the reduced penetration. When slant-nailing is proposed to hold down the rafters of large roof structures a detailed force analysis and design to select proper nail size and spacing is recommended. This can be done by resolving the joint load into components parallel and perpendicular to the nail, and choosing nail

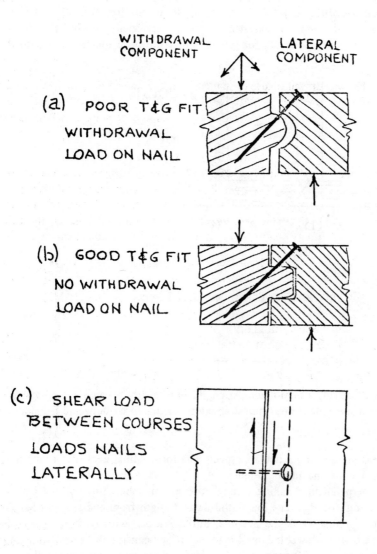

Figure 46. Slant-nailed decking

sizes to meet the lateral and withdrawal forces called for. Poorly designed slant-nail hold-down connections for large roofs are a common source of building failure due to wind uplift forces.

The necessity for slant-nailing is usually a matter of access to the joint area for fabrication. A joint with perpendicular-to-grain nailing (Figure 47c), if it can be physically made, can usually be designed for greater strength in withdrawal from side grain, since the potential for generous penetration is much better with the nail point in the deeper member.

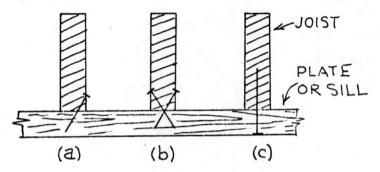

Figure 47. Joist and rafter connections

       (a) slant-nailed
       (b) cross-slant-nailed
       (c) straight-nailed

Cross-slant nailing equals or exceeds single-slant-nailing strength, presumably because the opposing forces exerted by the loaded nails resist lateral movement and impose greater bearing force between the sides of the nails and the wood.

Toe-nailing differs from slant-nailing in one particular respect. The longitudinal axes of the two members of a toe-nailed joint intersect in the plane of the joint (Figure 48). Unlike slant-nailing, toe-nailing can provide joints of greater strength than perpendicular nailing through the side member into the end grain of the main member. This is generally true because of the very low withdrawal strength from end-grain wood. The use of extremely long nails to compensate for this would be possible, but is seldom actually done. The allowable loads for toe-nailed joints are 83 percent of the allowable lateral load and 67 percent of the allowable withdrawal load for nails driven at an angle of approximately 30 degrees to the piece and started at approximately one-third of the nail length from the end of the piece.

Clinched Nails

Information on the performance of smooth-shank nails that have been clinched is found in the research literature. By clinching at least three diameters of the length of nail, withdrawal resistance can be increased 50 percent. If clinching is across the grain this increase will be 60 percent. The withdrawal resistance of seasoned nailed joints that were fabricated green normally falls off to about 25 percent, but clinching improves this to about 66 percent. However, such joints are likely to be loose after seasoning unless they can be reclinched in the field. This is not a very practical operation in the eyes of most contractors. See page 151 for clinched nails in plywood-lumber joints.

Nails in Wood Treated with a Fire-Retardant

Wood may be fire-retardant-treated by pressure impregnation with an aqueous solution of the fire-retardant chemical. Such treatment leaves the wood saturated with water and essentially unseasoned. It can then

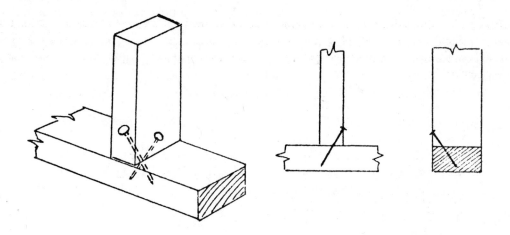

Figure 48. Toe-nailed connections stud to sill

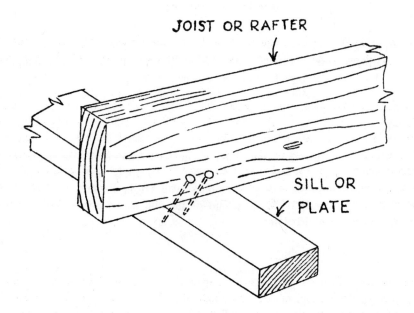

Figure 49. Slant-nailed joist or rafter connection

be kiln dried or allowed to season in service. The strength reduction factors related to moisture content that were described on page 144 also apply to wood that is unseasoned by virtue of fire-retardant treatment. In addition there is a 10-percent reduction in strength due to the effect of the fire-retardant chemical on the wood.

Fire-retardant-treated wood structures with joints fabricated wet and seasoned in service would require nail values of 90 percent by 25 percent of the values in Table 47 for withdrawal, and 90 percent by 75 percent of the values given in Table 48 for lateral loads for nails and spikes. For hardened threaded steel nails the 25 and 75 percent factors do not apply and only the 10 percent reduction is taken.

Nails in Wood Treated with a Preservative

Aside from the normal moisture content reduction factors previously described, preservative chemicals do not further affect the strength of wood in any adverse way. Certain of the oil-borne treatments actually protect the surface of the wood from weathering, and greatly reduce the rate of moisture change in wood.

Nails Other than Steel

Aluminum and stainless steel nails are sometimes used to avoid the consequences of certain corrosive conditions. Aluminum nails distort slightly more than steel under lateral load but sustain the same ultimate loads. If distortion is highly crucial the aluminum nails used would be 10 percent larger in diameter than steel for the same expected lateral performance. Aluminum nails have been observed to withdraw more easily than some steel nails, however, this may well be a function of nail smoothness rather than nail material.

Stainless steel nails perform much the same as regular medium carbon steel nails with respect to loading properties.

Casing Nails

The lateral load-bearing strength of casing nails are only about one-half that of common nails. Casing nails should not be used for withdrawal type loading, as a general rule, although with adequate penetration in both members, withdrawal resistance of casing nails could be developed equal to those for common nails.

Nailed Joints in Plywood

Nailed connections between plywood and lumber are very common in structural work. With the exception of the application of roofing shingles to plywood-sheathed roofs, the nail points are usually in the lumber members of the joints. Since plywood is commonly available in thicknesses 3/4-inch (the minimum standard lumber size) and less, the bearing of the head-end of the nail in the plywood can become the weakest element of such joints. You may recall that lateral nail load tests are normally made with 3/4-inch lumber side members.

It has been established that the full bearing strength of 6 penny common nails can be developed in 5/16-inch plywood, of 8 penny common nails in 3/8-inch plywood, of 10 penny common nails in 1/2-inch plywood, and of 16 penny nails in 5/8-inch plywood. Full bearing of all nails can be developed in 3/4-inch plywood. This presumes that the nails are driven into lumber of the same species group as the plywood, and at penetrations to develop full rated lateral nail loads.

Edge distances for laterally loaded nails in plywood should be 3/8-inch minimum when load direction parallels the plywood edge. For load direction perpendicular to the plywood edge, an edge distance of 1/2-inch for 6 penny nails up to 3/4-inch for 16 penny nails is recommended. Nail spacing in the direction of the grain of lumber member should be 4 inches in Group I and Group II woods such as Douglas fir, but can be reduced to 3 inches in Group III and IV species.

Common nails used in double-shear with plywood gusset plates on each side of a lumber member have twice the lateral load capacity of nails in single-shear for the same nail penetration into the lumber, provided the nails are clinched 3 diameters of the nail length, with the clinch perpendicular to the stress direction. The deformation of double-shear joints is less than that of single-shear joints.

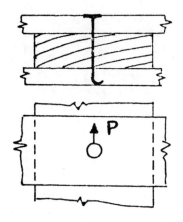

Figure 50

Plywood resists splitting much better than lumber, as one might reasonably expect. The nail-bearing performance is independent of face-grain direction.

Withdrawal resistance from plywood 1/2-inch thick and less, is about equal to that in the same species of lumber. At greater thicknesses the "per inch" withdrawal resistance of plywood decreases. Exact thickness related figures are not available, but a 30-percent reduction for withdrawal strength for nails in five or more plies would be a safe adjustment.

Plywood is manufactured dry and generally is dry when nailed. If the plywood becomes wet in service the withdrawal strength is not affected. However, if plywood structures should be fabricated under wet conditions and then become dry in service, the moisture content adjustments for lumber fabricated green and dried in service should be applied (25 percent for withdrawal; 75 percent for lateral load).

Load Sharing Between Nails

In designing compression or tension joints the nails are considered to share the total load on the joint, equally. The net section of the wood is considered the full section, unless the nails holes (prebored size) are subtracted from the full section to get the net section. Allowable stress is the allowable compression or tensile stress for the species and grade of lumber used.

In designing the spliced joints in bending members the nails are considered to share the load in proportion to their distances from the centroid of the nail pattern. The nail farthest from the center of gravity is regarded as stressed to the allowable lateral nail value, and the other nails to lower loading. This is very similar to conventional design of riveted steel splice plate joints.

Under some circumstances both moment and direct stress are carried by the spliced member. In that case the most highly stressed nail must be located by analysis, on the assumption that the direction of stress due to moment is perpendicular to the radius to the centroid, and the direct stress is parallel to the axis of the member.

Table 52. Check List for Design of Nailed Joints

ADJUSTMENT FACTORS FOR:

DESIGN FEATURES AND SERVICE CONDITIONS	Lateral Load	Withdrawal Load
	Table 48 at penetrations of 10D – GRI, 11D – GRII, 13D – GRIII, 14D – GRIV. Interpolate nail values down to 1/3 these penetrations – Table 49. Group Table 46.	Table 47 per inch of penetration specific gravity Table 46 Nail & spike sizes in Table 45.
Seasoned, used dry [1]	1.00	1.00
Unseasoned, used wet	0.75	1.00
Unseasoned, used dry	0.75	0.25
Moisture cycling	0.25	0.25
End grain	0.66	0.50
Metal side plates	1.25	1.00
Plywood	1.00	0.75
Treated wood:		
Preservative	1.00	1.00
Fire retardant	0.90	0.90
Toe nailing	0.83	0.67
Aluminum nails	0.85	0.85
Clinched:		
Seasoned, used dry	---	1.5 to 1.6
Unseasoned, used dry	---	1.66
Double shear:		
Member thickness ratio = 1/3	1.33	---
Member thickness ratio = 1	1.66	---
3/8" side member & clinched	**2.0 for 12d or smaller**	---
Diaphragms	1.30	1.30
Drilled holes	1.00	1.00

1. Moisture content adjustments do not apply to hardened nails.

CHAPTER 12

BOLTS AND BOLTED JOINTS

Although split ring connectors are of considerably greater efficiency in developing the strength potential of wood joints, common bolts are often adequate and are important fasteners for wood construction. The properties of bolted joints have been obtained from research and testing. Tables of bolted joint properties for a wide variety of North American wood species published in the "National Design Standard" and other handbooks are founded upon procedures described in the "Wood Handbook" and are essentially alike.

Bolted joints are used principally to resist load perpendicular to the axis of the bolt at angles to grain from 0° to 90°. Withdrawal values are not published for bolts, inasmuch as they are not driven into tight-fitting holes and their threads do not engage the wood. For axial loading, bolt strength would be a function of compressive bearing area under washers and compressive strength of the wood at that location.

When bolts are loaded perpendicular to their axis they bear upon the sides of the bolt hole, i.e., the projected area of the bolt. If bolts are large and stiff, this bearing pressure is uniform and the allowable bolt load is the product of the allowable bearing pressure and the projected area of the bolt.

On the other hand, if the bolt is slender it will not be stiff enough to distribute the bearing load uniformly, and the bearing stress will concentrate in that portion of the bearing surface near the surfaces of the member. These conditions are shown by the sketches in Figure 51.

Figures 52 and 53 are graphs of allowable load for bolts in double shear plotted against the length of the bolt in the main member of a three-member joint, with main member twice the side member thickness.

In Figure 52, the curves are linear up to a value of $\ell = 4$ bolt diameters. This indicates that allowable load is a function of projected bolt area multiplied by a wood bearing strength of about 1180 psi. Thus, for $\ell/d = 4$, the projected bolt areas and corresponding loads allowed are:

Bolt Diameter	ℓ	Area	Load
1/2	2.0	1.00	1180
5/8	2.5	1.53	1830
3/4	3.0	2.25	2660
7/8	3.5	3.16	3600
1"	4.0	4.00	4720

At bolt length in the main member exceeding about four diameters the bearing pressure concentrates more and more near the faces of the main members. This is reflected in Figure 52 where one observes that beyond $\ell = 4d$, the allowable bolt load ceases to increase directly with length and projected area. The allowable load becomes a constant maximum value at ℓ/d of about 6, and remains fixed regardless of how much the bolt length exceeds 6d.

An inspection of Figure 53, for load to grain angle of 90 degrees, shows this same linearity up to values of ℓ/d of about 7. The Figure 53 curves do not level out beyond $\ell/d = 7$, but rise to a maximum then diminish.

154

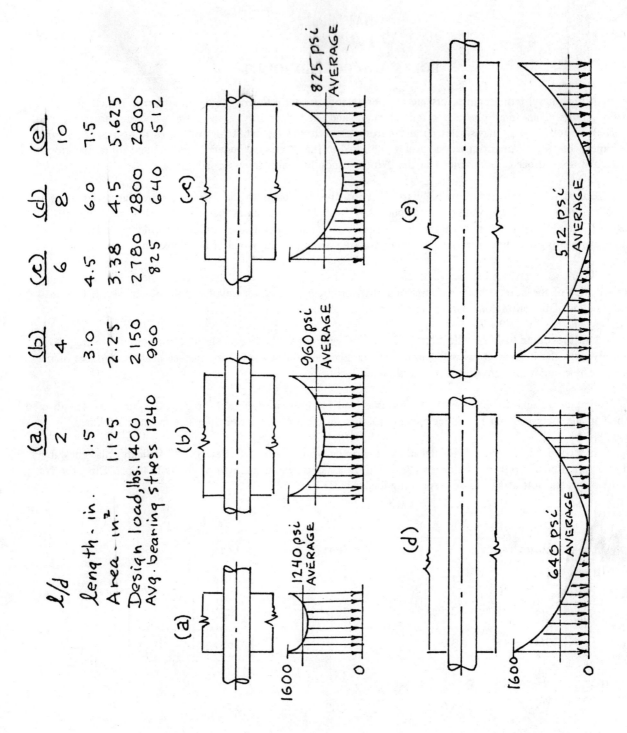

	(a)	(b)	(c)	(d)	(e)
l/d	2	4	6	8	10
Length - in.	1.5	3.0	4.5	6.0	7.5
Area - in²	1.125	2.25	3.38	4.5	5.625
Design load, lbs.	1400	2150	2780	2800	2800
Avg. bearing stress	1240	960	825	640	512

Figure 51. Distribution of stress in 3/4-inch bolted joint parallel to grain in main member.

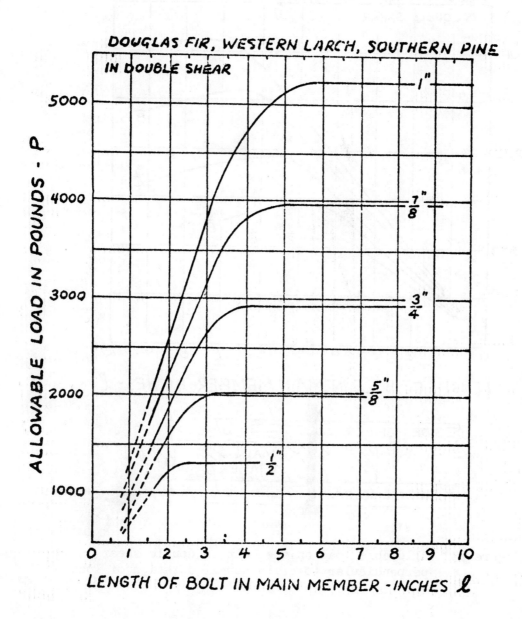

Figure 52. Allowable load on one bolt in double shear
parallel to the grain normal duration of load.

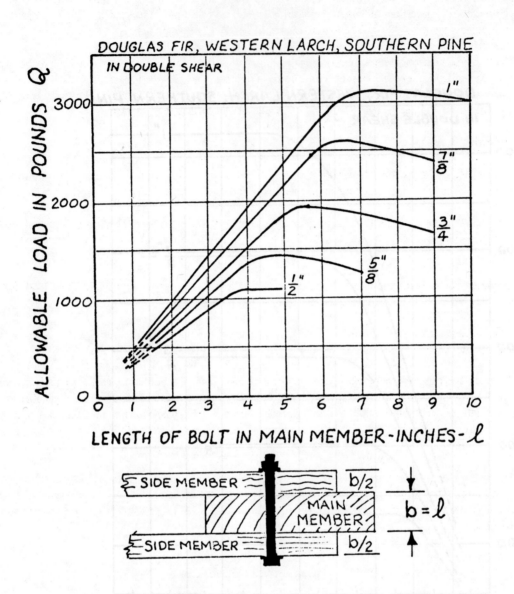

Figure 53. Allowable load on one bolt in double shear
perpendicular to grain normal duration of load

No clear-cut explanation for the difference in shape of these curves at high ℓ/d ratios is offered here. It is likely that the low elastic modulus of wood perpendicular to the grain, plus the fact that $F_{c\perp}$ is based on proportional limit strength (see page 27) rather than ultimate is involved in the explanation.

The explanation of this behavior is important only insofar as it helps the designer comprehend the type of behavior that is occurring under the various conditions described. The tabular information in the National Design Standard and other design manuals is sufficient for the selection of bolt and timber sizes to carry the design loads in the structure. Figures 52 and 53 are taken directly from NDS Table 12, column 4.

Load Parallel to Grain

The allowable design loads are "Normal" duration of load values for bolts in *double shear* with side member thickness equal to or exceeding one-half main member thickness.

If side member thickness is less than one-half main member thickness, a parallel-to-grain allowable load value is selected from the curves or tables for a bolt length in main member value equal to twice this side member thickness.

As an example: for a main member 3.5-in. thick and 1.5-in. side members, the allowable load for a 3/4-inch bolt in Douglas fir is 2660 lbs. from Figure 52 for $\ell = 3.0$ inches.

The allowable load for more than one bolt, of the same or of different sizes in a joint is the sum of the loads for the individual bolts.

Allowable loads for bolts in *single shear* can also be obtained from the published bolt load tables. Using a value of "ℓ" equal to twice the thickness of the smallest member of the two member joint, the allowable load in single shear is one-half the tabulated value. As an example: For a 1.5 in. piece bolted to either a 1.5-in. or larger piece, the allowable single shear load for a 3/4-in. bolt is one-half the value 2660 from Figure 52, that is, 1330 lbs.

Joints with more than three members (Figure 54) can be designed by treating each pair of members as a single shear joint, obtaining the single shear value for each joint or shear plane, and using the sum of these values. As an example, if two 2.5-in. members are joined to a 1.5-in. and a 3.5-in. member, the joint strength can be calculated as follows:

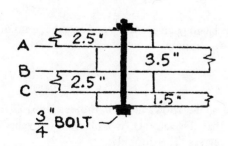

Figure 54.

Shear Plane A:

Using $\ell = 2 \times 2.5 = 5.0"$
$P = 2890/2 = 1445$ lbs.

Shear Plane B:

Using $\ell = 2 \times 2.5 = 5.0"$
$P = 2890/2 = 1445$ lbs.

Shear Plane C:

Using $\ell = 2 \times 1.5 = 3.0"$
$P = 2660/2 = 1330$ lbs.

Total Joint Strength of Bolts =
$1445 + 1445 + 4220$ lbs.

The parallel-to-grain load values can be increased 25% if metal side plates are used. With metal side plates, the tabular value for the joint is based on the length of the bolt in the wood main member. The steel plate, of course, must be designed for the joint load in bearing, tension, compression, and/or bending as the structure may require.

Load Perpendicular-to-Grain

Most structural joints involving perpendicular-to-grain bolt loading, and loading at angles between 0 and 90 degrees consist of one member loaded at the angle and the other member loaded parallel-to-the-grain. In designing such joints, one must determine the capacity of the parallel-to-grain loaded member and the angle-to-grain loaded member, then base the design on the lesser of these two capacities.

For a three-member joint with the load perpendicular-to-the-grain of the main member, Q is determined on the basis of main member thickness, without regard to the thickness of the side member. A value of P is then determined for "ℓ" equal to twice the thickness of the thinnest side member. The lesser of these two values is the joint strength.

An example of this situation would be a joint consisting of two 1.5-in. side members and a 4.5-in. main member, load perpendicular-to-the-grain of the main member, 3/4-inch diameter steel bolt. Q, for "ℓ" = 4.5 is 1650 lbs. from Figure 53. P, for ℓ = 2 x 1.5 = 3 inches is 2660 lbs. from Figure 52. Use Q = 1650 lbs. as the capacity of this joint.

For the same joint with the load perpendicular-to-the-grain of the side members, Q is determined for ℓ at twice the thickness of the thinnest side member; and P for the thickness of the main member. Thus, for the joint in the preceding example with the load perpendicular to the 1.5-in. side members: Q, for ℓ = 2 x 1.5 = 3 in., is 1120 lbs., from Figure 53; P, for ℓ=4.5 inches, is 2660 lbs., from Figure 52, and it is obvious that the joint strength is limited to 1120 lbs.

If the main member was thinner than the side members, and the load was perpendicular to the grain of the 1.5-in. side members, the result might be different. Suppose the main member was only 3/4-in. thick. Q, for side members, as before, is 1120 lbs. P for the main member is 780 lbs. from Figure 52. In this case, the parallel-to-grain loaded thin main member defines the strength of the joint. This example is not a usual condition, but it does occur from time to time.

For single shear joints, Q and P are both obtained from the tables or charts as half the allowable load for bolt lengths twice the thickness of the loaded member. The lesser of these two joint strengths is chosen for design.

In the case of steel plates associated with perpendicular-to-grain loaded wood members, no increase in Q is justified according to generally accepted practice based on test results.

Load at Angle to the Grain

At angles of load to grain between 0 and 90 degrees, the allowable load is determined as it was in the preceding discussion of load perpendicular to grain, except that the value Q, is replaced by a value N based on the Hankinson formula for load at angles between 0 and 90 degrees. This formula:

$$N = \frac{PQ}{P \sin^2\theta + Q \cos^2\theta}$$

can be conveniently solved by reference to the nomograph in Appendix B, Figure B1. P and Q are obtained on the basis of the thickness of the member for which the load direction is θ and used to obtain N. A parallel-to-grain load value is obtained for the member or members of the joint for which the parallel-to-grain load direction applies, and the lesser of the joint loads is used for the design.

Several examples of these procedures follow.

A three member joint consisting of two 1.5-inch. side members and a 3.5-in. main member is fastened with two 3/4-in. bolts. The angle of load to grain is 45 degrees in the main member. Assuming the species for the load data in Figures 52 and 53, Q for the main member (ℓ=3.5) is 1300 lbs., and P is 2800 lbs. N, from the nomograph is 1775 lbs. Compare this value of N and P for the side members, using ℓ = 2 x 1.5 = 3 inches, which is 2660 lbs. Joint load is limited to twice 1775 lbs., or 3550 lbs. total for two bolts.

If this same joint had been arranged so the load was applied at 45 degrees to the side members and parallel to the main member, then Q, for ℓ = 2 x 1.5 = 3 inches, would be 1120 lbs. and P would be 2660 lbs. This produces an N of 1500 lbs. The maximum parallel to grain load for the main member, ℓ = 3.5 in., is 2810 lbs. Now the maximum joint capacity is 1500 lbs./bolt or 3000 lbs. total.

Joints with only two members or with more than three members can be designed following this same procedure but using the single shear procedures described previously.

Load at an Angle of Axis to the Bolt

In cases where a joint member is not perpendicular to the bolt axis the allowable load is developed from a consideration of the load component that is perpendicular to the bolt axis or the projected area that is perpendicular to the load axis.

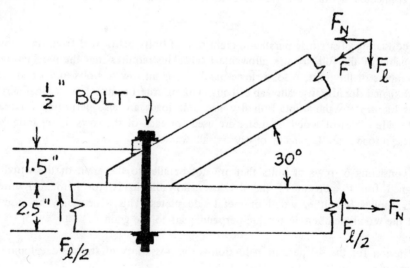

Figure 55.

$$F_N = F \cos 30 = 0.866F$$
$$\ell = 2 \times 1.5 = 3"$$

$$\frac{P}{2} = \frac{1290}{2} = 645 \text{ lbs.} \qquad \frac{Q}{2} = \frac{890}{2} = 445 \text{ lbs.} \qquad N = 580 \text{ lbs.}$$

$$F_N = N \qquad F = N/0.866 = 580/0.866 = 670 \text{ lbs.}$$

Some of the design manuals are not very clear that both P/2 and Q/2 must be obtained to find N in these circumstances. However, it is evident that F_N does not act parallel to the grain of the smaller member. If thickness of the horizontal member is less than the bolt length in the diagonal member, then one should find P/2 for ℓ = 2b, to establish which of the two allowable loads becomes limiting. If, in this example, b, was 1.5-inches, P/2 = $\frac{1290}{2}$ = 645 lbs. and this would be the limiting joint strength.

The published allowable bolt loads are for seasoned lumber used in dry locations at Normal durations of the load. Other load duration factors mentioned previously in Chapter 3 are applicable to the design allowable bolt loadings.

Moisture Content of Lumber and Service Conditions

For service conditions other than dry, the bolt loads are subject to the general provisions that (a) for wet conditions of service, near to and above fiber saturation, the bolt loads are 67 percent of those derived directly from the dry use condition tables, and (b) for dry use conditions where occasional extended periods of wet weather may bring the wood at the connections into the moisture range of 16 to 20 percent, use 75 percent of the dry use values.

With special reference to bolted connections, the effect of shrinkage and resulting stress perpendicular to the grain (a direction in which the tensile strength of wood is quite low), requires some special consideration. It is fairly common to build with unseasoned or only partially seasoned wood. This is necessarily the case for sawn lumber greater than 4-inches thick (glu-lam timber is an exception), often the case for lumber between 2-inches and 4-inches thick, and not uncommon when building with even thinner lumber.

Joints connected by one bolt are free to shrink in any direction without setting up severe shrinkage stresses.

Joints consisting of a single parallel-to-grain row of bolts, fabricated from unseasoned wood that seasons in place, are capable of the full dry use allowable loads. This requires that the parallel-to-grain row arrangement occurs in all members of the joint. Also, a single parallel-to-grain row of bolts in a wood member with metal side plates can be designed for dry use allowable loads. This is true because longitudinal shrinkage is too small to produce stresses harmful to the joint. Full dry use bolt loads are also permitted for multiple parallel-to-grain rows, if separate side plates of wood or metal are used for each of the rows. If separate side plates are not used for each row, design loads are 40 percent of dry use allowables.

Joints consisting of rows of bolts that are not parallel to the grain of the wood in all members of the joint, are designed for 40 percent of the dry use allowable loads, for fabricated unseasoned-used seasoned conditions. This applies for either wood or metal side plates. This is necessary because shrinkage stresses can develop to split the wood members in tension perpendicular to the grain.

The criterion for the 40 percent reduction is the possibility of stresses developing perpendicular-to-grain due to shrinkage.

Bolt Holes, Nuts & Washers

For holes in unseasoned lumber that will season in service, shrinkage will be five to eight percent of the bolt diameter. To avoid development of shrinkage stresses in the wood around a bolt, the hole size should be larger than the bolt, if drilled in unseasoned wood, by the amounts shown in Table 55.

It is generally necessary to have holes a minimum of 1/32-inch larger than the bolt diameter, even if no shrinkage is anticipated. When holes are drilled in seasoned wood, future wetting does not reduce bolt hold size. Therefore, for seasoned wood, holes may be 1/32-inch larger than bolts regardless of future service conditions.

Table 53. Design Checklist on Bolts.

	LOAD PARALLEL TO GRAIN	LOAD PERPENDICULAR TO GRAIN
Allowable load per bolt for "Normal" loading in <u>double shear</u> Table B1-B2	When b_1 and $b_2 \geqq b/2$: Obtain P for $\ell = b$ When $b_1 \leqq b_2 < b/2$: obtain P for $\ell = 2b_1$	obtain Q for $\ell = b$ obtain P for $\ell = 2b_1$; $b_1 \leqq b_2$ Use whichever of these is smaller, P or Q.
Allowable load per bolt for "Normal loading in <u>single shear</u> Table B1-B2	When $b_1 \leqq b_2$: Use $\ell = 2b_1$ and obtain P/2 for design	Obtain Q/2 for $\ell = 2b_2$ obtain P/2 for $\ell = 2b_1$; $b_1 < b_2$ Use whichever of these is smaller, P/2 or Q/2
Allowable load per bolt <u>per shear plane</u> for "Normal" Loading Table B1-B2	If $b_1 = b_2 = b_3 = b_4$: use $\ell = 2b_1$, and obtain P/2 for design of each shear plane. If b_1, b_2, b_3 and b_4 are not equal use ℓ =twice the smallest b to obtain P/2 for design for each shear plane.	Obtain Q/2 for $\ell = 2b_2$ Obtain P/2 for $\ell = 2b_1$ Use whichever is smaller, P/2 or Q/2

Table 53. (continued)

	LOADED 0° to 90° IN MAIN MEMBER	IN SIDE MEMBER
Allowable load per bolt for "Normal" loading in double shear Table B1-B2	 $b_1 \leqq b_2 < b$ Obtain P for $\ell = b$. Obtain Q for $\ell = b$. Use Hankinson formula or nomographs p. to get N. Obtain P' for $\ell = 2b_1$ Use P' or N, whichever is smaller, for design.	 $b_1 \leqq b_2 < b$ Obtain P for $\ell = 2b_1$. Obtain Q for $\ell = 2b_1$. Use Hankinson formular or nomographs to get N. Obtain P' for $\ell = b$. Use P' or N, whichever is smaller, for design.
Allowable load per bolt for "Normal" loading in single shear	 $b_1 < b$ Obtain Q/2 for $\ell = 2b$. Obtain P/2 for $\ell = 2b$. Obtain N/2 from nomograph. Obtain P'/2 fro $\ell = 2b_1$. Use N/2 or P'/2, whichever is less.	 $b_1 < b$ Obtain P/2 for $\ell = 2b_1$. Obtain Q/2 for $\ell = 2b_1$. Obtain N/2 from nomograph. Obtain P'/2 for $\ell = 2b$. Use N/2 or P'/2, whichever is less.

Table 54. Adjustment Factors for Unseasoned Wood,
Which Seasons in Service.

Side Members	Wood		Steel	
Load Direction	//	⊥	//	⊥
ONE BOLT JOINT	1.0P	1.0Q	1.25P	1.0Q
SINGLE ROW, // to grain	1.0P	1.0Q	1.25P	1.0Q
MULTIPLE ROWS, // to grain SEPARATE SIDE MEMBERS FOR EACH PARALLEL ROW	1.0P	1.0Q	1.25P	1.0Q
MULTIPLE ROWS, // to grain ALL ROWS IN THE SAME SIDE MEMBER	0.4P	0.4Q	0.5P	0.4Q
MORE THAN ONE BOLT IN MEMBERS NOT PARALLEL	0.4P	0.4Q	0.5P	0.4Q

Table 55. Hole Diameters for Unseasoned Wood

Bolt Diameter inches	BOLT HOLE SIZES FOR:			
	6% MC Service	12% MC Service	15% MC Service	Wet Service
1/2	9/16	17/32	17/32	17/32
5/8	11/16	21/32	21/32	21/32
3/4	13/16	25/32	25/32	25/32
7/8	31/32	15/16	29/32	29/32
1	1 31/32	1 1/16	1 1/32	1 1/32
1 1/8	1 7/32	1 3/16	1 3/16	1 5/32
1 1/4	1 11/32	1 5/16	1 5/16	1 9/32
Bolt Dia.	+ 3/32	+ 1/16		+ 1/32

Exceptionally loose holes permit the joints in a structure to slip as load is applied, and in large bolted trusses, this could lead to excessive sag under low load, or require special provisions for extra camber.

The safe load values are for loose or tight nuts and assume the use of standard washers or metal plates to prevent the nuts or bolt heads from working their way into the wood as the nuts are tightened or loaded.

Treated Wood

Bolt strengths and wood properties do not require any adjustment for preservatively treated timber, except insofar as the moisture content of the wood may be affected. Some wood preservatives are carried in a water solution and timber treated with these chemicals must be redried after the treatment if dry fabrication and use conditions are to govern the design.

Fire retardant treatments of the types in common use are somewhat hygroscopic and have an effect on strength. For wood treated with fire retardants, a 10 percent reduction is made for all bolt load and wood properties.

Dimensioning of Bolts in Joints

Economical design requires that bolts be grouped as efficiently as possible to minimize the overlapping of splices and the sizes of metal side plates. In joints with member axes at angles to one another, definite limitations exist on the available area of mating surfaces common to the joint members. Minimum bolt spacing is then necessary to avoid increasing a member size purely to accommodate bolts.

Certain practices have been developed to guide bolt spacing dimensions. All spacings, end and edge distances are measured from the centers of the bolts.

Except for seasoned wood to be used seasoned, or wet wood to be used wet, single rows of bolts parallel to grain are more economical than double rows, unless separate splice plates can be provided for each row. (See page 160)

Bolt spacing practices are not sufficiently refined to permit adjusting the allowable spacing with reference to the percent of full load that the bolt actually carries. An exception, for perpendicular to grain spacing of perpendicular to grain loaded bolts is mentioned on page 166. Also, spacing is not adjusted for intermediate angles of load to grain between zero and 90 degrees. Whenever the load direction is intermediate, the spacing is developed on the assumption that full load could occur in either or both directions.

Spacing of Bolts Loaded Parallel to Grain

The direction of a row of bolts may be parallel to the grain for parallel to grain loading or perpendicular to grain for perpendicular to grain loading. For intermediate angles of load to grain, spacing rules for both row directions are observed.

For loading parallel to grain, the bolt spacing in a row parallel to grain is a minimum of four diameters. Spacing between rows of bolts loaded parallel to the grain should permit a minimum edge distance of 1.5 bolt diameters, and a net section adequate to develop the total required member loading. (Figure 56)

For joints with two or more rows parallel to grain, the edge distance should equal half the row spacing when bolt ℓ/d exceeds 6 (Figure 57). This is an added precaution against splitting that might arise from the concentration of load near the lumber face when long slender bolts are used. The minimum edge distance remains 1.5 bolt diameters, so this means that when bolt ℓ/d exceeds 6, member width must be at least six bolt diameters for two rows and nine bolt diameters for three rows, etc.

It is a good general practice to space rows in the center of the portion of the total member cross section that receives its load from that row of bolts.

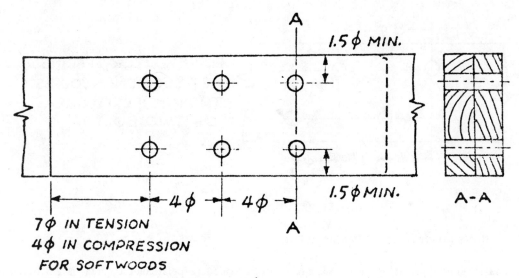

Figure 56

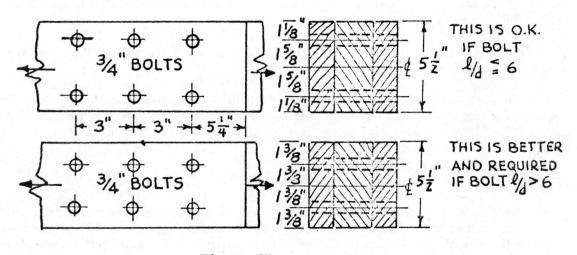

Figure 57

End distances parallel to the grain for softwoods should be 7 diameters or more if the member is in tension, and 4 diameters if in compression. *For hardwoods,* 5 diameters is permitted for tension loading, 4 diameters in compression.

In those rare instances where the distance between rows of bolts loaded parallel to grain in a single member exceeds 5 inches, separate splice plates must be used, *regardless* of wood moisture content conditions.

Bolts may be staggered, but if this is done all bolts in any 4 bolt diameter length of a piece must be considered in computing net section (Figure 58).

Bolt groups should be symmetrical and with the centroid of the group on the axis of the load.

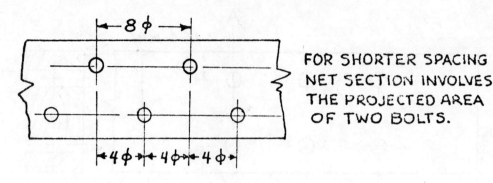

FOR SHORTER SPACING
NET SECTION INVOLVES
THE PROJECTED AREA
OF TWO BOLTS.

Figure 58

Spacing of Bolts Loaded Perpendicular to Grain

The minimum parallel to grain spacing of bolts loaded perpendicular to grain is 2.5 bolt diameters if bolt ℓ/d is 2 or less. Such short bolts are uncommon. If bolt ℓ/d is 6 or more, minimum spacing practice is 5 bolt diameters. At ℓ/d ratios between 2 and 6 minimum spacing can be interpolated on a straight line basis.

The minimum perpendicular to grain spacing is 4 bolt diameters if the bolts are fully loaded with reference to the side members. This may be proportionately reduced if the bolt loading in the side members is less than full capacity.

For steel side members, bolt spacing perpendicular to grain is 4 diameters if fully loaded in the main member, and proportionately less if not fully loaded.

The distance from the end of a member and bolts loaded perpendicular to grain is 4 diameters, minimum. The edge distance in the direction of load measured perpendicular to grain is called the "loaded edge distance." The minimum loaded edge distance is 4 bolt diameters. In the direction of the unloaded edge, the minimum distance is 1.5 bolt diameters.

Spacing of Bolts Loaded at Angles to the Grain

Bolts loaded at angles to the grain can be spaced to satisfy the requirements of both parallel and perpendicular to grain loading. As an example, for 1/2-inch bolts in a joint that loads the main member at 45° degrees to the grain, the wood is Douglas fir, the main member is 3.5 x 5.5 inches, and the two side members are 1.5 x 3.5 inches. The side members are loaded parallel to the grain (Figure 59).

The allowable load per bolt obtained from Figures 52 and 53 by the use of Hankinson's formula using P and Q based on twice the side member thickness, is:

$$N = \frac{1290 \times 900}{1290(0.5) + 900(0.5)} = 1060 \text{ lbs.}$$

Consider first the *main member* bolt spacing requirements and refer to Figure 59a. The parallel to grain spacing in each bolt row is four diameters for parallel to grain loading, but five diameters for perpendicular to grain loading. The bolts do bear some perpendicular to grain load so the five diameter practice governs, requiring a 2.5-inch spacing.

The unloaded edge (top edge in Figure 59a) distance must be at least 1.5 diameters on the basis of parallel to grain requirements, or 0.75 inch. The loaded edge distance is four diameters, or 2 inches in the main member.

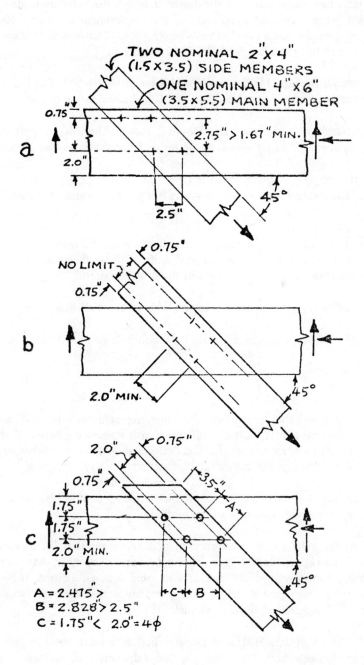

Figure 59

The row spacing in the main member depends on the degree to which the bolts are loaded perpendicular to the grain. At N = 1060 lbs. the perpendicular to main member grain component is 0.707 x 1060 = 750 lbs., which is 83.3% of 900. Row spacing in the main member may be 83.3% of four bolt hole diameters, or 1.67 inches as a minimum. Available space in this joint is 5.5-2.0 -0.75 = 2.75 inches.

Now consider the *side member* bolt spacing limitations and refer to Figure 59b. The bolt loading in this member is parallel to the grain. Edge distance must be 1.5 diameters, 0.75 inches, as a minimum.

Bolt spacing in each side member row is four diameters or 2 inches. There is no limit on row spacing when loading is parallel to the grain. Joint symmetry should be an objective however, insofar as possible.

To accommodate the bolts, the side member width must be 3/4" + 0.707(2.5)" + 3/4" = 3.27", so the 1.5" x 3.5" piece is wide enough. The distance on the side members is a parallel to grain end distance in tension, seven diameters, or 3.5 inches.

The spacing dimensions in Figure 59c will meet all the limitations of Figures 59a and 59b. These dimensions are chosen to allow the fabricator to use conventional units of linear measure, to avoid uncommon decimal dimensions, and permit a tolerance of 1/16" in laying out the drilling pattern.

Net section computations will involve the deduction of the areas of two bolt holes.

The cross sectional area of the members remaining after the bolt hole projected area is subtracted must be adequate to carry the loads.

Critical Section

The cross sectional area of a member remaining after the projected area of bolt holes has been subtracted is the net section. If the net section is located at the most highly stressed position in the member, it becomes the critical section with respect to member strength. The designer should consider whether or not this is the case, and if so, design the member to sustain the stresses at that section.

For simple tension and compression members, the allowable tensile or compressive stress for the grade of lumber or timber is the basis for determining adequacy of net section.

For a bolted joint with all the bolts at one cross section, it is important that the maximum allowable strength reducing growth characteristics (knots, sloping grain, wane) do not also occur at that section. Since the designer has little control over this, he must rely on the fabricator to avoid such a condition. If he cannot do so he would need to safeguard this in the drawings and design with more net section than otherwise. A procedure for handling this is rather complex, and is described by an example:

A piece of 1.5" x 5.5", No. 1 Structural J & P Douglas fir has a joint consisting of two 5/8-inch bolts in the same cross-section. (Bolt holes within 4-diameters of one another are considered to be in the same section for net section purposes.) What is the maximum load this member may take if the grade strength ratio condition actually existed at that section? (Figure 60a).

For this grade and species, F_t is 1000 psi and the tension strength ratio is 31%. This means the clear wood strength has been reduced by 69% to obtain F_t. If two 5/8" bolts, each in 11/16" holes are also present at the section, this further reduces the available section for carrying load by

$$\frac{2 \times 11/16}{5.5} = 25\%$$

for a total reduction of 94% or an effective tensile strength ratio of 6%. At 6% SR, the effective value of F_t would be

$$\frac{1000}{0.31} \times 0.06 = 194 \text{ psi.}$$

The maximum safe member load with the two 5/8-inch bolts then is 194 psi x 8.25 sq. in. = 1600 lbs.

The bolt load capacity is 1175 lbs/bolt, 2350 lbs. for the pair, exceeding the member capacity. However, by arranging the bolts in a row, parallel to the grain, (Figure 60b) the member capacity would be raised to:

$$\frac{1000}{0.31} \times 0.185 = 598 \text{ psi}$$

$$598 \times 8.25 = 4830 \text{ lbs.}$$

This is well above the 2350 lb. load. The example illustrates the highly limiting situation that can develop when bolt holes and maximum allowable defect are combined in a single section. Joints should never be purposely designed with bolts so close to knots or knot holes.

If joints contain several bolts, it is well to space them out parallel-to-grain as much as possible, when the fabricator cannot be relied upon to use very good judgment in keeping bolts well away from large defects. Sections containing large defects may extend as much as six inches along a piece.

With good fabrication control, it is recommended that calculations for required net section take the form:

$$\text{Net section} \times \frac{7}{8} F_t = \text{Allowable member load,}$$

$$\text{and} \quad \text{Net section} \times \frac{7}{8} F_c = \text{Allowable member load.}$$

This is the basis on which most designing has to be done. The importance of control of fabrication practice becomes quite important.

Wood properties (F_t & F_c) for net section strength calculations are subject to the same adjustment factors for service conditions at moisture, outlined in the discussion beginning on page 160.

Moment Resisting Bolt Groups and Shear

Under certain conditions of load, bolted joints are required to resist rotation. In such cases, the group is designed for bolt loading equal to the allowable bolt load in the direction of moment resisting force on the bolt, adjusted in proportion to the distance of the bolt from the centroid of the group (Figure 61).

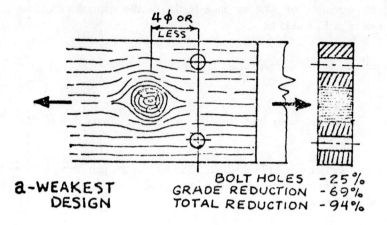

a-WEAKEST DESIGN

BOLT HOLES — 25%
GRADE REDUCTION — 69%
TOTAL REDUCTION — 94%

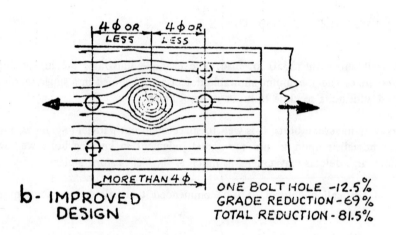

b- IMPROVED DESIGN

ONE BOLT HOLE —12.5%
GRADE REDUCTION —69%
TOTAL REDUCTION - 81.5%

Figure 60

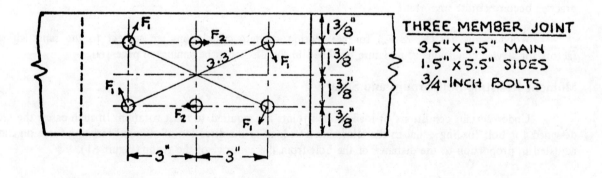

THREE MEMBER JOINT
3.5" x 5.5" MAIN
1.5" x 5.5" SIDES
¾-INCH BOLTS

Figure 61

Example:

Distance to Extreme Bolt Loaded F_1 = 3.3 in.

Angle of Load to Grain = 65.5°

Douglas fir: ℓ = 2 x 1.5 = 3

Fig. 49   P = 2660 lbs.

Fig. 50   Q = 1120 lbs.

$$N = \frac{PQ}{P\sin^2 + Q\cos^2} = \frac{2660 \times 1120}{2660(0.91)^2 + 1120(0.415)^2}$$

$$= 1245 \text{ lbs.}$$

Moment resistance per bolt = 1245 x 3.3 = 4120 in. lbs.

Bolt Loaded F_2

Angle Load to Grain = 0°
  ℓ = 3 P = 2660 lbs.

Moment Resistance Per Bolt = 2660 x $\frac{1.375}{3.3}$ x 1.375 = 1510 lbs.

Moment Resistance of Group

  4 x 4120 + 2 x 1510 = 19,500 in. lbs.

This group of bolts is fully loaded when the extreme bolt is fully loaded. If the bolts also resist an axial load in the member, the capacity of the group to resist moment is reduced.

Example: Determine the moment capacity of the bolt group if it carries a 4800 lb tensile load. The tensile load per bolt is 800 lbs.

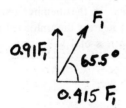

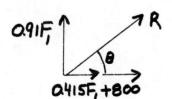

The angular relationship of the <u>moment</u> force on the bolt remains 65.5°.

In addition, there is a horizontal force of 800 lbs added to 0.415 F_1.

The resultant R, is:

$$\sqrt{(0.91F_1)^2 + (0.415F_1 + 800)^2}$$

It is necessary to find a value of F_1 such that R does not exceed:

$$N = \frac{2660\,(1120)}{2660\sin^2\theta + 1120\cos^2\theta}$$

Begin by choosing $0.91 F_1 = 1120$; $F_1 = 1231$; $0.415 F_1 = 511$

$$R = \sqrt{(1120)^2 + (1311)^2} = 1724$$

$\sin\Theta = 1120/1724 = 0.65$
$\cos\Theta = 1311/1724 = 0.76$ $\qquad \Theta = 40.5^\circ$

$$N = \frac{2660\ (1120)}{2660\ (.65)^2 + 1120\ (.76)^2} = 1645 \text{ lbs.}$$

An R of 1724 exceeds N of 1645 so a lower value of F_1 must be used. Try $0.91 F_1 = 1050$; $F_1 = 1154$; $0.415 F_1 = 479$

$$R = \sqrt{(1050)^2 + (1279)^2} = 1655 \text{ lbs.}$$

$\sin\Theta = 1050/1655 = 0.634$
$\cos\Theta = 1279/1655 = 0.773$ $\qquad \Theta = 39.4^\circ$

$$N = \frac{2660\ (1120)}{2660(.634)^2 + 1120(.773)^2} = 1675 \text{ lbs.}$$

An R of 1655 is less than allowable N of 1675 so is OK for design. (Actually, another trial might produce a slightly higher acceptable value of R and N.)

The moment capacity of the entire bolt group is:

$$4(1154 \times 3.3) + 2(1154 \times \frac{1.375}{3.3} \times 1.375) = 16,572 \text{ in. lbs.}$$

When the bolts in a joint form the support for a bending member, the shear in the member must be checked using an effective beam depth equal to the loaded edge distance to the bolt nearest the unloaded edge. For joint details of this kind, it is common practice to use a value of allowable shear stress of $1.5 F_v$

CHAPTER 13

DESIGNING WITH TIMBER CONNECTORS

Special hardware for joining wood members together with considerably greater efficiency than simple nails and bolts is readily available in North America and many other countries. This hardware provides shear strength at the connection considerably greater than that of nails and bolts. As an example, the bolted split ring connector joints which will be described in this chapter have four to five times the shear capacity of joints made with the bolts alone. The design properties and procedures for connectors commonly available in the United States and Canada are explained.

A variety of patented toothed plate connectors are used in the manufacture of floor and roof trusses. These are made from 16 to 20 gage galvanized steel sheet with teeth punched out and bent at right angles to the sheet. They are generally supplied only to franchised fabricators and, with a few exceptions, cannot be purchased for general use. Design properties are not published. The propertietors of the patents on these toothed metal plate connectors establish design properties by evaluative testing, and obtain approval for their use from the building code authorities. The proprietors then produce structural designs for approval in these building code jurisdictions, and supply the designs to their licensed fabricators. The characteristics of these toothed plate connectors will be discussed in Chapter 21.

Three types of readily available connector hardware are illustrated in Figure 62 and of these, *the split-ring* is probably the most widely used form. When installed between two members, it provides a large bearing surface. It fits tightly in wedge-shaped grooves cut by a special tool installed in a drill press or portable power drill. When the bolt and nut are drawn tight, the split ring expands slightly and fits perfectly into the groove making a connection that takes up shear load with very little slip or play in the joint. Both the inner and outer faces of the split ring participate in bearing action against end grain wood. Split ring connected joints are proportioned so there is a balance between the compressive bearing load and the strength of the wood in the required area contiguous to each ring. Note that the bolt itself does not function in bearing, but serves to hold the joint together.

Split-ring connectors are manufactured in two sizes, 2 1/2-inch and 4-inch. Design information supplied by the manufacturer in the form of Load Charts, Figures 63 and 65; and Spacing Charts, Figures 64 and 66.

Toothed rings[1] are corrugated steel rings with serrated sharpened teeth that serve to develop shear by increasing the bearing area over that which is possible with bolts alone. The wood members are not grooved to receive these rings. They are drilled for a bolt of the size specified on the load charts, in a location at the center of the proposed tooth ring location. The toothed ring is placed between the members and embedded by pressure, after which the bolt is fastened in place. Embedding may be done with a press, but usually a special embedding tool is used. This tool consists of a high strength steel rod of the same diameter as the bolt, a pair of heavy washers, slightly larger than the diameter on the toothed ring, and a ball bearing washer beneath a nut on an acme thread at one end of the bolt. This nut is tightened with a rachet wrench which jacks the members together, embedding the toothed ring between them. The tool is then removed and the permanent bolt is installed.

Toothed rings are intended for use where grooving is not possible, although they can be used for complete structures. They are made in four sizes: 2, 2 5/8, 3 3/8 and 4-inch, and their load and spacing characteristics are given in Figures 67 through 74. The manufacture of toothed rings has been discontinued by the U.S. manufacturer but may still be available in other countries. Joints made with 4-inch toothed rings are similar in strength to 2 1/2 inch split rings with spacing requirements approximating those of 4-inch split rings. Other sizes are lower in strength with closer spacing characteristics. They are not precisely interchangeable with split rings.

---

[1]Toothed rings are not currently manufactured in the United States but you may find them in old structures. Similar connectors are used in other countries.

174

SPLIT RING
CONNECTOR

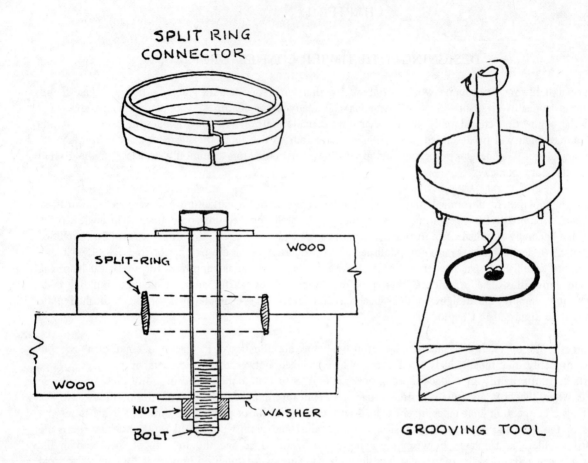

SPLIT-RING

WOOD

WOOD

NUT

BOLT

WASHER

GROOVING TOOL

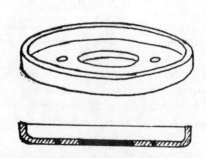

PRESSED STEEL
SHEAR PLATE

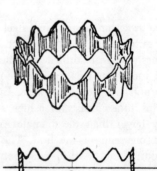

TOOTHED RING
CONNECTOR

Figure 62.

Table 56. Connector Load Grouping of Species When Stress Graded.

Connector Load Grouping	Species	
Group A	Ash, white Beech Birch Douglas fir, dense Elm, rock	Hickory Pecan Maple, hard Oak, red and white Pine, southern, dense
Group B	Douglas fir Elm, soft Larch, western	Maple, soft Pine, southern Gum, red and black
Group C	Cypress, southern and tidewater red Hemlock, western Pine, Norway	Redwood Poplar, yellow Spruce, eastern Spruce, Sitka
Group D	Cedar, western red Fir, white Hemlock, eastern Pine, ponderosa	Pine, sugar Pine, eastern white Pine, western white Spruce, Engelman

Table 56A. Load Capacity Adjustment for Wood Moisture Content
for Split Rings, Shear Plates and Toothed Rings

Fabricated:	Seasoned	Unseasoned	Unseasoned
Used:	Seasoned	Seasoned	Unseasoned
Adjustment:	1.0	0.80	0.67

Shear plates are cup-shaped connectors which fit into prebored grooves and daps in the wood members. Shear plates are intended for use in members that must be disassembled and reassembled, or in making connections between wood members and steel members. When used for demountable structures, or for field connection of preassembled sections, the shear plates are mounted in the mating members and secured with nails through small holes in the webs of the plates. Note that these plates transfer load between members by way of metal to metal bearing at the bolt.

Shear plates are used to attach columns to steel straps, to construct trusses with steel gusset plates, for heel straps in trusses, particularly in bowstring trusses, and quite extensively for field connections between glued laminated members of timber structures.

Shear plates are manufactured in two sizes, 2 5/8 and 4-inch. The 2 5/8-inch size is a pressed steel plate. The 4-inch size is a malleable iron plate. Figures 75 and 76 are load and spacing charts for 2 5/8-inch shear plates for wood-to-wood or wood-to-steel joints. Figures 77 and 78 are for 4-inch shear plates for wood-to-wood, and Figures 79 to 81 are for wood-to-steel joints.

The 2 5/8-inch shear plate capacity is similar to the 2 1/2-inch split ring, and the 4-inch plate is similar to the 4-inch split ring. The loads are not exact equivalents, but the spacing charts are identical for the split rings and shear plates in wood-to-wood applications.

The Timber Engineering Company is the manufacturer of this hardware, which is distributed through building materials dealers in major cities in the United States as well as many other countries. In the Nordic countries and Europe, other manufacturers may also be able to supply these connectors, but in Japan, Australia and Southeast Asia there are distribution outlets for the Timber Engineering Company hardware.

The designer may procure a copy of the "Design Manual for TECO Timber Connector Construction" directly from the manufacturer.

The use of the load and spacing charts for all of these connectors is quite similar and a discussion of their use for split rings will be sufficient to cover all three types.

SPLIT RING LOAD CHARTS

The load capacity of a split ring is related to wood species and is subject to the usual adjustments for moisture content and duration of load.

Species are grouped for connector load design in a slightly different way than for other metal fasteners discussed in other chapters. The groupings for connectors are given in Table 56.

Figure 63 is the load chart for 2 1/2-inch split rings in *single shear*. For Group D species, which are not included on this chart, use 86 percent of the load values shown on the chart for Group C woods. The chart presents values for various angles of load to grain. This makes it unnecessary to use Hankinson's formula for angles of load to grain between 0 and 90 degrees. Note that the load capacity of split rings depend upon the thickness of the member and the presence or absence of another split ring on the opposite face of the member on the same bolt axis. The series of load chart curves for each species group provides for these variables.

All of the thickness dimensions on the load chart are actual inches, not nominal. The use of connectors on lumber less than 1-inch thick is not recommended. In view of the recent reduction in standard lumber size from 1 5/8-inch to 1 1/2-inch dry—1 9/16-inch green, the split-ring values for *two-faces*, as given in the charts for 1 5/8" thick lumber should be reduced by 4 percent for 2 1/2" split-rings, and 8 percent for 4" split rings. For shear-plates, old lumber size chart values may be used with the new lumber sizes.

177

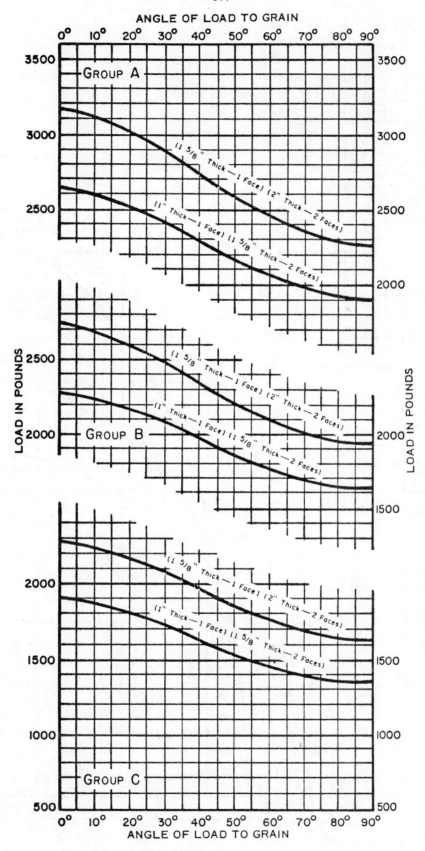

Figure 63. Load chart for normal duration loading for one 2 1/2"
split-ring and bolt in single shear. Courtesy TECO.

178

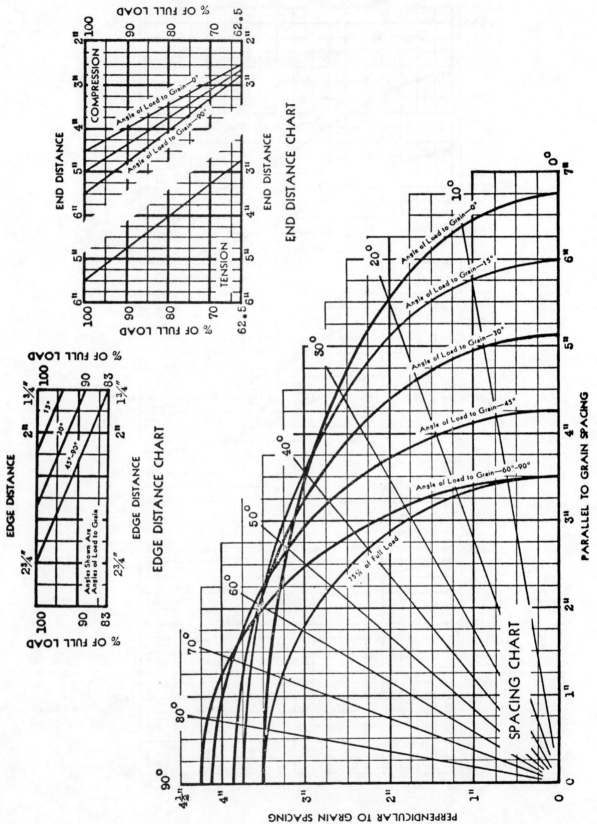

Figure 64. Spacing chart for 2 1/2" split-ring connectors. Courtesy TECO.

179

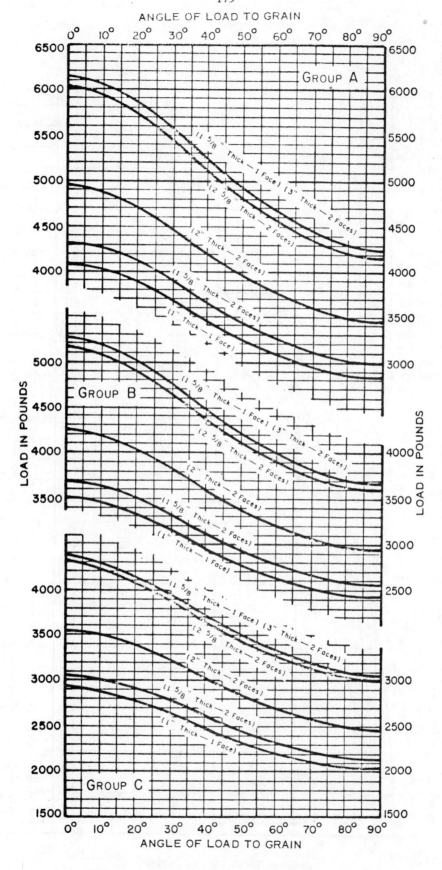

Figure 65. Load chart for normal duration loading for one 4"
split-ring and bolt in single shear. Courtesy TECO.

180

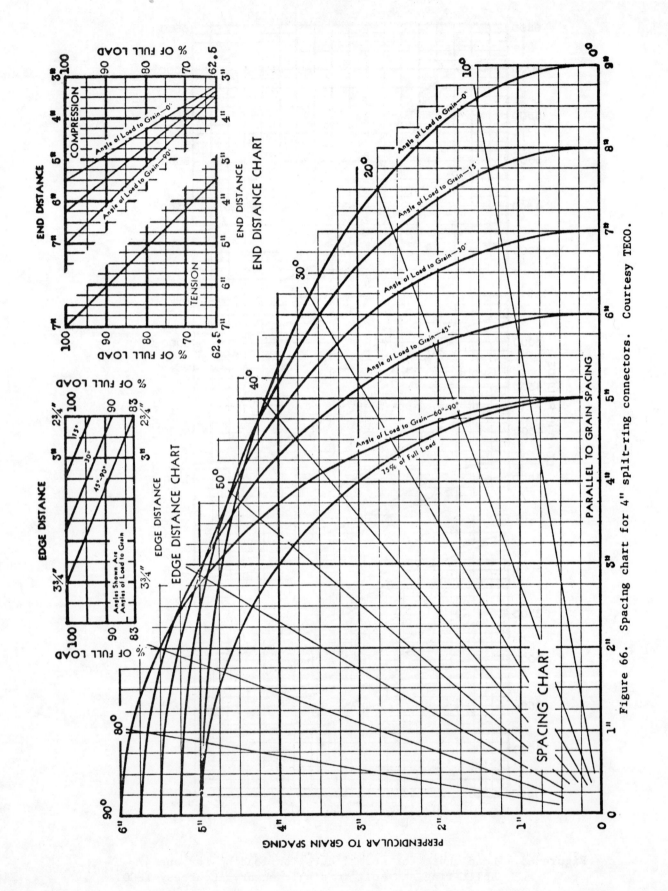

Figure 66. Spacing chart for 4" split-ring connectors. Courtesy TECO.

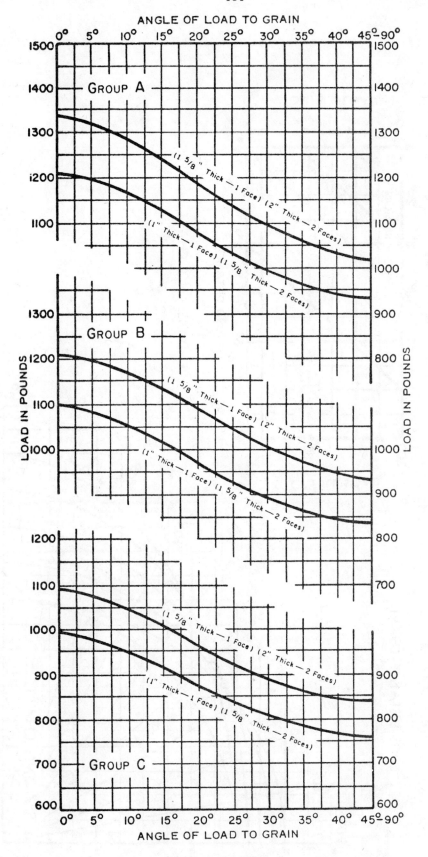

Figure 67. Load chart for normal duration loading for 2" toothed ring and bolt in single shear.

Courtesy TECO.

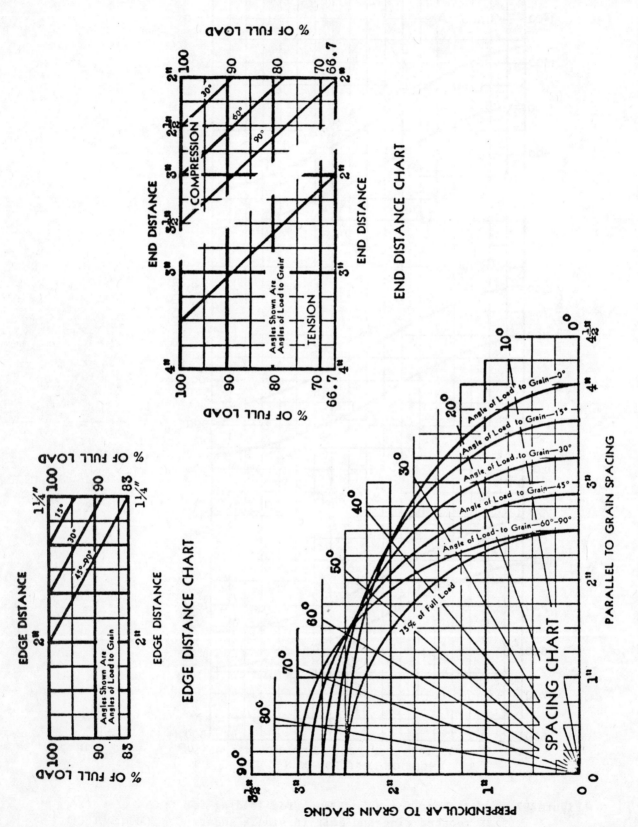

Figure 68. Spacing chart for 2" toothed ring connectors.

183

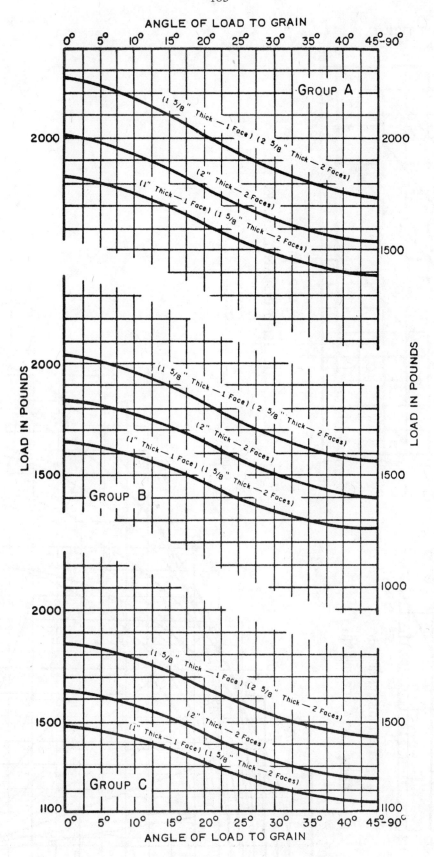

Figure 69. Load chart for normal duration loading for 2 5/8" toothed ring and bolt in single shear. Courtesy TECO.

184

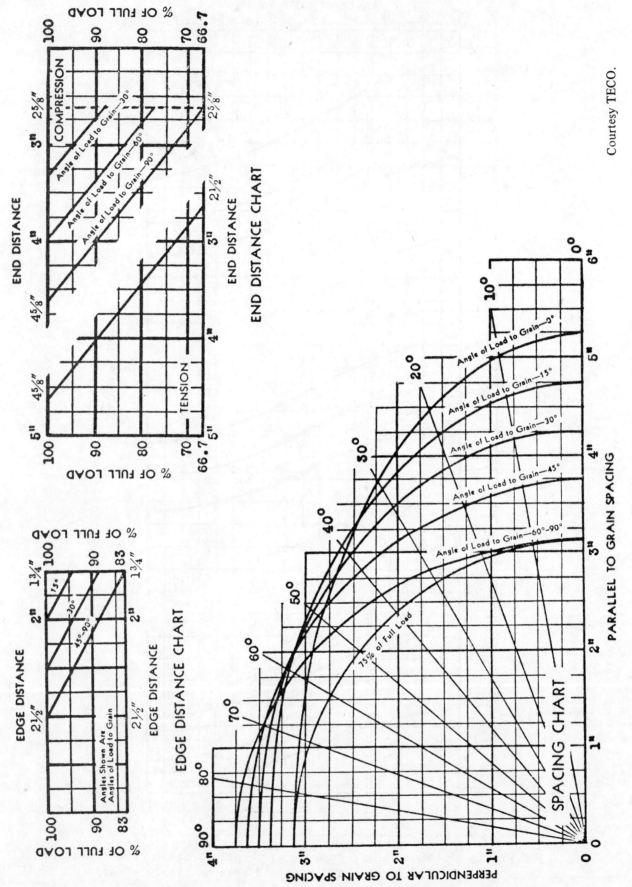

% OF FULL LOAD
END DISTANCE
100 · 90 · 80 · 70 · 66.7
COMPRESSION
2 5/8" · 3" · 4" · 4 5/8" · 5"
Angle of Load to Grain—30°
Angle of Load to Grain—60°
Angle of Load to Grain—90°
TENSION
2 1/2" · 3" · 4" · 5"
66.7 · 70 · 80 · 90 · 100
% OF FULL LOAD
END DISTANCE CHART

% OF FULL LOAD
EDGE DISTANCE
100 · 90 · 83
1 3/4" · 2" · 2 1/2"
15°
30°
45°–90°
Angles Shown Are
Angles of Load to Grain
EDGE DISTANCE CHART

PARALLEL TO GRAIN SPACING
0° · 10° · 20° · 30° · 40° · 50° · 60° · 70° · 80° · 90°
0 · 1" · 2" · 3" · 4" · 5" · 6"
Angle of Load to Grain—0°
Angle of Load to Grain—15°
Angle of Load to Grain—30°
Angle of Load to Grain—45°
Angle of Load to Grain—60°–90°
75% of Full Load
PERPENDICULAR TO GRAIN SPACING
0 · 1" · 2" · 3" · 4"
SPACING CHART

Courtesy TECO.

Figure 70. Spacing chart for 2 5/8" toothed rings.

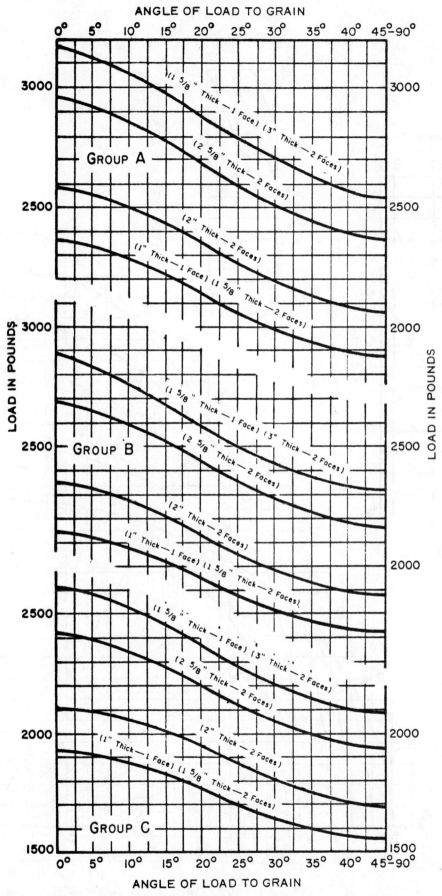

ANGLE OF LOAD TO GRAIN

Figure 71. Load chart for normal duration loading for
3 3/8" toothed ring and bolt in single shear.

Courtesy TECO.

186

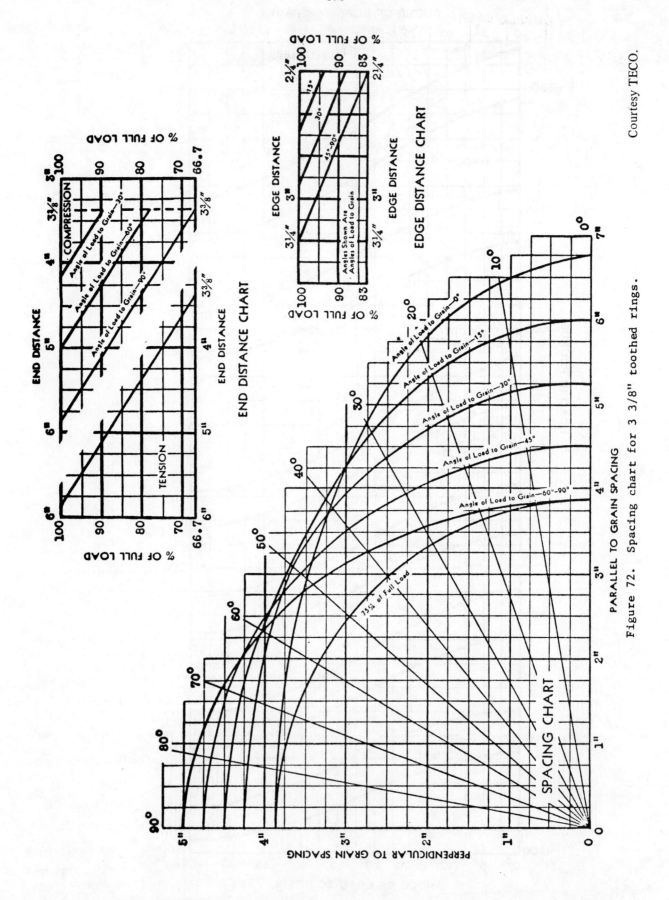

Figure 72. Spacing chart for 3 3/8" toothed rings.

Courtesy TECO.

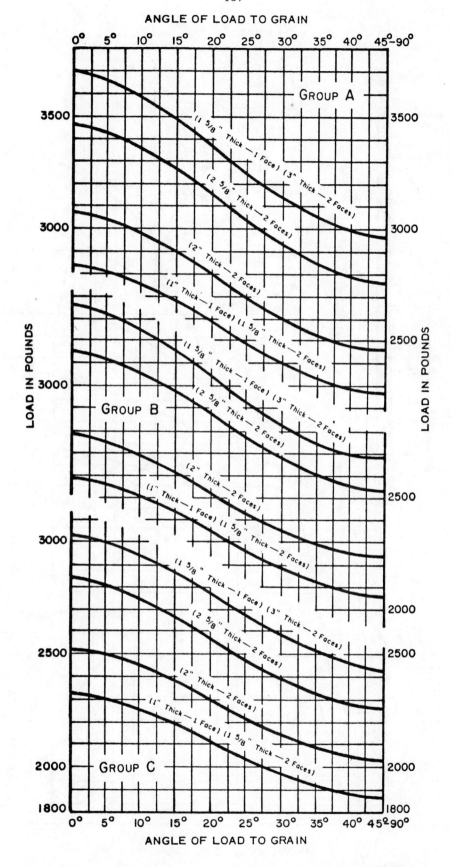

Figure 73. Load chart for normal duration loading for 4" toothed ring and bolt in single shear.   Courtesy **TECO.**

188

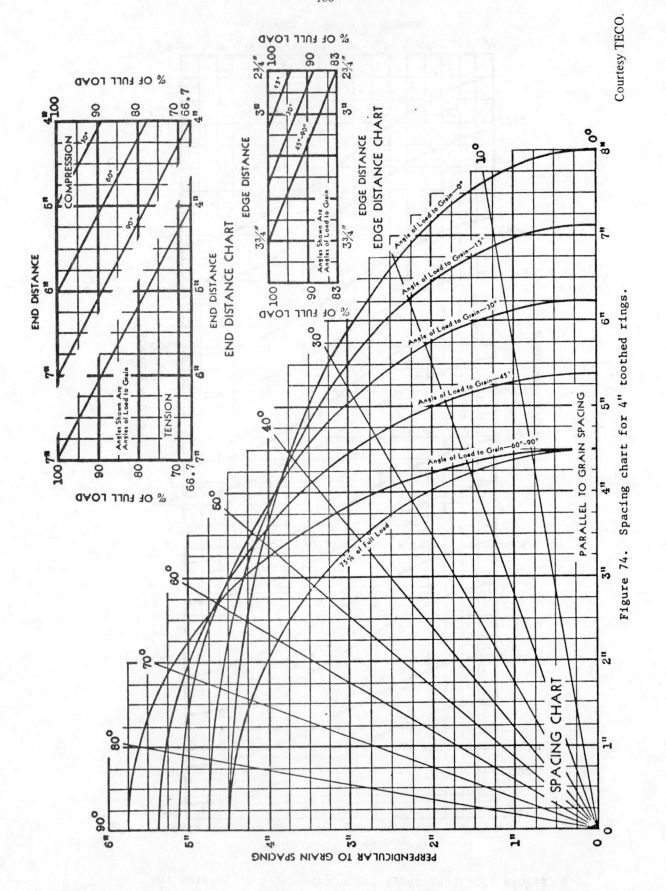

Figure 74. Spacing chart for 4" toothed rings.

Courtesy TECO.

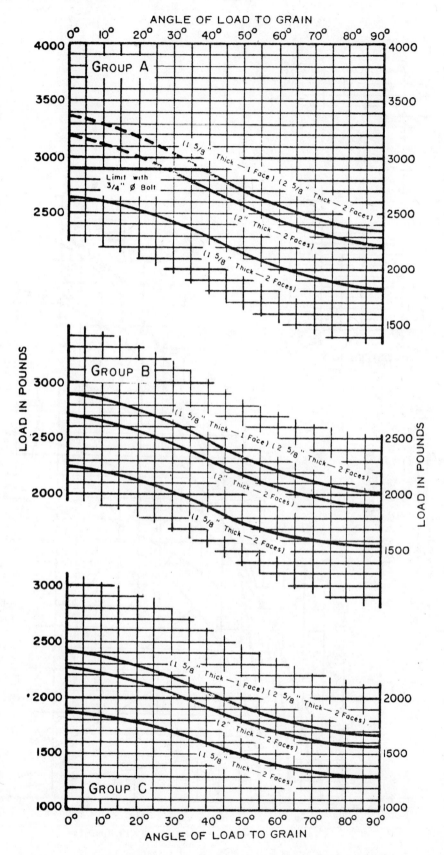

Figure 75. Load chart for normal duration load for one
2 5/8" shear-plate unit and bolt in single shear.

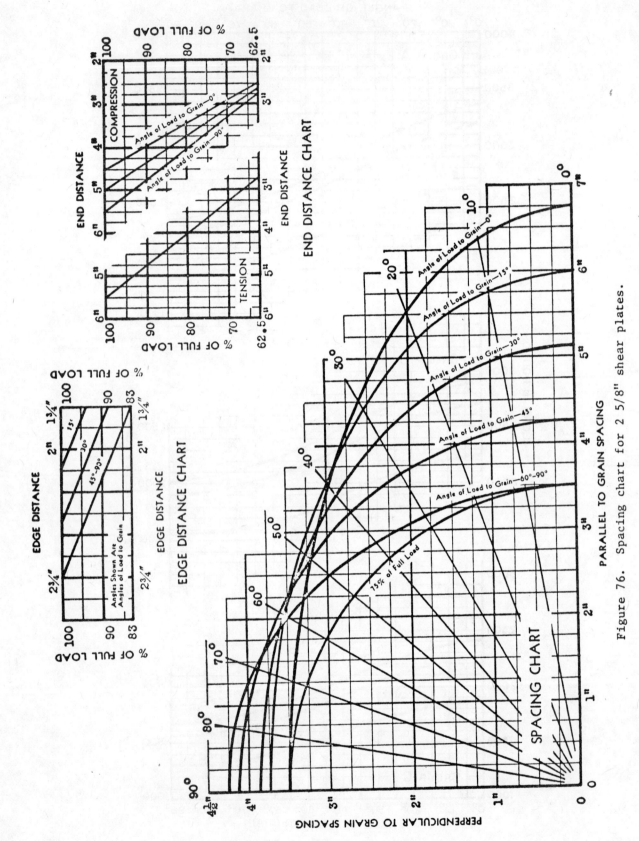

Figure 76. Spacing chart for 2 5/8" shear plates.

Courtesy TECO.

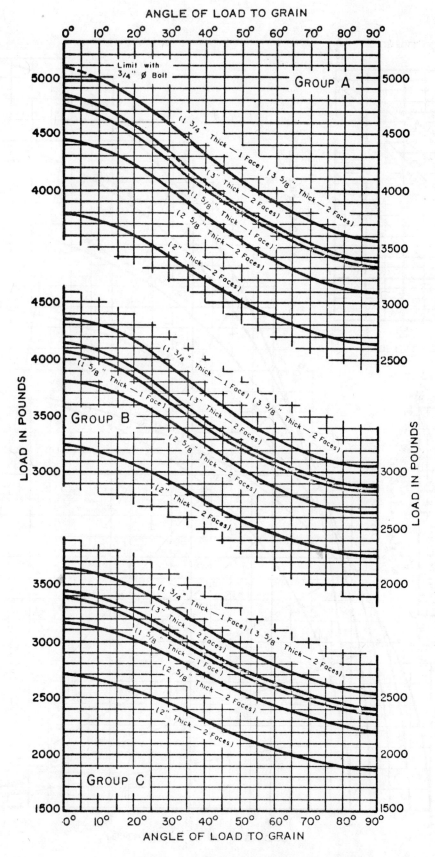

Figure 77. Load chart for normal duration load for one 4"
shear plate unit and bolt in single shear.

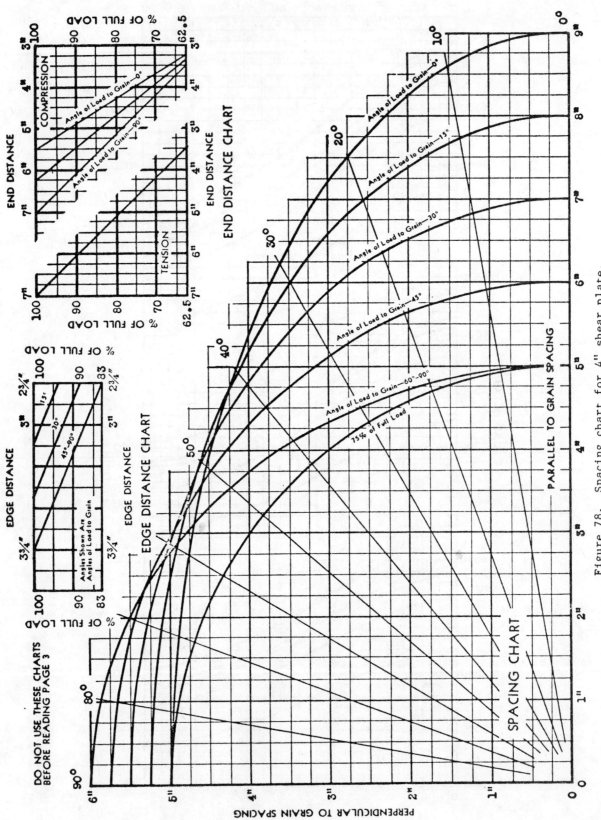

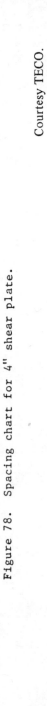

Figure 78. Spacing chart for 4" shear plate.

Courtesy TECO.

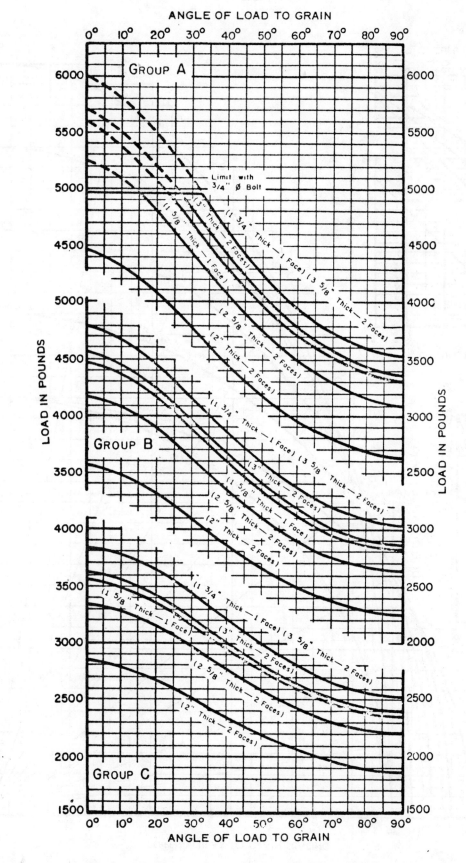

Figure 79. Load chart for normal duration load for one 4" shear plate unit and bolt in single shear, wood-to-steel.

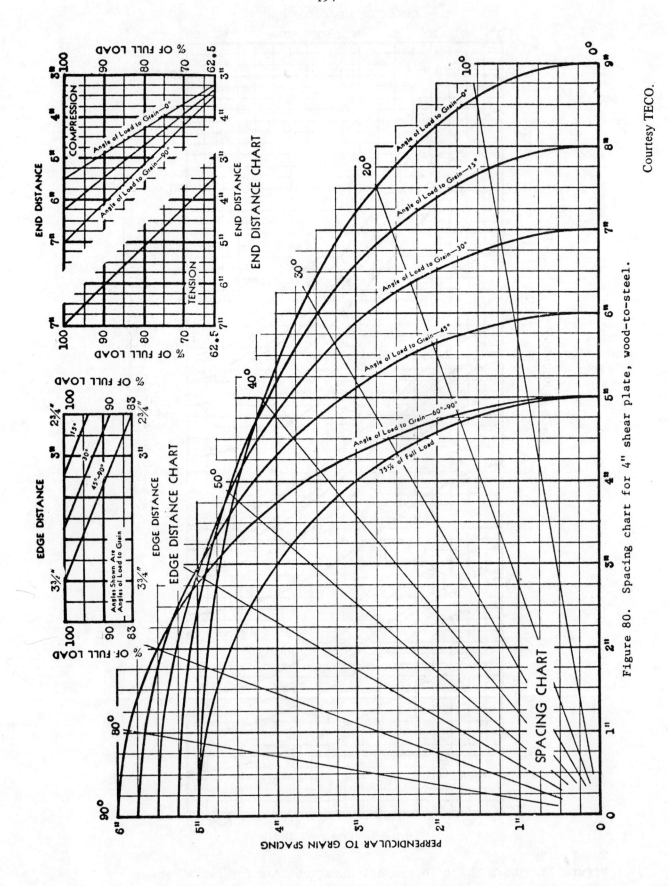

Figure 80. Spacing chart for 4" shear plate, wood-to-steel.

Courtesy TECO.

Examples of Uses of Load Charts

Example 1. A lap joint between two pieces of seasoned 2" x 4" (1 1/2" x 3 1/2") Douglas fir lumber is made with two 2 1/2" split rings. The maximum allowable load for the joint in either tension or compression, for normal duration loading from Figure 63 is 2740 pounds. This is read from the 1 5/8" thick-1 face curve for Group B·species. Since the rings are only installed in one face of each member, the 4% new lumber size adjustment does not apply.

Example 2. A truss joint consists of a nominal 2" x 8" horizontal chord, a 2" x 6" vertical compression member and a 2" x 6" tension diagonal at a 45 degree angle to the other members. The wood is Group B species. The truss is fabricated of unseasoned wood for use in a dry location, so all allowable load values from the charts must be reduced 20 percent.

Adjacent wood members are connected by 4" Split Rings, and both rings are on the same bolt axis. Duration of load is "Normal."

This problem contains many different angles of load to grain and various associated split ring capacities. The forces on all elements of the joint are interrelated. It is necessary to determine these capacities and interrelationships to establish a strength for the joint.

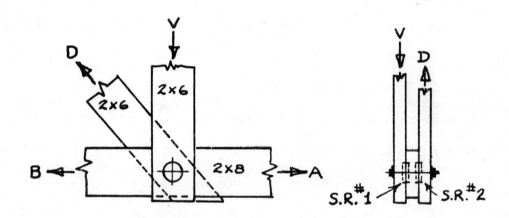

Figure 81. Chord as Middle ·Member (Example 2)

For equilibrium of forces: A - B = D sin 45° = 0.707D = V

The capacities of the split rings in the various angle of load to grain directions at which they must function in this joint are tabulated using information from load chart, Figure 65; reduced 20% for unseasoned lumber (and 8% for new lumber size where rings are installed in two faces, in the chord).

Split Ring	In Member	Angle of Load to Grain	Thickness And Faces With Rings	Capacity From Chart (lbs)	Adjusted (lbs)
1	Vertical (V)	0°	1 1/2 - 1	5275	4220
1	Chord (AB)	90°	1 1/2 - 2	2560	1885
2	Chord (AB)	45°	1 1/2 - 2	3025	2225
2	Diagonal (D)	0°	1 1/2 - 1	5275	4220

The lowest ring capacity is 1885 lbs at 90 degrees to the grain of the chord. When loaded to full capacity at this point, the forces in the joint would be V = 1885 lbs; D = 1885 ÷ 0.707 = 2663 lbs and A - B = 1885 lbs. SR No. 2 under these conditions produces a load on the face of the chord of 2663 lbs at 45 degrees to the grain. This exceeds the allowable load of 2225 lbs, which appears to be the limiting feature of this joint. To avoid overloading, that connection, D must not exceed 2225 lbs, thus limiting V and A - B to 2225 x 0.707 = 1575 lbs. [V = 1575 lbs, D = 2225 lbs., A-B = 1575 lbs.]

Note that the vertical member cannot react against horizontal loads, and the horizontal chord cannot react against vertical loads except insofar as it is restrained by the vertical member to function as a link in transferring vertical force from the vertical to the diagonal member. See Figure 82.

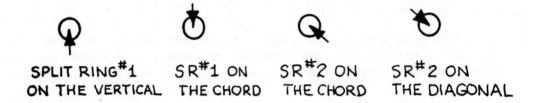

SPLIT RING #1 ON THE VERTICAL   SR #1 ON THE CHORD   SR #2 ON THE CHORD   SR #2 ON THE DIAGONAL

Figure 82.   Forces Exerted by the connector on the member.

Example 3. A different condition exists when the vertical strut and the 45 degree diagonal are directly connected by a split ring. In this case, the chord does not transfer any vertical load from the diagonal to the vertical. The transfer occurs by a direct path via connector No. 1.

If the diagonal is the middle member, as in Figure 83, no member of the joint will be loaded at 90 degrees to the grain. Both connectors will load the diagonal at 45 degrees to the grain. Chord and vertical will be loaded parallel to their grain.

Split Ring	In Member	Angle of Load to Grain	Thickness And Faces With Rings	Capacity	
				From Chart (lbs)	Adjusted (lbs)
1	Vertical (D)	$0°$	1 1/2 - 1	5275	4220
1	Diagonal (D)	$45°$	1 1/2 - 2	3025	2225
2	Diagonal (D)	$45°$	1 1/2 - 2	3025	2225
2	Chord (AB)	$0°$	1 1/2 - 1	5275	4220

The capacity of SR No. 1 and SR No. 2 in the diagonal at 45 degrees to grain is 2225 pounds = A - B = V. This permits load D to be 22255 ÷ 0.707 = 3150 pounds. This arrangement of members permits better overall joint capacity by avoiding $90°$ angle to grain member loading. [V = 2225 lbs., D = 3150 lbs., A-B = 2225 lbs.]

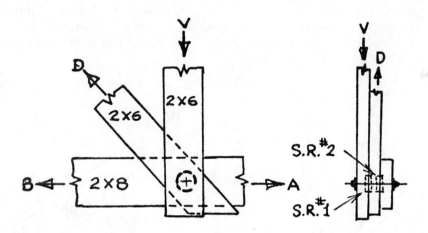

Figure 83. Diagonal as middle member (Example 3).

Example 4. If the vertical strut is the middle member (Figure 84), the chord is free of any angle-to-grain loads. The vertical strut is loaded at 45 degrees to its grain via SR No. 1, and at 90 degrees to grain by SR No. 2. The diagonal is loaded parallel to its grain.

Split Ring	In Member	Angle of Load to Grain	Thickness And Faces With Rings	Capacity	
				From Chart (lbs)	Adjusted (lbs)
1	Diagonal (D)	0°	1 1/2 - 1	5275	4220
1	Vertical (V)	45°	1 1/2 - 2	3025	2225
2	Vertical (V)	90°	1 1/2 - 2	2560	1885
2	Chord (AB)	0°	1 1/2 - 1	5275	4220

From this one sees that A - B is limited to the 90 degree angle to grain load capacity of SR No. 2 in the vertical member. This is 1885 lbs, which would make the load in the diagonal 2663 lbs as in Example 2. This is a parallel to grain load in the diagonal, and since its capacity is 4220 lbs, it can be safely carried. V = 1885 lbs, an improvement over the arrangement with the chord as the center member, but not equal to the arrangement with the diagonal as the middle member. [V = 1885 lbs., D = 2663 lbs., A-B = 1885 lbs.]

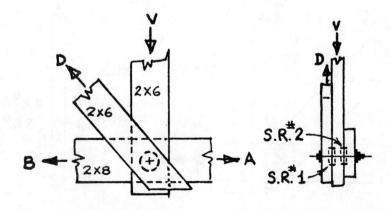

Figure 84. Vertical strut as middle member (Example 4).

Example 5. A design with a pair of chord members enclosing the web members of the joint, as in Figure 85, is often used for a number of reasons (stability, end-support of compression strut, buckling resistance of compression chords, and stiffness of truss for purposes of erection). This complicates the analysis of forces in the joint and Figure 86 is an exploded development of such a joint to illustrate how these forces are distributed.

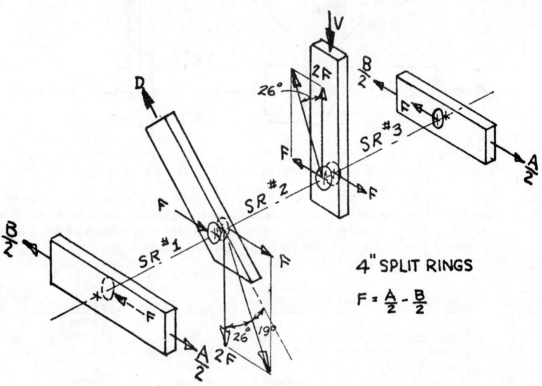

$$F = \frac{A}{2} - \frac{B}{2}$$

4" SPLIT RINGS

Figure 86. Loads at split rings.

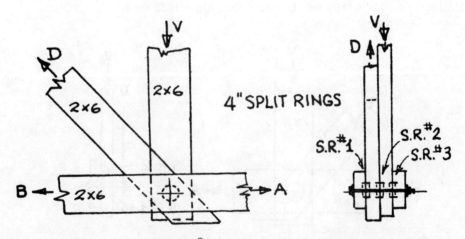

Figure 85. Two member chord.

Split Ring	In Member	Angle of Load to Grain	Thickness And Faces With Rings	Capacity From Chart (lbs)	Adjusted (lbs)
1	Chord $\left(\dfrac{A-B}{2}\right)$	0°	1 1/2 - 1	5275	4220
1	Diagonal	45°	1 1/2 - 2	3025	2225
2	Diagonal	19°	1 1/2 - 2	3500	2575
2	Vertical	26°	1 1/2 - 2	3400	2500
3	Vertical	90°	1 1/2 - 2	2560	1885
3	Chord	0°	1 1/2 - 1	5275	4220

To determine which of these capacities controls the capacity of the joint, determine which ring can be fully loaded without overloading any of the others. In the following tabulation the underlined loads are the trial loads and the other loads in each column are the corresponding loads at other parts of the joint.

Split Ring	In Member	Load Distribution	Trial #1	Trial #2	Trial #3
1	Chord	F at 0°	1885	1130	1120
1	Diagonal	F at 45°	1885	1130	1120
2	Diagonal	2.23F at 19°	4210	2575	2500
2	Vertical	2.23F at 26°	4210	2575	2500
3	Vertical	F at 90°	1885	1130	1120
3	Chord	F at 0°	1885	1130	1120

A load of 4220 lbs on the chord will quite obviously overload other rings in the joint. A load of 1885 lbs on the connection of chord to vertical strut (Trial No. 1) will overload the connection between diagonal and vertical. A load of 2575 lbs on the vertical to diagonal SR No. 2 connector exceeds the capacity of ring SR No. 2 in the vertical (Trial No. 2). A load of 2500 lbs on this connection (Trial No. 3) will not overload any of the split ring connections. The resulting member forces will be:

A - B = 2240 lbs   V = 2240 lbs   D = 3170 lbs

These results are identical with those for example 3, which suggests that design arrangements which minimize 90 degree angle of load to grain conditions lead to stronger designs.

Heel joints in pitched trusses are sometimes a problem to students. Such joints may be designed so the truss is supported by its top chord (Figure 87b), or its bottom chord (Figure 87a). The load to grain angles in the members depend upon which arrangement is followed. The distinction should be fairly self evident, yet it is a common source of error.

These examples have been confined to joints that have one split ring, or several split rings aligned on a single bolt. These have been truly pin-connected joints, with members free to rotate. No moment transfer through the joints has been considered.

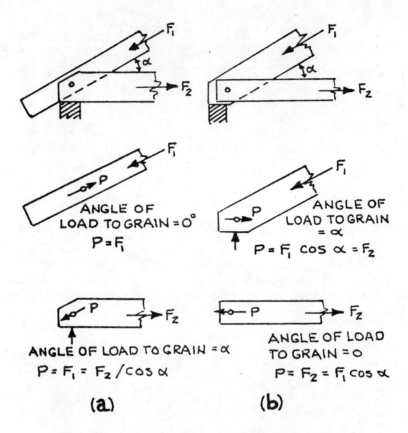

Figure 87.   Heel joint arrangements for ring-
connected trusses.

Plane joints may have several bolts and connectors. Usually, they are still treated as pin-connected joints without moment transfer. The load is distributed equally among connectors of equal size. However, connector groups may be designed in the fashion of riveted joint groups developing moment about their centroid with connector loads regarded as proportional to distance from the centroid. A common application is to the splices in loaded top chord members of long trusses.

Controlling Loads

The preceding examples have indicated how the load charts are used. They have also shown the importance of developing a clear concept of the distribution of load among connectors and the directions of the reactions of the connectors upon the wood members.

The controlling load in a joint made up of several members cannot always be identified by rules of thumb. A thorough consideration of each connector and its relationship to each of the connected members is necessary. The member with the lowest allowable load per connector is a worthwhile starting point in an investigation, but if that member also happens to be lightly loaded some other member with a higher allowable connector capacity coupled with a higher imposed load may control. The generalization that the members loaded at the greatest angle of load to grain controls the design is often used, but can mislead if members of different thicknesses or species are used. These analyses are not simple and the designer should make adequate use of free body sketches and equilibrium equations to verify any intuitive feeling he may have in connection with a design.

Split Ring Spacing

Of all the mechanical connectors at our disposal, the spacing requirements for split rings and similar shear-developers have been defined in the most adequate way for the convenience of the designer and the efficiency of his design. Spacing affects load capacity and determines the feasibility of providing enough connectors in a member of a given size to load it efficiently. It is often more practical to use a medium to low grade of structural lumber, than a higher grade of narrower width, to provide space for the installation of connectors.

Standardized spacing charts for each of the connector types shown in Figure 62 are presented on the pages facing the load charts.

The following terms are illustrated in Figure 88.

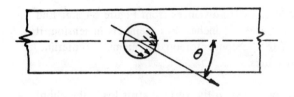

θ = Angle of load to grain

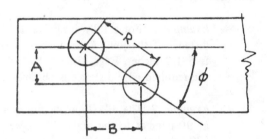

φ = Angle of axis to grain
A = Perpendicular to grain Spacing.
B = Parallel to grain spacing.
R = Spacing

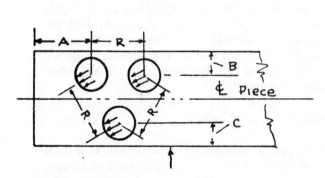

A = End distance
B = Unloaded edge distance
C = Loaded edge distance
R = Spacing

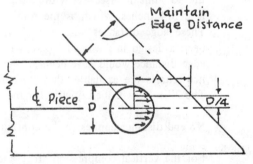

A = End distance   D = Connector diameter

Figure 88. Connector Design Terminology.
Courtesy of TECO.

Angle of load to grain is measured with reference to the longitudinal axis of members.

Angle of axis to grain refers to the angle between a line through the center of a pair of connectors in a member face, to the longitudinal axis of the member.

Distances between connectors are measured center to center. Parallel-to-grain spacing is the projection of this distance on the member's longitudinal axis. Perpendicular-to-grain spacing is the projection on a perpendicular to the longitudinal axis of the member.

End distance is measured from the center of the connector to the end of square end cut members. For members with ends cut at an angle, end distance is measured from a point on the diameter of the connector drawn perpendicular to the member axis, and located one-half the radius from the center of the connector. The minimum end distance is the critical dimension.

Use of the end and edge distance charts may be shown by determining the edge distances for some of the members in the preceding examples.

Example 1. For a fully loaded 2 1/2" SR the end and edge distances from Figure 64 are: End distance if the joint is for members in compression is 4 1/2 inches. For members in tension, it is 5 1/2 inches. Edge distance is 1 3/4 inches. With the connector on the member centerline, the required edge distance is obtained in 2 x 4 members.

Example 2. The 4" SR in the chord on the side connected to the vertical strut loads the chord at 90 degrees to the grain. The lower edge of the chord is the loaded edge. V = 1775 lbs. is 83% of the capacity of the connector so the distance to the lower edge must be 2 3/4 inches, from the 90° line intersection with the 83% of full load line on the edge distance chart of Figure 66. The unloaded edge distance may be the minimum edge distance figure at the right hand ordinate of this chart, 2 3/4 inches. These add up to 5 1/2 inches. There is adequate space in the 2 x 8 to provide these edge distances.

The side of the chord connected to the diagonal is 100% loaded at 45 degrees to the grain. The distance to loaded edge (which is the top edge in this case) is 3 3/4 inches, the intersection of the 45° line intersection with 100% of full load line in Figure 66. The unloaded edge distance is 2 3/4 inches, which is the minimum physical edge distance recommended for any 4" SR. These edge distances add up to 7 1/2 inches, the width of an unseasoned 2" x 8". Had this been a design in seasoned wood, with the seasoned lumber width of 7 1/4 inches, the sum of edge distance would have been greater than the 2" x 8" would provide. It is believed that when new charts are available, they will allow slightly reduced edge distances for seasoned lumber. The 2" x 8" will then qualify for the edge distance requirement.

No end distance applies to the continuous chord at this panel point.

For the vertical compression strut, the 1575 lb. load at zero degrees angle of load to grain is 37% of full load. Edge distances are the minimum of 2 3/4 inches from Figure 66. End distance in compression is 3 1/4 inch, since 37% is less than 62.5% the minimum load ratio on the chart.

For the diagonal member, the load of 2225 lbs. is 53% of full load (4220 lbs.) and minimum edge distances of 2 3/4 inches apply. The end distance for this tension member is 3 1/2 inches, the minimum value on the end distance chart for tension at and below 62.5% of full load. This would be measured as described in Figure 88, making the centerline distance from the connector to the bias cut end equal to 4 1/2 inches.

When joints contain several split rings between a pair of members, it is necessary to determine the spacing between connectors. A simple illustration of the use of the spacing chart can be made for a tension splice containing several split rings.

Example 6. A 3" x 8" Group B species acting as a tension chord and containing a splice made with 2" x 8" side plates will serve as an example. The splice contains three 4-inch split rings in each face of the main member as in Figure 89. The spacing and capacity of the rings are to be determined for fabrication unseasoned and use seasoned.

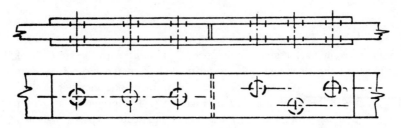

Figure 89.

The capacity of 4" SR's in one face of a 1 1/2" member loaded parallel to the grain are 5275 lbs. each from Figure 65 directly. For 4" SR's in two faces of a 2 1/2" member, capacity is 5160 lbs. each. Reduce 20% for fabrication unseasoned, use dry, to 4130 lbs. If the rings are placed in a single row, the angle of axis to grain is zero degrees. The angle of load to grain is zero degrees. From the chart in Figure 66, the spacing between rings is 9-inches. The end distance is 7-inches and the minimum edge distance is 2 3/4-inches. There is adequate edge distance (7.5 ÷ 2 = 3.75 inches).

By moving the rings into two rows, each 2 3/4-inches from the edge, a more compact grouping of rings is possible. The spacing between rows will be 7.5 - 2 (2.75) = 2.0 inches. This permits a perpendicular-to-grain spacing of 2-inches. Using Figure 66 the intersection of the perpendicular-to-grain spacing line of 2-inches with the angle of load to grain curve of zero degrees gives a parallel to grain spacing of 8.25-inches. The angle of axis to grain for this intersection is 13 degrees. The spacing between rings measured along the axis is $\sqrt{2^2 + 8.25^2} =$ 8.5-inches. This can also be estimated by swinging an arc about the origin through the intersection mentioned above to the intersection with the base of the chart, also giving 8.5 inches. The dimensions of this joint and ring spacing are summarized in Figure 90.

For either the one or two-row arrangement, the total ring capacity of this joint, if fully loaded is 6 x 4130 = 24,780 lbs.

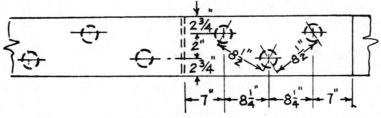

Figure 90.

Example 7. If the required strength of the joint is only 20,000 lbs. the rings will be 80% loaded. In that case, a shorter spacing is permissible. For a single row, interpolate between 9-inches for fully loaded rings to 5-inches for 75% loaded rings to obtain 5.8-inches. For rings in two rows, spaced 2-inches apart, interpolate between 8.25-inches at 100% to 4.625-inches at 75% to obtain 5.35-inches, and use 5.5 inches for ease of fabricating measurement. End distance in this case will be 5.125-inches.

204

When several members come together as at a panel point in a truss, and two or more rings per face are required, it is necessary to work out some mutually consistent and acceptable spacing which will not be optimum, but will satisfy the minimum spacing requirements for all the members. Usually, this is done by establishing the minimum spacing requirements for each member of the joint separately, using the maximum row spacing permissible. With this information, the designer can establish ring centers that will satisfy the requirements of all the members of the joint. It is sometimes necessary to increase member size to accommodate the ring spacing requirements.

Net Section

The strength of a member containing connectors is limited to the strength of the net section remaining after the area occupied by the rings and bolts is subtracted from the gross cross sectional area of the member.

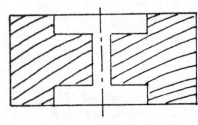

Figure 91.

The area for a pair of rings in one member is the projected area of the rings and bolts as in Figure 91. The projected area of rings and bolts for various lumber thicknesses and connector types are given in Table 57. Rings in two rows are only considered to be at the same section if the parallel-to-grain spacing is equal to or less than the connector diameter.

Using the net section and the applicable compression or tension strength property for the grade of lumber used, the strength of the member is obtained as the product of net section times allowable stress, with a factor of 7/8 to account for possible presence of knots in the region of connectors. This method of determining member strength at the connector locations is used in preparing shop drawings for the fabricator. It accepts the assumption that the knots ordinarily allowed might encroach upon the working area at connector locations.

It is rarely practical to specify that all connectors be located in knot-free positions in the lumber. Under certain circumstances, a person may be called upon to assess the strength at an existing connector location, for purposes of increasing the load on an existing structure. In cases of this kind, the strength may be determined by subtracting the projected area of rings and bolts, plus the cross-sectional area of knots occurring in the critical plane, but outside the area of bolts and connectors, from the member gross cross-section. This net section multiplied by the strength of values in Table 58 will give the member strength.

Calculation of strength of net sections at the critical plane for several of the examples used in this chapter will illustrate the procedure.

Example 1. Assume the Douglas fir 2" x 4" in this example is No. 1 Structural Light Framing with F_c = 1250 psi and F_t = 1050 psi. The projected area of one 2 1/2" SR in one face of one member is 1.8 sq. in. from Table 57. The gross cross-section is 5.25 sq. in. The net section is 5.25-1.8 = 3.45.

Strength in tension is 3.45 x 1050 x 7/8 = 3160 lbs.

Strength in compression is 3.45 x 1250 x 7/8 = 3780 lbs.

The connector value of 2740 lbs. determines the joint capacity.

Example 5. Assume the chords are Douglas fir No. 2 Structural Joists and Plank and the vertical and diagonal are No. 1 Structural Joists and Plank.

Table 57. Projected Area of Connectors and Bolts

(For use in determining net sections)
Courtesy TECO

Connectors		Bolt Diam.	Placement of Connectors	Total Projected Area in Square Inches of Connectors & Bolts in Lumber Thickness of				
No.	Size			1-5/8"	2-5/8"	3-5/8"	5-1/2"	7-1/2"
SPLIT RINGS		1/2	One Face	1.80	2.36	2.93	3.98	5.11
1	2-1/2	1/2	Two Faces	2.69	3.25	3.82	4.87	6.00
		3/4	One Face	3.15	4.00	4.78	6.30	7.93
2	4	3/4	Two Faces	4.99	5.80	6.61	8.14	9.76
TOOTHED RINGS		1/2	One Face	1.59	2.15	2.71	3.77	4.89
1	2	1/2	Two Faces	2.26	2.83	3.39	4.44	5.57
		5/8	One Face	2.02	2.71	3.40	4.69	6.06
2	2-5/8	5/8	Two Faces	2.93	3.62	4.31	5.60	6.97
		3/4	One Face	2.53	3.34	4.15	5.68	7.30
3	3-3/8	3/4	Two Faces	3.74	4.55	5.36	6.89	8.51
		3/4	One Face	2.82	3.63	4.44	5.97	7.59
4	4	3/4	Two Faces	4.32	5.13	5.95	7.47	9.09
SHEAR PLATES		3/4	One Face	2.14	2.95	3.76	5.28	6.91
1	2-5/8	3/4	Two Faces	2.95	3.76	4.57	6.10	7.72
		3/4	One Face	2.01	2.82	3.64	5.16	6.79
1	2-5/8 LG	3/4	Two Faces	2.70	3.52	4.33	5.85	7.48
		3/4	One Face	3.38	4.19	5.01	6.53	8.15
2	4	3/4	Two Faces	--	6.25	7.07	8.59	10.21
		7/8	One Face	3.50	4.44	5.38	7.14	9.01
2-A	4	7/8	Two Faces	--	6.42	7.36	9.12	10.99

Connectors		Bolt Diam.	Placement of Connectors	Total Projected Area in Square Inches of Connectors & Bolts in Lumber Thickness of				
No.	Size			1½"	2½"	3½"	5½"	7½"
SPLIT RINGS		½	One Face	1.71	2.27	2.84	3.89	5.02
1	2½	½	Two Faces	2.60	3.16	3.73	4.78	5.91
2	4	¾	One Face	3.01	3.86	4.64	6.16	7.79
		¾	Two Faces	4.85	5.66	6.47	8.00	9.62
SHEAR PLATES		¾	One Face	2.00	2.81	3.62	4.14	6.77
1	2⅝	¾	Two Faces	2.81	2.68	4.43	5.96	7.58
1	2⅝ LG	¾	One Face	1.87	2.68	3.50	5.02	6.65
		¾	Two Faces	2.56	3.38	4.19	5.71	7.34
2	4	¾	One Face	3.24	4.05	4.87	6.39	8.01
		¾	Two Faces	—	6.11	6.93	8.45	10.07
2-A	4	⅞	One Face	3.33	4.27	5.21	6.97	8.84
		⅞	Two Faces	—	6.25	7.19	8.95	10.82

Table 58. Constants for Use in Determining Required Net
Section in Square Inches or Strength in Tension
or Compression.

Thickness of Wood Member – In.	Constants for Species Group			
	A	B	C	D
4 inches or less	2350	2000	1650	1300
Over 4 inches	1850	1600	1300	1050

Courtesy of TECO.

Chords

No. 2 Structural J&P
F_t = 825 psi

Vertical and Diagonal

No. 1 Structural J&P
F_c = 1250 psi
F_t = 1000 psi

Projected area of 4" SR and bolts, one face = 3.15 sq. in.
Area of 2" x 6" = 8.25 sq. in.
Strength of chord = (8.25 - 3.15) x 825 x 7/8 = 3680 lbs. (tension)
This exceeds the 1120 lb. load on the member.

Projected area of 4" SR and bolts in two faces of diagonal = 4.99 sq. in.
Strength of diagonal = (8.25 - 4.99) x 1000 x 7/8 = 2850 lbs. (tension)

The load on this diagonal is 3170 lbs., and the 2" x 6" member will not sustain that load. By using a 2" x 8" member, the strength will be increased to (11.25 - 4.99) x 1000 x 7/8 = 5470 lbs. which is adequate.

Strength of vertical = (8.25 - 4.99) x 1250 x 7/8 = 3560 lbs. (compression)

This exceeds the 2240 lbs. load on the member.

Example 7. Using Douglas fir No. 1 Strudctural Joist and Plank, F_t = 1000 psi. Projected area of one 4" SR in two faces of a 3" x 8" member is 5.8 sq. in. Member gross cross section is 18.1 sq. in. Strength in tension is (18.1 - 5.8) x 1000 x 7/8 = 10,780 lbs. This is insufficient for the 20,000 lb. load, but by increasing the member to 4" x 10", the projected area becomes 6.61 sq. in., member gross section is 32.3 sq. in., and net section is 25.69 sq. in. The tension strength is 25.69 x 1000 x 7/8 = 22,500 lbs, which is adequate. The 2" x 8" side plates will not be adequate, but for 3" x 8" side plates with rings in one face, net area is (18.1 - 3.15) x 1000 x 7/8 = 13,100 lbs. per plate, which is adequate for the load per plate of 10,000 lbs.

Net Section for Glued Laminated Timber

Calculations of member strength at the joint or required net section for glued laminated timber are based upon the allowable compressive strength parallel to grain for the grade of laminated timber. The 7/8 reduction factor is not applied, and no special consideration need be given for knots in the member. If the allowable tensile strength is less than the compression strength, it shall be used for this design.

CHAPTER 14

LAG BOLTS AND WOOD SCREWS

Lag bolts are produced in the same diameter range as machine bolts, the principal difference being that they have a screw thread tapering to a point, designed to anchor itself in the main member when installed in a prebored hole. Lag bolts (often called lag screws) function as bolts in joints where the main member is too thick to be economically penetrated by regular machine bolts. They are also used when one face of a member is not accessible for the installation of nuts and washers. Lag bolts are sometimes used in conjunction with split-rings, shear plates and toothed ring connectors.

The particular feature of both lag bolts and wood screws is their withdrawal resistance. A comparison of the withdrawal resistances of lag bolts and of wood screws, with nails of equal diameter illustrates this rather well.

A No. 9 wood screw has the same diameter as a 20 penny nail (0.177-in.). The withdrawal resistances in dry Douglas-fir are 131 and 49 lbs. per inch of penetration, respectively. A 1/4-inch lag bolt and a 50 penny nail are about the same diameter (0.25 versus 0.244-inches) and the withdrawal resistances are 232 and 63 lbs. per inch, respectively.

Screw fasteners of these kinds are difficult to dislodge, perform well where vibration is a factor, and can be used to develop considerable pressure to bring members into good alignment and to make field repairs with or without adhesives.

Wood screws do not have many structural uses in building construction. They are of considerable structural importance in furniture and fixture design and manufacture. Wood screws are generally smaller than lag bolts and are furnished in a variety of head shapes.

The properties of the two fasteners will be described separately, using allowable load recommendations from the "National Design Standard for Stress Grade Lumber and Its Fastenings."

LAG SCREWS OR LAG BOLTS

Withdrawal Resistance

The withdrawal resistance of a lag bolt is a function of its diameter, the length of the threaded part in engagement with the member containing the point, and the specific gravity of the wood (Table 46 and B1). For purposes of allowable withdrawal, load determination values are selected on the basis of average specific gravity of the species, rather than by grouping. This is done partly because different wood properties control withdrawal load than control lateral load (for which groping classes are used) and partly because withdrawal loads are much more sensitive to specific gravity than lateral loads.

Table B5 in Appendix B lists the withdrawal loads for lag bolts. Note that these values are given in pounds per inch of penetration of the threaded part into the member holding the point. They are for axial load perpendicular to the grain or fiber direction and are for dry use. They are normal duration loads. Duration of load adjustments apply.

The values are for single lag bolts or for bolts in a single row parallel to grain, installed in either seasoned or unseasoned wood. The moisture adjustments for multiple rows described in Chapter 12 for bolted joints, apply to lag bolted joints.

For unseasoned timber in service or timber used wet, a factor of 0.67 applies in addition. For wood exposed to weather in such a way as to exceed 16 percent moisture content, the factor is 0.75.

SCREWS

· An added factor of 0.90 is required when fire retardant pressure treatments are applied to the wood, but no reduction is necessary for preservatively treated wood, other than such moisture content reductions as may be appropriate.

To determine withdrawal resistance for a specific design certain lag bolt dimensions are necessary. These are given in Table 59.

Table 59. Lag Bolt Dimensions.

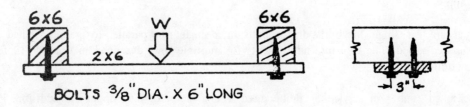

D. in.	D_r, in.	E, in.
3/16	0.120	5/32
1/4	0.173	3/16
·5/16	0.227	1/4
3/8	0.265	1/4
7/16	0.328	9/32
1/2	0.371	5/16
9/16	0.435	3/8
5/8	0.471	3/8
3/4	0.579	7/16
7/8	0.683	1/2
1	0.78	9/16

L,in.	D, in.	S, in.	T, in.
1	3/16 - 1/2	1/4	3/4
1 1/2	3/16 - 1/2	3/8	1 1/8
2	3/16 - 5/8	1/2	1 1/2
2 1/2	3/16 - 1/4	1	1 1/2
2 1/2	5/16 - 3/8	7/8	1 5/8
2 1/2	7/16 - 5/8	3/4	1 3/4
3	3/16 - 1	1	2
4	3/16 - 1 1/4	1 1/2	2 1/2
5	3/16 - 1 1/4	2	3
6	3/16 - 1 1/4	2 1/2	3 1/2
7	3/16 - 1 1/4	3	4
8	3/16 - 1 1/4	3 1/2	4 1/2
9	3/16 - 1 1/4	4	5
10	3/16 - 1 1/4	4 3/4	5 1/4
11	3/16 - 1 1/4	5 1/2	5 1/2
12	3/16 - 1 1/4	6	6

For Design use threaded length = TL = T - E

Courtesy of NFPA.

The use of lag bolts in end-grain, that is with axis parallel to fibers, should be avoided. If it should be necessary to install bolts in this way loads obtained for perpendicular to grain withdrawal should be multiplied by 0.75.

Withdrawal loads should not exceed the tensile strength of the bolt at its root section. For ASTM A36 steel, this is 22,000 psi. As a general practice, NDS recommends limiting the load on a bolt to that which would be permitted for penetrations of the threaded portion of 7 diameters for Group I, 8 diameters for Group II, 10 diameters for Group III, and 11 diameters for Group IV.

Example: Determine the load that will be supported by the bolts in the plank in Figure 92, if the wood is installed unseasoned, and seasons in place. The species is commercial white fir.

BOLTS 3/8" DIA. X 6" LONG

Figure 92.

From Table B5, the allowable withdrawal load for commercial white fir (Table 46 or B1), which has a specific gravity of 0.40, is 217 lbs. per inch of thread engagement when used dry.

Length of threaded portion of bolt is 3 1/2"-1/4" = 3 1/4" from Table 59. As this will all be in engagement, the load per single bolt is 3 1/4 x 217 = 705 lbs.

Because there are two rows of bolts spaced so that seasoning shrinkage can produce tensile stress perpendicular to the grain, only 40% of this value can be used.

Total strength, W = 4 x 705 x 40% = 1129 lbs.

Lag bolt holes must be prebored to a diameter equal to the diameter for the unthreaded shank, and a diameter slightly less than the root diameter for the threaded portion. The Uniform Building Code specifies the hole for the threaded portion at 75 percent of the shank diameter. The hole may be smaller for lower density species as long as splitting does not occur. NDS recommends the lead hole for the threaded portion have a diameter of 65 to 85 percent of shank diameter for Group I species, 60 to 75 percent for Group II species, and 40 to 70 percent for Groups III and IV species. The lead hole should extend to the depth of the threaded part, and the shank diameter to the depth of the shank. The large percentage figure is for the larger diameter bolts in Table 59 and the lower percentage figure for the smaller diameters.

Washers should be used under the heads of lag bolts.

Lateral Resistance

Tables B3 and B4 in Appendix B list the lateral load capability for lag bolts with wood and metal side members. Values are given for directions of load parallel to and perpendicular to grain direction. For other angles of load to grain, the Hankinson formula and the Scholten nomographs, Figure B1 of Appendix B may be used.

The values in Tables B3 and B4 are for single shear for wood that is seasoned. Spacing considerations for lag bolts are the same as those given in Chapter 12 for bolts. Where multiple rows of lag bolts are used, the 40 percent strength reduction for bolts installed in unseasoned wood that seasons in place must be considered. For single lag bolts or single rows of lag bolts, or multiple rows with separate side plates, the full tabular value may be used when installed in unseasoned wood that seasons in place.

The moisture content and duration of load adjustments mentioned previously in this chapter apply to allowable loads of both lateral and withdrawal types.

Lag bolts are sometimes used with timber connectors instead of regular bolts with nuts. NDS makes specific recommendations for this kind of lag bolt use. The lag bolt must have cut threads and not rolled threads. The prebored holes must equal the shank diameter for the shank, and 75 percent of the shank diameter for the threaded length of penetration. When used with connectors, lag bolt diameters equal to the recommended bolt diameter for the connector are required.

To obtain full connector load values, the penetration of the threaded portion of the lag bolt must meet specific requirements as outlined in Table 60. Seventy-five percent of the full connector load is permitted at lesser penetrations as listed, with straight-line interpolation allowed for intermediate loads.

For 2 5/8" shear plates used with *lag bolts and metal side plates,* full connector load is allowed at the penetrations shown in the 75 percent column of Table 60. Other connectors, when used with metal side plates, require the penetrations shown in Table 60, at the loads indicated.

Table 60. Diameters of Penetration for Lag Bolts with Connectors.

Species Group Table 46 or Table Bl	100% Load 2 1/2" & 4" Split Rings 4" Shear Plate	100% Load 2 5/8" Shear Plates	75% Load 2 1/2" & 4" Split Ring 2 5/8" & 4" Shear Plates
I	7	4	3
II	8	5	3 1/2
III	10	7	4
IV	11	8	4 1/2

By permission of TECO.

Table 61a. Preboring Diameters for Wood Screws.

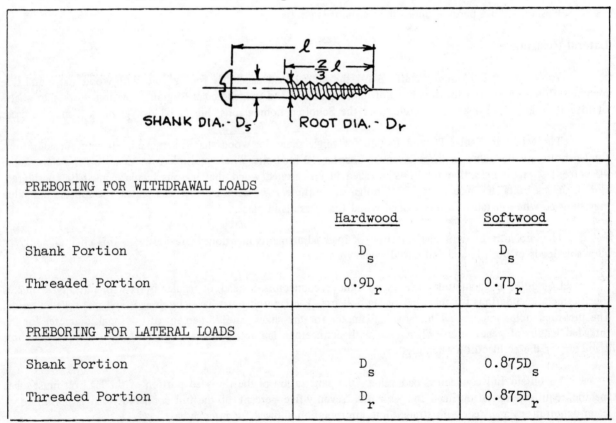

	Hardwood	Softwood
PREBORING FOR WITHDRAWAL LOADS		
Shank Portion	D_s	D_s
Threaded Portion	$0.9D_r$	$0.7D_r$
PREBORING FOR LATERAL LOADS		
Shank Portion	D_s	$0.875D_s$
Threaded Portion	D_r	$0.875D_r$

Table 61b. Screw Gages for Various Lengths.

Gage Nos.	1 - 6	2 - 11	3 - 12	5 - 14	7 - 16	9 - 18	12 - 20
Lengths	1/2"	3/4"	1"	1 1/2"	2"	2 1/2"	3"

By permission of NFPA.

WOOD SCREWS

Withdrawal Resistance

The withdrawal resistance of wood screws is a function of screw diameter, length of engagement of the threaded portion into the member containing the point, and the specific gravity of the species of wood.

Wood screw dimensions, Table 61a, are necessary for determining the load capacity. Wood screws are manufactured in various lengths for different screw diameters or gages. The corresponding gages and diameters are listed in load table (B6 and B7 of Appendix B). The screw gages in which different lengths may be obtained are listed in Table 61b.

Threaded lengths are approximately two-thirds of total length of the screws.

Prebored holes for wood screws are necessary for their use in dense species, and desirable for all species. The lead hole for the threaded portion should be 70 percent of the root diameter for softwoods (conifers) and 90 percent for hardwoods (the broadleaved deciduous species). Prebored hole diameters at the shank are not critical for withdrawal use.

Withdrawal load capacity for wood screws are given in Table B7 of Appendix B for normal duration loading. End grain loads on wood screws are unreliable and wood screws should not be used for that purpose.

The tensile strength of the screw at the root diameter should not be exceeded.

Spacing, end and edge distance rules for wood screws are not well-established and should be adequate to preclude splitting of the wood. Nail spacing rules would be a good guide to wood screw spacing requirements. See Chapter 11.

Example: Design a joint between a piece of 1/2" Douglas-fir plywood and two 2" x 8" Douglas-fir joists arranged as in Figure 93. The plwyood is to carry a load of 180 lbs. per sq. foot. The material will be seasoned when fabricated and when used. The load will be permanently applied.

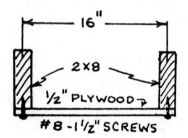

Figure 93.

The load per lineal foot of section will be

$$\frac{14.5}{12} \times 180 = 218 \text{ lbs. per lin. foot.}$$

To obtain full penetration of the threaded part into the joist, a screw length of 1 1/2" or larger would be desirable, for a 1" penetration. Douglas-fir has a specific gravity of 0.51 and an 8 gage screw has a normal duration load capacity of 121 lbs. per inch. Its permanent load capacity is 90% of 121 = 109 lbs. for the 1-inch penetration.

The number of screws per foot of length of the plywood would be

$$\frac{218}{109} = 2$$

Therefore, one screw per foot into *each joist* should support this load.

Lateral Resistance

Table B6, Appendix B, gives allowable lateral loads for wood screws, for single shear, seasoned wood, normal duration. These values apply for any direction of lateral load to grain. *For full lateral load, penetration of a screw into the member holding the point should be seven diameters.* Proportionally lower loads downs to four diameters of penetration are permitted. In figuring allowable lateral load, penetration includes shank penetration, and is not limited to threaded length engagement as in the case of allowable withdrawal load determination.

Prebored holes for lateral resistance should be 7/8 the shank diameter for the part holding the shank and 7/8 for the root diameter for the part holding the thread, for softwoods. In hardwoods, the hole should closely fit the shank, and be equal to the root diameter for the threaded portion.

Wood screws may be laterally loaded in end grain to 2/3 the loads given in Table B6.

Wood screws holding metal side plates to wood members have design loads for lateral bearing 25 percent greater than those tabulated for wood side members.

Moisture Content in Service.—Joints made with wood screws are considered to have 75 percent of dry strengths, if exposed to weathering, and 67 percent if used wet (as in boat construction, for example). This applies to both lateral and withdrawal loads.

Example: The bow post of a boat is secured to the planking with fifty 12 gage by 1 1/2" brass screws. The bow post is southern cypress, 0.49 specific gravity—Group III, and the planking is 1/2-inch thick western red cedar, specific gravity 0.36, Group IV. Determine the maximum force that can be applied to the bow post without stressing the screwed joint beyond the allowable load.

The penetration into the bow post is 1-inch. A 12-gage screw has a diameter of 0.216 inches, so the penetration of thread is 1.0/0.216 = 4.63 diameters. The allowable lateral load per screw for Group IV species is 118 lbs. (Table B6) seasoned, or 79 lbs. wet use. However, at 4.63 diameters penetration, this must be reduced to 79 x 4.63/7 = 52 lbs. The total load on the post must not exceed 50 x 52 = 2600 lbs.

This is for normal load and could be adjusted for other durations. A mooring or towing line should not be fastened to a bow post, but to a capstan anchored to the keel, deck and frame of the hull. Bow post lines are generally limited to rather small and lightweight boats.

CHAPTER 15

GLUED-LAMINATED TIMBER

Designers may make use of glued laminated wood members in structures without actually becoming involved in the details of designing and constructing the individual glu-lam members. The designer will be concerned primarily with selection of the sizes and grades of glued laminated products, which are produced to standard specifications. U.S. Commercial Standard CS253-63 is the basis for most glued-laminated timber in the United States. Similar standard specifications are used in Canada, Britain, Australia, New Zealand, South Africa, Germany and the Nordic countries. These specifications are limited to conventional products made from a relatively few species of wood. Some manufacturers have developed structural laminated products which have not yet found their way into standard specifications. These products are usually described in the special new product approval publications of the building code jurisdictions where they are marketed. These new product approvals can generally be secured from the manufacturer.

The American Institute of Timber Construction (AITC) represents many United States laminators. This organization publishes "Standard Specifications for Structural Glued Laminated Timber," AITC 203-70, portions of which form a part of this chapter. In addition, AITC publishes manufacturing quality control procedures and operates an inspection service for certifying conformance to standards. As inspection and testing service is the principal business of numerous privately owned firms, inspection services other than those of AITC are also functioning in this field of work. Their quality marks vary, but they generally reference the same standards and use the same procedures recommended by AITC along with the aforementioned product standards.

Individuals who become engaged in the direct design and production of laminated timber items would want more technical background than that presented here. What follows will provide the basis for incorporating glued laminated timber into structures with some background related to its design.

General Characteristics of Glued-Laminated Timber

Laminating is a practical means of obtaining a high degree of control over the properties of wood products. Grading and seasoning of sawn lumber are first steps—laminating permits added control over the location of material of different quality within the member. By placing the strongest material in the regions of greatest stress, i.e., the top and bottom surfaces and the sections of greater imposed bending moment, performance can be maximized. Likewise, by placing the material with greatest elastic modulus as far as possible from the neutral axis, deflection can be minimized.

Arranging the laminations in this way improves performance by 10 to 20 percent, depending upon the amount of top quality material placed near the tension and compression faces.

The concept of laminating not only optimizes the location of material of differing quality with respect to the neutral axis, but also disperses the strength reducing defects to advantage, Figure 94 illustrates this point. If the solid sawn member was to be cut into several thinner laminations, then reassembled with the sections containing the knot dispersed longitudinally, the section modulus and moment of inertia of the laminated member would be higher than in the case of the solid member. In practice, the material losses due to sawing and resurfacing each of the laminations would yield a laminated member of less depth than the solid piece, which is a negative economic factor in laminating.

In practice lumber of the higher quality is the source of laminations for the outer layers of bending members, while that of lower structural quality supplies the material for the central portion of the beam. A laminated wood beam is more likely to look like the member shown in Figure 95, than Figure 94, on that account.

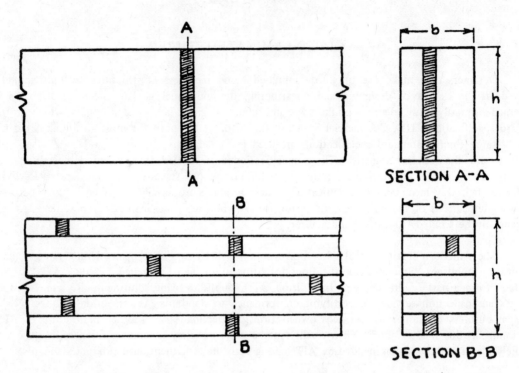

Figure 94. Effect of knot dispersion in laminating.

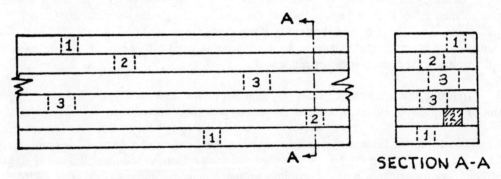

1 - Knot 1/4 the width of the beam.
2 - Knot 1/3 the width of the beam.
3 - Knot 1/2 the width of the beam.

Figure 95. Knot dispersion longitudinally and laterally
plus gradation from neutral axis to outer faces.
(An example)

Laminating lumber thicknesses range from 3/4-inch to 2-inches actual size. The 3/4-inch size is generally used for sharply curved members. Thorough seasoning is economically feasible in this range of thickness. As a consequence, laminated timber has the advantage of dry lumber design values. Furthermore, it looks better because the large seasoning checks one learns to live with in heavy solid sawn timber are avoided in glued-laminated material. The major shrinkage problems connected with solid sawn timber are avoided, the allowable load values for fastenings can be used at their best level, and both design and fabrication are simplified.

When used in covered structures which do not house wet process operations, glued-laminated timber produced at 10 to 12 percent moisture content is practically free of shrinkage or swelling variations. Bolted connections and closely fitted joints remain tight. If exposed to the elements, as for the overhanging end portions of beams favored by some designers, wood's usual shrinkage and swelling checks can develop, unless these areas are protected by properly designed flashings and end caps.

Glued-laminated timber is normally manufactured in the range of 10 to 16 percent average moisture content. By specifying a moisture content within plus or minus three percent of the average service conditions, the designer can avoid dimensional change problems.

The laminating process is versatile, enabling the designer to obtain a variety of physical shapes that are not possible with solid sawn timber. Beams may be curved to provide camber, roof drainage, or generate arches and rigid frames. Tapered members of considerably greater strength and reliability than one could expect from sawn tapered solid members are practical. Reversed curvature is not uncommon, and instances of glued-laminated timber with a twist about the longitudinal axis for the plates or headers of hyperbolic paraboloid roof structures are not uncommon. Circular and spiral shaped members have been produced.

Sawn timber is limited to uses that do not require large pieces. The size of trees and the size of sawmill equipment constrain the size of wood structural members. Laminating permits size versatility limited only by the equipment to transport the product to the customer. The practical limits on sawn timber sizes are approximately 12" x 18" x 26'. Laminated members 12" x 72" and 100 feet long are not uncommon. Inefficient mechanically spliced joints are avoided and aesthetics are served well.

Laminated timber meeting the size requirements of Heavy Timber Construction (see Chapter 23) receives the fire ratings of that particular category of materials. This is considerably better than light frame wood construction and unprotected steel. Heavy timber structures rarely are consumed by fire. They support their structural loads under extremely intense thermal exposure, permitting safe access to the structure by firemen in establishing control and suppression.

The adhesives used in laminating are not combustible, nor do they melt, soften or lose their strength under the effects of high temperature. The insulating effect of wood further protects the glue lines and the wood on the interior of the members.

Sawn timber, if it can be obtained in the sizes required, and if the limitations on connection strength and the disadvantages of shrinkage and creep in service will not present problems, is usually equal in strength to glued laminated material of the same width and board foot content of laminating stock.

As an example, a No. 1 Structural sawn Douglas fir timber, 8" x 18" nominal size on a 24-foot span will carry a normal duration load of about 550 lbs. per foot, uniformly distributed. The deflection at this load will be 0.77 inches ($\ell/375$). If the dead load is one-third of the total load, the creep over a period of time will add one-third to this deflection for a total load deflection of about one inch ($\ell/280$).

A 2400 psi grade laminated beam produced from the same amount of material will measure 6 3/4" x 13.25". (Note that a solid sawn 8" x 18" contains 12 board feet per lineal foot and a 6 3/4" x 13 1/4", is constructed from 9 pieces of nominal 2" x 8" or the equivalent of 12 board feet of laminating lumber per foot of beam length.) It will carry 530 lbs. per foot, normal uniformly distributed load on a 24-foot span, at its allowable bending strength. The deflection at this load will be 1.7 inches ($\ell/166$). The laminated beam can be cambered to any desired amount. Normally, camber would be built into the beam to compensate for dead load deflection and for creep, plus possibly a small amount for drainage if the roof is flat. If cambered for dead load and creep, the total load deflection below the horizontal would be 1.16-inches ($\ell/248$), which is greater than for the solid sawn 8" x 18" member without camber. The load at a deflection of $\ell/280$ would be 485 lbs. per foot.

The performance of this laminated beam is not equal to the 8" x 18" solid sawn member.

If the same quantity of material was laminated to form a narrower but deeper member, a superior beam would result. Using nominal 6-inch lumber, twelve layers would make 12 board feet per foot. A beam size of 5 1/8" x 17 3/4" would be possible. Such a beam would carry 725 lbs. per foot as its allowable stress, with a deflection of 1.25 inches ($\ell/227$). By cambering for 1/3 of this deflection and for creep the actual deflection below the horizontal would be 0.85 inches ($\ell/340$), which is considerably less than the deflection of the solid sawn member.

This illustrates that size for size, sawn timber may bear greater loads than laminated timber of the same size, but with the same quantity of wood suitably rearranged, a superior laminated beam will result.

Laminated beams cost about three to four times as much as solid sawn timbers, so their use must be justified on factors other than structural bearing capability. Despite the cost differential, laminated timber offers values that allow them to compete successfully with structural steel and solid sawn wood materials.

Factors favorable to laminated wood structural members are their appearance and aesthetic attributes, uniformity of quality and dimensional stability, and the simple fact that large sizes and curved shapes are not available in solid sawn wood members. Timber laminators provide engineering design service as a part of their custom laminating price structure, and will assemble all the materials and hardware needed for a building. This service is not usually available from the producers of commodity sawn timber and is a value item that should receive consideration in any cost comparisons the designer wishes to make. Laminators will fabricate members to exact dimensions, provide end-cuts, connector hardware and prefabricated detailing that would otherwise need to be accomplished in the field, at a cost to the contractor and owner.

Types of Glued Laminated Products

The most common glued laminated beam is the *horizontally laminated type*. The load is applied perpendicular to the wide face of the laminations. These beams are designed on the basis of knot distribution studies of the laminating stock from which specifications such as AITC 117-71 (Standard Specifications for Structural Glued Laminated Timber) have been established. A detailed description of this procedure may be found in USDA Technical Bulletin 1069, "Fabrication and Design of Glued Laminated Wood Structural Members" by Freas and Selbo. Allowable stresses for these beams are based upon a 99 percent probability that the strength ratios of the beams will exceed the nominal strength ratio specified. This, coupled with a 98 percent probability that clear wood stress values will be exceeded, produces a probability of safe performance in the order of about 1 in 5000.

Vertically laminated beams, with load direction perpendicular to the edges of laminations are not as common as the horizontal types. The simple and conservative approach to this type of glued laminated beam is to set the allowable stress at the average allowable stress for the laminations used, increased by 15 percent for defect distribution. This procedure applies to beam of three or more laminations.

A procedure for designing vertically laminated beams with considerably more efficiency and reliability was developed by L. J. Nemeth[1] and has been used for a number of years as the basis for the design of

[1]Nemeth, L. J. 1967. "Determination of Allowable Working Stresses for Vertically Laminated Beams," Forest Products Journal, V. 4, p. 23.

commercially produced beams. This procedure involves knot-moment studies of the laminating stock, as contrasted to knot-area studies which are the basis for horizontally laminated timber-properties. Several model building codes recognize vertically laminated beams designed on this basis.

The use of machine-stress-rated lumber in laminating is a recent innovation of some significance, and machine-stress-rated horizontally laminated beams are produced commercially. These beams are particularly uniform in their properties and meet the reliability criteria of structural products generally. Beams made with machine-stress-rated laminating lumber also meet the acceptance criteria of major building codes.

Other types of structural laminated wood products are glued laminated decking, electric utility poles and transmission arms, heavy duty railroad car flooring, keels and frames for modern wood commercial and naval vessels, sheet piling, and a wide assortment of special custom structures.

Standard Specifications for Structural Glued Laminated Timber

The bulk of laminated timber made in the U.S.A. and Canada is Douglas fir or southern pine. Some western larch beams, (a species comparable to Douglas fir) are produced. Because of cost, California redwood beams appear to be of primary interest for appearance purposes. From a technical point of view, laminated structural products may be designed from most of the commonly available species of wood. Some manufacturers do make beams from the true firs, white pine, western hemlock and western red cedar. In Europe, the true firs and some pine are used for laminating. In New Zealand, Australia and South Africa, Radiata (Monterey) pine is a raw material well suited to glued laminated timber. Hardwoods are occasionally used for glued laminated timber, particularly ship building and flooring for railway freight cars and industrial plants.

In general, the designer is most likely to use glued laminated timber manufactured in accordance with U. S. Commercial Standard CS253-63 or some more recent revision of that document. To use laminated decking or any of the vertically laminated beam products, the specifications which have been reviewed and accepted by building code agencies in the geographic area where the structure will be located will apply. Manufacturers of such products are able to furnish that documentation.

Grades and Allowable Unit Stresses

Tables A9 and A10 of Appendix A list the allowable design properties of the two principal species of laminated members. Values are for normal load duration and are listed separately for dry use and wet use.

Laminated timber grades are called "combinations," from the practice of combining different grades of laminations in specific ways to produce members of the best economy for different end uses. Table A9 is for members supporting loads where the principal effect is to produce bending stresses. Laminators manufacture simple span beams more economically than continuous beams in which bending moment changes direction, with compression and tension faces alternating from top to bottom at positions between and over supports. Some laminators supply straight beams from stock inventories to obtain cost advantages both for themselves and the consumer. Curved arches are more costly than straight beams and the designer might investigate the relative cost of curved arches and arches consisting of straight members to be assembled in the field. Shipping costs on curved members are also likely to be higher than for straight members.

The beams in Table A9 generally have higher allowable bending stresses than the members in Table A10. The Table A10 members are intended for use as columns and chords of trusses in tension and compression. Since axial loaded members are likely to be subject to secondary bending, the values given for F_b and F_v in Table A10 are of two levels, reflecting the position of the neutral axis with reference to the bending stress. It is interesting to note that the bending stresses allowed when the neutral axis is parallel to the wide faces of laminations (the $F_b \perp$ column) are larger than for the other direction. This occurs because laminations of higher grade are disposed to the greatest advantage for this load direction. In the case of the shear stress, F_v the highest allowable value also occurs when the shear plane (or neutral axis) is parallel to the glue lines in the beam.

The $F_{c\perp}$ allowable stresses in Table A9, for the tension and compression faces of bending members are different because the quality of laminating material is characteristically different for these two faces, for Douglas fir beams. The designer and contractor should note that these beams have a definite top side which must be oriented properly at time of erection. The built-in camber in laminated beams will signify the proper top side, but in the case of straight beams, factory marking of the top or bottom side is necessary if this positioning is important.

It is becoming increasingly difficult to obtain the 26F combination, particularly in sizes deeper than 16 1/4-inches. Experiences has shown that often the use of beams of basically lower strength can be a more economical choice, than the use of higher strength members. Depending upon prevailing prices, 24f, 22f, 20f and even 18f beams may produce the optimum load capacity per unit cost.

Sizes

Laminated members are not tallied on a board foot basis, as is the practice for lumber and solid sawn timber. They are priced and ordered according to exact size and length.

Member depth is in multiples of the lamination thickness and varies from producer to producer, depending upon the size of the laminating timber. Some producers use freshly precision finished standard dry lumber. Others using the same basic material may need to resurface it prior to laminating to remove dirt and provide flat surfaces to meet quality control specifications. Some laminators purchase rough dried lumber which they surface and grade to minimize waste and reduce costs. These varied practices lead to a variety of member depths.

After the laminations have been securely bonded together, the members are surfaced on the sides to remove all excess glue "squeeze-out" and provide smooth faces. The exposed wide faces of the top and bottom laminations may be either sanded or machine surfaced with a planer.

For purposes of design, it is recommended that the designer assume a *beam depth* equal to some multiple of 3/4 inches for curved beams and 1 1/2 inches for straight or cambered beams, less 1/4-inch for surfacing. U.S. manufacturers have generally standardized on beam widths as given in Table 62.

Table 62. Standard Widths of Laminated Structural Members

Nominal Width of Laminating Lumber	Net Finished Width of Laminated Member
3"	2 1/4"
4"	3 1/8"
6"	5 1/8"
8"	7 1/8"
10"	8 3/4"
12"	10 3/4"
14"	12 1/4"
16"	14 1/4"

By permission of AITC.

Conditions of Use and Load Duration

The boundary moisture content between dry use and wet use conditions is 16 percent.

The duration for load factors for laminated timber are identical to those cited on page 32 of Chapter 3 of structural timber. These increases are not cumulative. They do not apply to E, except in the determination of allowable unit loads on columns.

Depth Effect on Size Factor

The depth effect factor was mentioned on page 96, Chapter 9. Recent research at the U.S. Forest Products Laboratory has produced a new depth factor equation for glued-laminated timber in the form:

$$c_d = \left(12/h\right)^{\frac{1}{9}}$$

Figure 96 is the depth effect factor curve from this equation. This factor should be applied to the allowable bending stresses from Table A9 and A10, for all bending calculations for which the depth (h) is greater than 12 inches. The depth effect adjustment results in a reduced allowable bending stress.

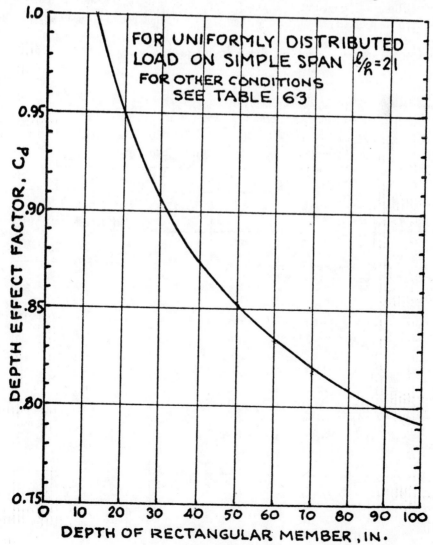

Figure 96.   By permission of AITC.

This depth factor is for simply supported members with a uniformly distributed load and a span-to-depth ratio of 21. For other loading conditions and span-to-depth ratios, C_d may be adjusted per Table 63.

Table 63. Depth Factor Correction for Load Conditions and Span-to-Depth Ratios.

Span to Depth Ratio	% Change	Loading Condition for Simply Supported Beams	% Change
7	+6.3		
14	+2.3	Center Point	+7.8
21	0	Uniformly distributed	0
28	-1.6	Third Point	-3.2
35	-2.8		

By permission of AITC.

Curvature of Beams

Curved beams are formed by bending straight laminations to a form or template, with adhesive between them and clamping in position until the adhesive is cured. This is a cold bending operation which causes prestress in shear, compression and tension. These reduce the ability to assume added load in service. In laminating practice the minimum radius of curvature is related to lamination thickness as shown in Table 64. In this table the tangent end condition is defined as a straight end portion equal to or exceeding the depth of the member plus 6 inches.

Table 64. Minimum Radius of Curvature for the Laminations of Structural Glued Laminated Members.

Lamination Thickness (in.)	Species		
	Douglas fir, larch and redwood		Southern pine
	Tangent ends, in.	Constant Curvature, in.	
1/4	31	31	25
3/8	48	56	38
1/2	72	86	50
5/8	92	118	63
3/4	112	150	75
1	180	244	100
1 1/4	248	336	125
1 1/2	330	426	150
1 5/8	384	480	163
1 3/4	432	540	175
2	540	672	200

By permission of AITC.

The allowable bending stress in the curved portion of a beam must be reduced according to the equation:

$$C_c = 1 - 2000 \left(t/R\right)^2$$

in which t = thickness of lamination
R = radius of curvature

This reduction factor does not apply to the straight portion of a partly curved member. However, the depth effect factor for straight beams previously described applies both to curved and straight portions of beams. Therefore, a 24" deep Douglas fir beam made with 3/4 inch laminations to a minimum radius of 150 inches is subject to a bending stress reduction of

$$C_c \times C_d = \left[1-2000(0.75/150)^2\right] \sqrt[9]{12/24}$$

$$= (0.95)(0.93) = 0.884$$

Lateral Stability

When beam depth exceeds beam width, attention should be given to adequate support against buckling on the compression side of bending members. Procedures for computing allowable bending stress for beams susceptible to lateral buckling are described on pages 112, 113 and 114 of Chapter 9.

The computed reduction in bending stress on the basis of lateral buckling is not cumulative with the depth effect factor reduction. Allowable stress is limited to the lesser of the two values determined on the depth effect and lateral stability bases.

Radial Tension and Compression

When curved laminated beams or arches are loaded to stress the concave face in tension parallel to grain, the wood is subject to stress in tension perpendicular to grain. If the applied load places the convex face of the member in tension parallel to the grain, the wood is subjected to stress in compression perpendicular to grain. The magnitude of these stresses may be calculated using the equation:

where F_r = 3M/2Rbh = radial stress, psi
M = bending moment, in.-lbs.
b = width of member, inches
h = depth of member, inches
R = radius of curvature of centerline of the member, inches

The derivation of this equation is explained by consideration of a semi-circular section of curved beam as in Figure 97.

For a summation of forces in the vertical direction:

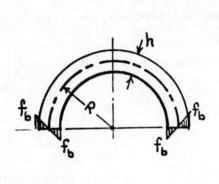 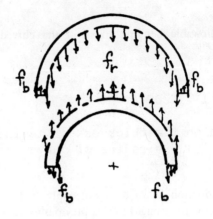

Figure 97.

$$2 \left[\frac{f_b}{2} \quad X \quad \frac{bh}{2} \right] = 2Rbf_r$$

$$f_b = 6M/bh^2$$

$$f_r = \frac{6M}{bh^2} \times \frac{bh}{2} \times \frac{1}{2Rb} = \frac{3M}{2Rbh}$$

The allowable tension stress perpendicular to grain should not exceed $F_v/3$ for southern pine and should not exceed 15 psi for Douglas fir. It has been observed that the internal stress due to the bending of laminae are relieved by creep over a period of time in the case of southern pine, while they tend to remain for Douglas fir members, possibly explaining the differences in allowable radial tensile stress for these two species.

If radial tension will exceed these allowable values, reinforcement to sustain radial tension should be provided in the form of bolts in the radial direction.

When radial stress is compressive, it should be limited to the minimum allowable values for compression perpendicular to grain for the species as listed in Table A9.

Tapered Beams

Laminated beams sawn to provide a taper provide an attractive architectural effect. These may be straight beams with single taper, or a double taper rising to a ridge line or gabled shape. Curved beams are also produced with a sawn double taper to provide a cambered lower surface and a pitched upper face.

The design of tapered beams is a considerably more elaborate procedure than straight or curved members. This topic is not treated in this text. The reader is referred to the AITC Timber Construction Manual for a detailed explanation of tapered beam design.

Adhesives

Adhesives for laminating are classed as dry-use and wet-use types.

Wet-use adhesives are suitable for all conditions of moisture in service. In the United States, the majority of glued laminated timber is made with wet-use adhesives. Wet-use adhesives are generally more expensive formulations and a factor of some importance in manufacturing economics. The wet-use types require somewhat more costly plant facilities for economical production. Wet-use adhesives are the phenol-resorcinol and melamine types and certain combinations thereof. The urea synthetic resins are not recommended, unless heavily fortified with melamine resins. Some melamine-urea adhesives are suitable for wet-use applications. These requirements are defined by AITC in their laminating specifications and in CS 253-63.

Dry-use adhesives are suitable for members used in environments where the maximum repeated, periodic or prolonged periods of moisture do not raise the wood moisture content above 16 percent. The most common dry-use adhesive is casein, fortified with pentachlorophenol or some equally effective preservative to prevent bacteriological degradation. Well-made casein bonded laminated timber has an excellent performance record in dry-use applications.

Urea formaldehyde adhesives have been used for dry-use laminating in Europe for a period of time extending back beyond the origin of the U.S. timber laminating industry and with proper controls in manufacture have performed adequately.

Laminating adhesives produce bonds between radial and tangential surfaces, that is, parallel-to-grain bonds, that will develop the full strength of wood in shear, and tension perpendicular to the grain. For this reason, several pieces which are laminated together can be regarded as equal to a single member in shear. The adhesives are rigid, free of undesirable creep properties, and form very thin gluelines. As a consequence, the section properties of glued laminated members may be regarded as identical to those of solid members of the same dimensions.

Glued End Joints

Laminating timber is generally supplied in 10 to 20 foot lengths and must be joined end to end for use in longer beams. The scarf joint with a slope of 1 in 8 to 1 in 12 has been the traditional end jointing method. Such scarf joints, when well-mated and bonded, have strength properties in the order of 75 to 85 percent of the clear wood. Since scarf joints are usually made in portions of the lumber where defects are very minor, it is possible to join together pieces without adversely affecting their allowable design stresses.

Structural end joints consisting of sharply pointed, precision machined, glued fingers have been successfully developed for end jointing lumber. These joints are of various lengths, ranging from 5/16-inch to 1 1/2-inches. Length, however, is not closely related to the effectiveness of the joint, but is related to the production procedure and manufacturing costs. Any of these finger joints produce savings of laminating lumber in the order of eight percent over the costs when scarf joints are used. The angles of finger cuts and the sharpness of finger points are crucial to structural efficiency of end joints.

Laminators pay particular attention to the control of manufacturing quality in end jointing operations.

Quality Control

Laminating is very exacting business. The process is not complex nor are the plant facilities necessarily costly, although some laminators have invested liberally in mechanized processing facilities. Production laminating in volume will justify costly machinery. Custom laminating will generally not justify elaborately mechanized facilities. Most laminators are engaged in both types of business.

Careful attention to the preparation of the materials, their storage and conditioning, and the curing and pressing procedures are vital. Sampling and quality testing of glue bonds and the conformance of material to grade and moisture specifications occupy the full time attention of several people in a successful laminating business.

The most successful quality control methods have been those conducted under the supervision of quality control specialists both in the plant and from independent testing and inspection agencies. Quality problems, when they occur are often traceable to relaxed inspection activities or personnel who have allowed the inspection process to become a rote process. Perceptive and knowledgeable people must be involved in good quality control procedures. Several excellent independent agencies perform glued laminated timber quality control work, with the endorsement and approval of regulatory agencies. Their mark of acceptance on the product is the designers best assurance of conformance to manufacturing standards.

CHAPTER 16

PLYWOOD FOR SHEATHING

The term "sheathing" denotes a product end-use to enclose space, the material used to cover framed structures. The structural characteristics of plywood sheathing have been summarized in the form of tables of grades, sizes and application methods in such a way that the designer does not need to compute the deflection, bending stress and shear stress for each individual application. Sheathing is the layer of material applied directly to the framing joists, rafters and wall studs. Usually a secondary layer is applied over the sheathing, such as weatherproof roofing materials; brick, wood bevel siding, hardboard or composition siding, plywood siding; and hardwood flooring, particleboard underlayment and composition flooring materials or carpeting. Where thin composition floor coverings such as vinyl tile or linoleum are used, the surfaces of floor sheathing must be smoothly sanded and the plywood must be of a grade that will not contain knotholes in the surfaces or interior plies that would allow show-through of surface irregularities or puncturing of the covering under concentrated loads. Such plywood is classed as "underlayment." Particleboard and hardboard underlayment may also be used over standard sheathing to provide the required support for flexible floor covering materials.

Table 22, Chapter 6, is a span table for various grades and thicknesses of plywood for subflooring and roof decking. The spacing of supports indicated in this table is predicated on the orientation of face grain at right angles to the supports. In those rare instances where plywood must be used with face grain parallel to the supports, the thickness must be selected to provide moment of inertia in the stress perpendicular to grain direction equal to that for the stress parallel to grain direction indicated in Tables 23 or 24 of Chapter 7, for the thickness specified in Table 22.

As an example, it might be desirable to build a panelized floor system with face grain parallel to joists to obtain the highest level of composite action (stressed skin panel action) of sheathing and joists. From Table 22, 1/2-inch thick Structural I, C-D INT Group I plywood is required for a 16-inch joist spacing with face grain perpendicular to joists. The EI product of this plywood is 1,800,000 x 0.10. For use with face grain parallel to joists, the required thickness in this grade of plywood should be 3/4-inch, for which EI is 1,800,000 x 0.132 = 238,000, which exceeds 180,000. The 5/8-inch size would not be sufficiently stiff since its EI would be 1,800,000 x 0.056 = 104,000.

It is important when specifying sheathing plywood to include the span index from Table 22 as a part of the description.

PLYWOOD FLOOR SYSTEMS

Performance requirements for floor sheathing as set forth by the UBC specify that flooring, including the finish floor, underlayment and subfloor, where used, shall:

1.   Deflect not more than 1/360 of span between supporting joists or beams.

2.   Support a concentrated load of 200 lbs. applied to a 1-inch diameter area at midspan without exceeding a deflection of 1/8-inch when supports are 24 inches on center or less, and without exceeding 1/360 of span when span exceeds 24-inches.

3.   Support all uniform design loads without failure.

4.   Support 300 lbs. of concentrated load on a 3-inch diameter bearing area, at any location on the floor, without failure.

Grades and sizes of plywood for subfloor may be chosen from Table 22. This table gives consideration to both uniformly distributed loads and concentrated loads. Table 65 summarizes American Plywood Association recommendations on plywood sizes for subflooring.

Table 65.

Plywood subflooring (a)(c)(d)

For direct application of T&G wood strip and block flooring and lightweight concrete.
(Plywood continuous over two or more spans, face grain across supports)

Panel Identification Index (b)	Plywood Thickness (inch)	Maximum Span (e) (inches)	Nail Size & Type	Nail Spacing (inches)	
				Panel Edges	Intermediate
30/12	5/8 (j)	12 (f)	8d common	6	10
32/16	1/2, 5/8	16 (g)	8d common (h)	6	10
36/16	3/4 (j)	16 (g)	8d common	6	10
42/20	5/8, 3/4, 7/8	20 (g)	8d common	6	10
48/24	3/4, 7/8	24	8d common	6	10
1-1/8" Groups 1 & 2	1-1/8	48	10d common	6	6
1-1/4" Groups 3 & 4	1-1/4	48	10d common	6	6

(a) These values apply for STANDARD C-D INT-DFPA, STRUCTURAL I C-D INT-DFPA, C-C EXT-DFPA and STRUCTURAL I C-C EXT-DFPA grades only.

(b) Identification Index appears on all panels except 1-1/8" and 1-1/4" panels.

(c) In some nonresidential buildings, special conditions may impose heavy concentrated loads and heavy traffic requiring subfloor construction in excess of these minimums.

(d) Edges shall be tongue-and-grooved or supported with blocking for square-edge wood flooring, unless separate underlayment layer is installed. Minimum thickness of this underlayment layer should be 1/4" for subfloors up to 48/24, and 3/8" for thicker panels on 48" or longer spans.

(e) Spans limited to values shown because of possible effect of concentrated loads. Allowable uniform loads vary, but at indicated maximum spans, floor panels carrying Identification Index numbers will support uniform loads of more than 170 psf.

(f) May be 16" if 25/32" wood strip flooring is installed at right angles to joists.

(g) May be 24" if 25/32" wood strip flooring is installed at right angles to joists.

(h) 6d common nail permitted if plywood is 1/2".

(j) Check dealer for availability in your area.

By permission of APA.

To provide a suitable surface for thin resilient floor surfacing materials, plywood underlayment should be sized and installed as indicated in Table 66.

It is often economical to use a grade of plywood for subflooring that will serve both as a *subfloor and an underlayment,* to avoid the labor costs of laying down two separate layers for these purposes. Choice of plywood and installation recommendations are provided in Table 67 developed by the APA. The use a single layer combination subfloor-underlayment requires good continuity between panels. This may be obtained by installing nominal 2-inch wood blocking under all edge joints that do not normally fall upon supporting joists, or by using plywood with tongued and grooved edges on the long side of the panel which do not rest upon joists. It is worthwhile noting that many plywood producers provide tongue and grooved edge panels by running standard 48" x 96" panels to a pattern on the 96-inch edge. This results in reduction of actual face width of approximately 3/4-inch but does not affect the length of panels. Tongue and groove patterns on three-ply panels are not reliable unless they are machined so both tongues and flanges of the grooves have a strong cross-ply construction, which is extremely difficult to do.

Table 65 includes recommendations for the use of 2-4-1 (1 1/8" - 7 ply) plywood which permits wider joist spacing, with reduced joist installation labor and fewer pieces to handle in the construction operation. 2-4-1 plywood is manufactured with tongues and grooves on all edges, on two edges, and without tongues and grooves, all to the full face dimensions of 48" x 96".

In general, it is good practice to leave a spacing between plywood panels in floor systems to prevent stresses developing at the nailed connections if joist shrinkage is likely to be substantial. (1/16" for 2-4-1 plywood and 1/32" for thinner plywood.) Such stresses are likely to loosen the nailed connection. The tongues and grooves of 2-4-1 plywood are designed for a good vertical fit even when this shrinkage gap is provided. In buying tongue and grooved plywood of other thicknesses the purchaser should be certain that an appropriate tongue and groove design is furnished. Ordinary lumber tongue and groove patterns are not usually suitable for plywood. Threaded nails are usually superior to smooth shank nails to prevent nail loosening and reduce the chance that floor squeaks will occur. Floor squeaks can be a serious source of user dissatisfaction.

Underlayment should be protected from wetting during construction to eliminate the possibility of grain raising and surface roughening leading to show-through. This is essential if thin, high gloss, resilient vinyl floor covering is to be used.

The availability of new construction adhesives has led to their use in floor system construction. Floor systems with subflooring-to-joist bonds made with casein glues and certain floor tile adhesives were installed in the early 1960's and have served effectively. Since that time, use of these systems has grown. The APA has established an adhesive testing and approval procedure and offers a list of proprietary adhesives recommended for field or factory gluing.

Glued floor systems have the advantages of an exceptionally continuous bond that reduces nailing requirements and problems associated with floor looseness. They also provide a degree of structural continuity between framing and sheathing that produces an *integral structural action* (T-beam effect) leading to economy in the amount of joist material required, through a reduction in joist depth requirements. The APA publishes load span information for field glued floor systems on the basis of required performance of the Uniform Building Code and the Basic Building Code. While these tables are rather extensive for inclusion in this text, Table 68 presents some comparisons of the span capabilities for glued floor systems and conventionally nailed systems. The increased spanability, while not large, may sometimes enable the designer to use a lower size than would be necessary if the integral action of joist and plywood was ignored.

As examples, with normal width of supporting plates, Douglas fir/larch No. 2 Structural J & P would span 14 ft. with 5/8" plywood glued to 2" x 8" joist. With nailed plywood, it would be necessary to use 2 x 10 joist on 14 ft. span. (Span is 14', less width of two nominal 6" plates, or 13'-1")

Table 66.

Plywood underlayment — For application of tile, carpeting, linoleum or other non-structural flooring.

Plywood Grades and Species Group	Application	Minimum Plywood Thickness	Fastener size (approx.) and Type (set nails 1/16")	Fastener Spacing (inches)	
				Panel Edges	Inter-mediate
Groups 1, 2, 3, 4 UNDERLAYMENT INT-DFPA (with interior, intermediate or exterior glue) UNDERLAYMENT EXT-DFPA C-C Plugged EXT-DFPA	over plywood subfloor	1/4"	18 Ga. staples or 3d ring-shank nails (a) (b)	3	6 each way
	over lumber subfloor or other uneven surfaces	3/8"	16 Ga. staples (a)	3	6 each way
			3d ring-shank nails (b)	6	8 each way
Same grades as above, but Group 1 only.	over lumber floor up to 4" wide. Face grain must be perpendicular to boards.	1/4"	18 Ga. staples or 3d ring-shank nails	3	6 each way

(a) Crown width 3/8" for 16 ga., 3/16" for 18 ga., staples; length sufficient to penetrate completely through or at least 5/8" into, subflooring.

(b) Use 3d ring-shank nail also for 1/2" plywood and 4d ring-shank nail for 5/8" or 3/4" plywood.

Installation: Apply UNDERLAYMENT just prior to laying finish floor or protect against water or physical damage. Stagger panel end joints with respect to each other and offset all joints with respect to the joints in the subfloor. Space panel ends and edges about 1/32". For maximum stiffness, place face grain of panel across supports and end joints over framing. Unless subfloor and joists are thoroughly seasoned and dry, countersink nails 1/16" just prior to laying finish floor to avoid nail popping. Countersink staples 1/32". Fill any damaged, split or open areas exceeding 1/16". Do not fill nail holes. Lightly sand any rough areas, particularly around joints or nail holes.

From American Plywood Association's Guide to Plywood Sheathing for Floors, Walls & Roofs, by permission.

Table 67.

Combined subfloor-underlayment

For direct application of tile, carpeting, linoleum or other non-structural flooring. (Plywood continuous over two or more spans; grain of face plys across supports. Seasoned lumber is recommended.)

Plywood Grade (c)	Plywood Species Group	Maximum Support Spacing (a) (b)								Nail Spacing (inches)	
		16" o.c.		20" o.c.		24" o.c.		32" (e) or 48" o.c.		Panel Edges	Inter-mediate
		Panel Thickness	Deformed Shank Nail Size (d)	Panel Thickness	Deformed Shank Nail Size (d)	Panel Thickness	Deformed Shank Nail Size (d)	Panel Thickness	Deformed Shank Nail Size (d)		
UNDERLAYMENT INT-DFPA (with interior, intermediate or exterior glue)	1	1/2"	6d	5/8"(f)	6d	3/4"(g)	6d	—	—	6	10
	2 & 3	5/8"(f)	6d	3/4"(g)	6d	7/8"	8d	—	—	6	10
UNDERLAYMENT EXT-DFPA (C-C Plugged EXT-DFPA)	4	3/4"(g)	6d	7/8"	8d	1"	8d	—	—	6	10
2•4•1	1, 2 & 3	(2•4•1 specifications are so written that panels from all groups have equal properties.)						1-1/8"	8d (or 10d common smooth shank if supports well-seasoned)	6	(h)

(a) Plywood edges shall be tongue & grooved, or supported with framing.
(b) In some non-residential buildings, special conditions may impose heavy concentrated loads and heavy traffic requiring subfloor-underlayment constructions in excess of these minimums.
(c) For certain types of flooring such as wood block or terrazzo, sheathing grades of plywood may be used.
(d) Set nails 1/16" (1/8" for 2•4•1 panels) and lightly sand subfloor at joints if resilient flooring is to be applied. Don't fill nail holes.
(e) 2" wide supports for 32" o.c.; 4" wide supports for 48" centers.
(f) May be 19/32".
(g) May be 23/32".
(h) 10" for 32" o.c. 6" for 48" o.c. supports.

From American Plywood Association's Guide to Plywood for Sheathing for Floors, Walls & Roofs   By permission.

Table 68. Spans for Conventional Nailed and Nail-Glue Floor Systems using Plywood on 16-in. Support Spacing.

Species & Grade	Size	5/8" or 3/4" Plywood Without Glue	5/8" Plywood With Glue	3/4" Plywood With Glue
Douglas fir/larch	2 x 6	9'-3"	10'-4"	10'-7"
No. 2 Structural	2 x 8	12'-7"	13'-7"	14'-1"
Joist & Plank	2 x 10	15'-9"	16'-5"	16'-9"
	2 x 12	18'-3"	18'-8"	19'-2"
Hem-fir	2 x 6	8'-8"	9'-3"	9'-4"
No. 2 Structural	2 x 8	11'-10"	12'-7"	12'-7"
Joist & Plank	2 x 10	14'-11"	15'-10"	16'-1"
	2 x 12	17'-4"	18'-1"	18'-5"
Lodgepole pine	2 x 6	8'-3"	8'-10"	8'-10"
No. 2 Structural	2 x 8	11'-2"	12'-2"	12'-2"
Joist & Plank	2 x 10	14'-2"	15'-4"	15'-5"
	2 x 12	16'-7"	17'-6"	17'-11"

Based on FHA deflection criteria at 50 Psf, integral action stiffness; and bending stress computed on basis of joist alone.

A 2" x 10" Hem-fir No. 2 Structural J & P will span 16 ft. in practice if plywood is glued to joist. If not glued, a 2" x 12" is required to obtain the span.

A 2" x 8" Lodgepole pine No. 2 Structural J & P will span 12 ft. if glued construction is used, but nailed construction requires a 2" x 10" member.

The entire topic of design procedures which recognize integral action between connected members of wood structural systems is just beginning to receive serious attention. As this design technology develops, some extremely worthwhile building economies are likely to appear.

PLYWOOD WALL SHEATHING

Plywood wall sheathing serves as a base for the application of siding, as a weatherboard if certain exterior grades of suitable veneer quality are used, and as a structural element. In the structural sense, sheathing provides racking resistance and transmits wind loads to the wall studs. No doubt it also furnishes definite load bearing capacity to stud walls by stiffening the studs in both directions of their section. The extent to which walls receive structural credit for the contribution made by the plywood is usually limited to the resistance to racking and to buckling of studs in the narrow direction, but this need not be so.

Traditional on-site building methods having no consistently reliable form of quality control, and often carried out by workmen with limited experience and skill, do not inspire building authorities to grant recognition to these structural potentials. Factory built structural systems may be able to provide the control necessary for generating this confidence. To a limited extent, the capabilities of integrated performance of members in a system is becoming recognized in factory built structures produced under good quality inspection and control procedures.

Wall sheathing furnishes an important structural element in wood buildings as shear walls. Techniques for the design of shear walls developed by various forest products research organizations and reduced to practice by the APA are presented in Chapter 19 on Shear Walls and Diaphragms.

Plywood size and nailing information for simple wall constructions that provide racking resistance for residential structures and lateral support to wall studs is found in Table 69.

Table 69. Plywood wall sheathing[a][b] (Plywood continuous over 2 or more spans)

Panel Identification Index	Panel thickness (inch)	Maximum stud spacing (inches) Exterior covering nailed to:		Nail size (c)	Nail spacing (inches)	
		Stud	Sheathing		Panel edges (when over framing)	Intermediate (each stud)
12/0, 16/0, 20/0	5/16	16	16[d]	6d	6	12
16/0, 20/0, 24/0	3/8	24	16 24[d]	6d	6	12
24/0, 32/16	1/2	24	24	6d	6	12

(a) When plywood sheathing is used, building paper and diagonal wall bracing can be omitted.

(b) In dry conditions space panel edges ⅛", panel ends ¼". In wet or humid conditions double spacing.

(c) Common smooth, annular, spiral-thread, or galvanized box, or T-nails of the same diameter as common nails (0.113" dia. for 6d) may be used. Staples also permitted at reduced spacing.

(d) Apply plywood with face grain across studs.

from American Plywood Association's Guide to Plywood Sheathing for Floors, Walls and Roofs.

By permission.

The Minimum Property Standards for the Federal Housing Administration permit the use of 5/16" plywood on stud spacings up to 16 inches and 3/8" plywood on stud spacing up to 24 inches. Nailing must be 6d common on 6" centers along edges and on 12-inch centers along intermediate members. The direction of plywood face grain may be either perpendicular or parallel to studs. This is consistent with Table 69 based on APA recommendations, which also suggests that where shingles are used, or where exterior siding is connected to sheathing rather than through sheathing into studs, the face grain of 5/16" and 3/8" plywood be at right angles to the studding.

There is little actual design involved in these recommendations, and for most residential construction it isn't needed. However, for other uses, the choice of wall sheathing should be based on shear wall performance and resistance to wind loads without exceeding a deflection of 1/240 of the spacing between supports.

PLYWOOD ROOF SHEATHING

Structural roof sheathing performance requirements are set forth by the UBC and require that the sheathing shall:

1. Deflect not more than 1/180 of the span between supporting rafters and beams under uniform design live and dead load.

2. Deflect not more than 1/240 of the span between supports under uniform design live load.

3. Support the uniform design live and dead loads without failure.

4. Support a concentrated load of 300 lbs., on a 3-inch diameter bearing area at any location.

The UBC requires that plywood for roof sheathing be manufactured with an intermediate or exterior glue.

Table 70 is published by the APA to meet the above requirements as well as those of the Basic Building Code, the Southern Standard Building Code and most codes in common use. Two allowable roof loads are given in each box in Table 70. The top value is the load recommended for the 1/240 of span deflection limitation, and is therefore the maximum live load. The lower value, in parentheses, is the load that will cause 1/180 of span deflection or stress the plywood to its allowable maximum design stress. Under certain conditions, the load at 1/240 deflection and the load at allowable stress are equal or nearly so, and the two figures are identical. In using the table, check plywood span for total load on the basis of the number in parentheses and for live load on the basis of the loads whichre not in parentheses.

In designing diaphragms and shear walls, and where wind conditions induce high uplift loads, closer nail spacing may be necessary. See Chapters 8 and 19.

If the roof is subject to traffic, some differential deflection might occur between one panel and the next as the traffic proceeds. If this will damage the roof coating, edge support should be provided.

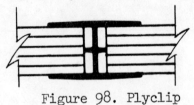

Figure 98. Plyclip

Plyclips are H-shaped pieces of hardware which can be installed in lieu of blocking on roofs to give edge support. Ply-clips (Figure 98) are available from plywood distributors.

Plywood decking is generally an economical material for use over open-web joists and trusses spaced 24", 32" and 48" on centers.

Plywood of 3/4" thickness on 48" support spacing is a common roof design in commercial buildings and apartment houses.

Table 70. Plywood Roof Decking Continuous Over Two or More Spans with Face Grain of Panels at Right Angles to Supports. (a)(b)(c)

Panel Ident. Index	Plywood Thickness inch	Max. Span (d) inches	Unsupported Edge - Max. Length (e) inches	Allowable Roof Loads, psf (f)(g) Spacing of Supports—Inches Center to Center										
				12	16	20	24	30	32	36	42	48	60	72
12/0	5/16	12	12	100 (130)										
16/0	5/16,3/8	16	16	130 (170)	55 (75)									
20/0	5/16,3/8	20	20		85 (110)	45 (55)								
24/0	3/8,1/2	24	24		150 (160)	75 (100)	45 (60)							
30/12	5/8	30	26			145 (165)	85 (110)	40 (55)						
32/16	1/2,5/8	32	28				90 (105)	45 (60)	40 (50)					
36/16	3/4	36	30				125 (145)	65 (85)	55 (70)	35 (50)				
42/20	5/8,3/4 7/8	42	32					80 (105)	65 (90)	45 (60)	35 (40)			
48/24	3/4,7/8	48	36						105 (115)	75 (90)	55 (55)	40 (40)		
2-4-1	1 1/8	72	48							175 (175)	105 (105)	80 (80)	50 (50)	30 (30)
1 1/8 Grp 1&2	1 1/8	72	48							145 (145)	85 (85)	65 (65)	40 (40)	30 (30)
1 1/4·Grp 3&4	1 1/4	72	48							160 (165)	95 (95)	75 (75)	45 (45)	25 (35)

NOTES: See page 234.

From American Plywood Association's "Guide to Plywood Sheathing for Floors, Walls and Roofs"

By permission.

Notes on Table 70

(a) These load values apply for STANDARD C-D INT-DFPA, STRUCTURAL I and II INT-DFPA, C-C EXT-DFPA, and STRUCTURAL I C-C EXT-DFPA grades only.

(b) For applications where the roofing is to be guaranteed by a performance bond see Table 71 on page 235.

(c) Use 6d common smooth, ring-shank, or spiral-thread nails for 1/2" thick or less, and 8d common smooth, ring-shank, or spiral-thread nails for plywood 1" thick or less. Used 8d ring-shank or spiral-thread or 10d common smooth shank nails for 2-4-1, 1-1/8" and 1-1/4" panels. Space nails 6" at panel edges and 12" at intermediate supports, except that where spans are 48" or more nails shall be spaced 6" at all supports.

(d) These spans shall not be exceeded at any load conditions.

(e) Provide adequate blocking, tongue and groove edges, or other suitable edge support such as Plyclips, when spans exceed values in this column. Use two Plyclips for 48" or greater spans and one for shorter spans.

(f) Uniform load deflection limitation: 1/180 of the span under live load plus dead load, 1/240 under live load only. Numbers without parentheses are allowable live loads. Numbers within parentheses are allowable total loads. The allowable live load should in no case exceed the total load less the dead load supported by the plywood including its own weight.

(g) Allowable roof loads were established by laboratory tests and calculations assuming uniformly distributed loads.

While the spacings and loads in Table 70 have proven satisfactory for most built-up asphalt and felt roofs, roofing companies who offer 20-year guarantees sometimes prefer that supports be spaced closer than the recommendations of Table 70. Roof constructions that will assure bonding companies of superior performance are described in Table 71.

Fire Resistance

Fire insurance rates comparable to unprotected metal roofs are granted in most states of the U.S.A. with fire retardant treated plywood and steel or fire retardant treated wood joists. Roof and floor constructions using plywood in combination with gypsum and with mineral acoustical ceiling panels can be built to qualify for one-hour fire resistance ratings. The "Building Materials List" of the Underwriters' Laboratories shows a large variety of these one-hour assemblies.

The 1 1/8-inch thick 2-4-1 plywood with exterior glue is accepted broadly throughout the U.S.A. as equal to 2-inch lumber and qualified for the "Heavy Timber Construction" fire resistance rating for roof decks.

Table 71. Plywood Roof Decks for 20-Year Bonded Roofs (a)

Allowable Grades	Panel Ident. Index	Plywood Thickness inches (b)	Support Spacing inches (c)	Edge Support - Plyclips (number as shown), Blocking T & G, or other means
STRUCT I	24/0	3/8,1/2	16	1
STRUCT II	30/12	5/8	24	1
C-C EXT	32/16	1/2,5/8	24	1
STANDARD C-D INT	36/16	3/4	24	1
STANDARD C-D INT w/EXT glue	42/20	5/8,3/4,7/8	32	1
STANDARD C-D INT w/intermediate glue	48/24	3/4,7/8	48	2

NOTES:

(a) Roofing nails per roofing manufacturers recommendation. Annular ring-shank nails are recommended.

(b) Plywooc continuous over two or more spans, grain of face plys across supports.

(c) See Table 70 for allowable loads and nailing requirements.

From American Plywood Association's "Guide to Plywood Sheathing for Floors, Walls and Roofs

By permission.

Acoustics

Structural systems using plywood floors may be designed to produce Sound Transmission Class Ratings above the lower limit of STP45, and Impact Noise ratings above the INR-8 to +5 values required in multi-family dwellings by the Federal Housing Administration. Such systems depend upon the combined use of acoustical insulating materials, resilient mounting channels, carpeting, mastic adhesives and gypsum panels. Acoustically superior structural systems in common use are carefully designed from a number of elements. Information on such designs can be obtained from the Federal Housing Administration; Report FHA No. 750 on "Impact Noise Control"; Owens-Corning Fiberglas Corporation, Report "Solutions to Noise ControlProblems in the Construction of Apartments, Motels and Hotels; and from the Wood Construction Research Section of the Pacific Northwest Forest and Range Experiment Station (see bibliography).

PLYWOOD SIDING

Plywood is used for exterior wall finish either with or without a layer of sheathing beneath it. There are many plywood exterior sheathing panel styles and textures on the market. Plywood is also manufactured in the form of horizontal-lapped bevel siding. The product is not highly standardized with respect to appearance, species, texture or prefinish paint or stain. Plywood siding should conform to certain fundamentals of construction worked out by the plywood manufacturers associations.

All plywood siding should be manufactured with exterior glue using grades of veneer that will withstand the weathering of outdoor exposure, unless protected by a weather resistant overlay material. Usually grades are C and better for textured siding with tight knots or filled or plugged knotholes. When siding is grooved to form vertical accent effects, the grooves should not penetrate deeply enough to expose voids in the crossbands or centers. Panels are generally run to a shiplap pattern along the edges for a tight joint that will not open due to shrinkage in service.

Medium density overlays are used for panels that give the best performance with smooth painted surfaces. Medium density overlay is a resin inpregnated fiber surface that is heat-fused to the panel faces.

Machine textured surfaces of a variety of types look well when stained.

Finely grooved surfaces are manufactured to relieve surface stress and minimize surface checking. Surface checking is a common problem with ordinary plywood and special consideration is necessary in choosing exterior plywood products to avoid this type of failure. Generally A-grade veneers are recommended.

The APA evaluates plywood finishes for exterior service and offers a list of approved finishes in their "Qualified Coatings for Plywood," (Form No. 68-910). Their publication "Finishing Softwood Plywood," is a valuable reference (Form No. 63-60).

While plywood siding as thin as 5/16-inch is used over plywood or other types of wall sheathing on 16-inch to 24-inch stud spacing, exterior plywood sidings of greater thickness may be more economically used in lieu of sheathing, as a single layer outside wall surface. Table 72 from APA's "Guide to Plywood Siding" summarizes construction features of single-layer plywood exterior walls.

Table 72. Plywood Siding Nailed Direct to Studs.

APA Single-Wall® construction

Panel sidings are normally installed vertically, but may be placed horizontally (face grain across supports). 303 plywood siding bearing the designation "303 - 24 o.c." on the grade-trademark may be applied vertically directly to studs spaced 24" on center. 303 - 16 o.c. may be used vertically over studs spaced 16" on center. All panels shown in the table may be used on studs 24" o.c. when applied with face grain horizontal.

All edges of panel siding should be backed with framing or blocking. To prevent staining of siding, use hot-dip galvanized, aluminum, or other non-corrosive nails. No corner bracing is needed with plywood panel siding.

Plywood descriptions are similar for plywood siding whether used direct to studs, or over sheathing. Joint detailing, however, differs. With any type of panel sheathing, building paper may be omitted. It may also be omitted in single-wall construction if joints are shiplapped or battened. Building paper is required for unbattened square butt joints in single-wall construction.

Plywood lap or bevel siding

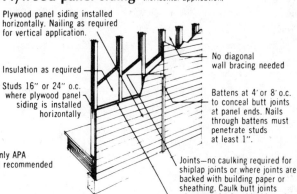

Shingle wedge under vertical joints
1" x 4" let-in diagonal brace
Stagger butt joints over studs
Insulation as required
Building paper
EXTERIOR plywood siding
No wedge required for bevel siding

Plywood panel siding
(regular vertical application)

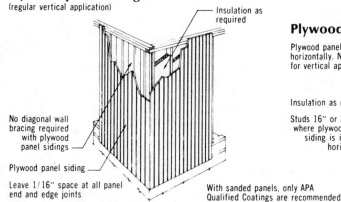

Insulation as required

No diagonal wall bracing required with plywood panel sidings

Plywood panel siding

Leave 1/16" space at all panel end and edge joints

With sanded panels, only APA Qualified Coatings are recommended for a quality finish.

Plywood panel siding (horizontal application)

Plywood panel siding installed horizontally. Nailing as required for vertical application.

Insulation as required

Studs 16" or 24" o.c. where plywood panel siding is installed horizontally

No diagonal wall bracing needed

Battens at 4' or 8' o.c. to conceal butt joints at panel ends. Nails through battens must penetrate studs at least 1".

Joints—no caulking required for shiplap joints or where joints are backed with building paper or sheathing. Caulk butt joints where required and inside and outside corners.

2x4 blocking at horizontal joints

APA single-wall construction
(Recommendations apply to all species groups)

Type	Plywood Siding Description	Nominal Thickness (in.)	Max. Stud Spacing (in.) Face Grain Vertical	Face Grain Horizontal	Nail Size (Use non-corrosive box, siding or casing nails)	Nail Spacing (in.) Panel Edges	Intermediate
Panel Siding	A-C EXT-DFPA B-C EXT-DFPA	⅜	16	24	6d for panels ½" thick or less; 8d for thicker panels.	6	12
	C-C Plugged EXT-DFPA MDO EXT-DFPA	½ & thicker	24	24			
	T 1-11 EXT-DFPA	⅝	16	24			
	303-16 o.c. Siding EXT-DFPA	5/16 & thicker	16	24			
	303-24 o.c. Siding EXT-DFPA	7/16 & thicker	24	24			
Lap Siding	A-C EXT-DFPA B-C EXT-DFPA	⅜	—	16	6d for siding ⅜" or less; 8d for thicker siding.	4" @ vertical butt joints; one nail per stud along bottom edge.	8" @ each stud, if siding wider than 12".
	C-C Plugged EXT-DFPA MDO EXT-DFPA MDO EXT-DFPA	½ & thicker	—	24			
	303-16 o.c. Siding EXT-DFPA	5/16 or ⅜	—	16			
	303-16 o.c. Siding EXT-DFPA 303-24 o.c. Siding EXT-DFPA	7/16 & thicker	—	24			

CHAPTER 17

DESIGN OF LUMBER-PLYWOOD BOX BEAMS

By combining lumber and plywood to form beams with an I or box-shaped section, wood may be used with a high degree of efficiency. Such beams may be straight or cambered, and can be designed in the form of rigid frames and three-hinged arches. Lumber is used for flanges to function as chords and carry most of the bending moment. Plywood is used for webs to carry the shear stresses. The plywood and lumber are joined together with adhesives, using clamps, presses, or nails to obtain the pressure for good mating of the surfaces while the adhesive cures. Vertical stiffeners of lumber are placed between the flanges to prevent web buckling and transfer load and bearing forces between the flanges. End joints in flanges and webs may require scarfing, finger jointing, or splicing.

In designing these types of beams, economies may be obtained by proportioning the sizes of flange and web material differently along the beam length to match bending moment and shear requirements. The portion of total deflection due to shear deformation as mentioned in Chapter 9 for lumber members, may be an even more significant factor in plywood-lumber beam performance.

Several section designs are illustrated in Figure 99. Sections A are for a beam of uniform box section throughout its length. Sections D are for a beam of uniform I section from end to end. Such beams have more than enough flange lumber at their ends and more than enough web material at their centers. However, the simplicity of manufacture may well offset material economies in justifying these uniform cross-section beams.

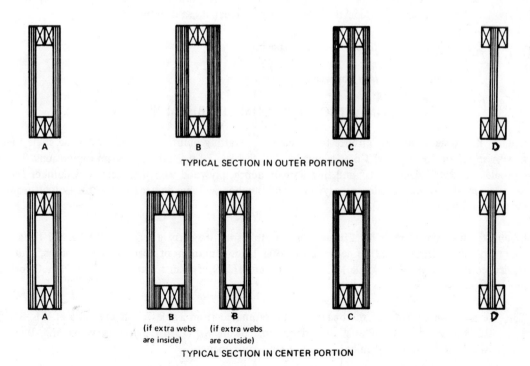

A   B   C   D

TYPICAL SECTION IN OUTER PORTIONS

A   B   B   C   D

(if extra webs are inside)   (if extra webs are outside)

TYPICAL SECTION IN CENTER PORTION

Figure 99. Plywood-lumber beam sections

By permission of APA.

BOX BEAMS

Sections B and C are for beams with more efficiently proportioned web material along their length. B requires two layers of plywood to resist the shear at the ends, and only one layer for the shear at midspan. Center section B illustrates a beam of uniform width throughout its length, using plywood or lumber shims to fill the space between web and flange in the central portion. Center section B' is for a beam that is not of uniform width along its entire length. Its appearance is less attractive than if it were uniformly wide, but it is easier to make and uses less wood.

Sections C illustrate a beam of uniform width with 50 percent more web material at its extremities.

Each flange, of course, may be one to several members and under certain circumstances may be fabricated from small laminated beams instead of lumber. Webs may be one or several layers of plywood.

Beams of type A can easily be produced by nail gluing. The other sections are more difficult to make with nail gluing methods and pressure gluing with clamps or presses is recommended.

To design a plywood beam for a specific set of load, span, and deflection criteria the design procedure consists of several distinct steps as follows.

1. *Estimate the approximate size* of beam required.

2. Determine the *bending moments* and required moment of inertia and section modulus.

3. Determine the *horizontal shear* and required plywood thickness.

4. Determine the *shear at the flange-web* joint and choose web and flange dimensions and arrangement to provide adequate rolling shear area.

5. Calculate the *deflection* based upon the section properties and compare it to the criteria, altering the section properties if necessary to meet those criteria.

6. Determine *bearing stiffener* size and spacing.

7. Determine *splice details* for webs and flanges.

ESTIMATING APPROXIMATE BEAM SIZE

Usually the designer has the criteria for a beam as a starting point, and he must choose some flange and web sizes. APA's "Guide to Plywood Components" offers Table 73 for estimating beam dimensions. To use this table one should calculate WL and WL^2 and find a beam depth, plywood web thickness, and number and size of flange lumber from the tables. Grades of plywood and lumber will be determined as the actual beam design calculations are developed.

Example: Design a beam to be 20 feet long, simple span, to carry a load of 300 lbs. per lineal foot total load. Dead load is one-third of total load. Duration of load is two months, and service conditions will be dry. Deflection criteria are 1/240 of span for total load and 1/360 for live load only.

The size and construction of the beam may be estimated from Table 73 on the basis of WL = 6000 lbs. and WL^2 = 120,000 ft. lbs. A nominal 16" deep box beam with 5/8" plywood webs and flanges each constructed of two 2" x 4" lumber members meets these requirements.

Table 73.   Size Estimating Table for Box Beams

Nominal Depth (in.)	WL (lbs.)	WL^2 (ft. lb.)	Nominal Plywood (in.)	Nominal Flange No. - Size
8	2,290	22,980	3/8	1 - 2" x 3"
8	3,500	32,170	1/2	1 - 2" x 4"
12	3,490	53,180	3/8	1 - 2" x 4"
12	5,350	81,645	1/2	1 - 2" x 6"
12	6,165	93,035	5/8	1 - 2" x 4"
16	4,690	74,190	3/8	1 - 2" x 4"
16	7,170	113,904	1/2	1 - 2" x 6"
16	8,275	136,815	5/8	2 - 2" x 4"
24	10,800	177,405	1/2	1 - 2" x 6"
24	12,450	223,015	5/8	2 - 2" x 4"
24	14,100	342,470	3/4	2 - 2" x 6"
30	13,550	225,790	1/2	1 - 2" x 6"
30	15,625	288,685	5/8	2 - 2" x 4"
30	17,700	443,320	3/4	2 - 2" x 6"
36	16,300	376,225	1/2	1 - 2" x 8"
36	18,800	544,170	5/8	2 - 2" x 6"
36	21,300	785,440	3/4	3 - 2" x 6"
42	19,050	645,020	1/2	2 - 2" x 6"
42	22,000	938,895	5/8	3 - 2" x 6"
42	24,900	1,204,335	3/4	4 - 2" x 6"
42	34,600	1,652,400	1	4 - 2" x 8"
48	21,800	1,074,710	1/2	2 - 2" x 6"
48	25,150	1,414,340	5/8	4 - 2" x 6"
48	28,500	1,934,660	3/4	4 - 2" x 8"
48	39,400	2,331,665	1	5 - 2" x 8"
48	42,750	2,963,980	1 1/8	5 - 2" x 10"

From A.P.A. "Guide to Plywood Components"

Courtesy American Plywood Association

BENDING MOMENTS & SECTION PROPERTIES

Bending moment at maximum load and moment of inertia are calculated and used to determine the bending stress at the extreme fiber. The allowable stress in the flanges will be the allowable stress in tension or compression parallel to the grain, whichever is the lower property value, usually F_t. The flanges are actually subject to axial tension and axial compression, plus bending. The bending stress is so small compared to the axial stresses, that the design may be carried out on the basis of axial stresses rather than using the refined combined axial stress and bending formulas given in Chapter 9. Proceeding on this basis then:

$$M = \frac{w\ell^2}{8} = \frac{300}{12} \cdot \frac{240^2}{8} = 180,000 \text{ in. lbs.}$$

The net moment of inertia, I_n, is the sum of the flange and web moments of inertia, $I_f + I_w$. The designer makes an estimate at this point, of the material that will likely be required. A trial choice of Douglas fir No. 1 Structural Light-Framing 2" x 4" flange lumber (E = 1,800,000 psi) and 5/8" int. plywood, Structural II C-D (E = 1,200,000 psi) is made as an estimate of probable minimum grades required. Allowing 1/8" for kerf and trim waste in cutting 16" web plywood from 48" sheets an estimated actual depth is 15.75". The 2 x 4's should be surfaced on the faces that must receive glue and on the exposed edge when the box beam is trimmed to final size (15.75") after gluing. This is likely to amount to 1/8" off each 2 x 4 dimension, making the finished dimensions of flange lumber 1 3/8" x 3 3/8".

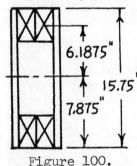

Figure 100.

$$I_f = 4\left[\frac{1.375(3.375)^3}{12} + 1.375(3.375)(6.185)^2\right] = 729 \text{ in.}^4$$

The effective thickness of the webs is the total thickness of the plys with grain parallel to the longitudinal axis of the beam. The effective web thickness for this moment of inertia calculation is not the same as the "Effective Thickness for Shear" given in Table 23, Chapter 7. To obtain the effective thickness for the moment of inertia calculations use the "Area for Tension and Compression" figure from Table 23 as follows:

$$\frac{\text{Area for tension or compression}}{\text{Gross area of one-foot-wide section}} \times \text{gross thickness}$$

$$\frac{4.586}{5/8 \times 12} \times 5/8 = \frac{4.586}{12} = 0.382 \text{ inch}$$

Since the elastic modulus of the web material is less than the elastic modulus of the flange material, web thickness should be transformed for use at the E-value of the flanges. Thus:

$$0.382 \times 1.2/1.8 = 0.254 \text{ inch}$$

The moment of inertia of web material is:

$$I_w = 2\left[\frac{0.254(15.75)^3}{12}\right] = 166 \text{ in.}^4$$

Total moment of inertia is:

$$I_n = I_f + I_w = 729 + 166 = 895 \text{ in.}^4$$

Using this section property the required allowable stress for lumber and plywood can be determined.

Flange stress, $f = M(h/2)/I_n = 180,000(7.875)/895 = 1584$ psi.

The lumber in the flanges must be of a grade that will have allowable tension and compression stress equal to or exceeding 1584 psi. No. 1 Structural Light Framing grade 2 x 4 per Table A2 shows $F_t = 1050$ psi and $F_c = 1250$ psi for Douglas fir. These are normal duration of load stresses and may be increased 15% for two-months duration as stated in the example. Thus, $F_t = 1210$ psi and $F_c = 1440$ psi, which are too low for the 1584 psi imposed stress. By specifying "MC15" lumber, these values may be raised to $F_t = 1310$ psi and $F_c = 1730$ psi, according to Table 15. For use at moisture conditions below 15 percent, *No. 1 Structural Light Framing MC15 grade Douglas fir* is adequate for the 2 x 4 compression flange, but not strong enough for the tension flange.

By specifying a "dense" grade, i.e., Dense No. 1 Structural Light Framing MC15 Douglas fir, the allowable stress will be further increased by 17% (Chapter 3, Table 9, footnote 3) to $F_t = 1535$ psi. This is still too low for the job. It is necessary to use a higher stress grade of lumber:

Select Structural Light Framing Douglas fir has $F_t = 1.15 \times 1200 = 1380$ psi which is not adequate. Specifying MC15 will only raise this 8% to 1490 psi. *Dense Select Structural grade Douglas fir* with $F_t = 1.15 \times 1.17 \times 1200 = 1620$ psi, would be adequate for the purpose.

The foregoing is based on the assumption that the flanges will be fabricated using nails to achieve the gluing pressure. If it is practical to bond the beam using positive clamp pressure, a 10% stress increase would be justifiable. In that case, the Dense No. 1 Structural Light Framing MC15 at $F_t = 1.1 \times 1535 = 1690$ psi would be satisfactory. Also non-dense, Select Structural Light Framing MC15 with $F_t = 1.1 \times 1490 = 1640$ psi would be adequate.

One should not overlook the possibility of using Machine Stress Rated lumber for high performance requirements of this kind. Referring to Table A6 the grade 2100f–1.8E has adequate $F_t = 1.15 \times 1575 = 1810$ psi and adequate modulus of elasticity (E = 1,800,000 psi) for the job. This could be obtained in a variety of species, all with equal primary strength properties as given in Table A6.

An alternative way to reduce the stress requirements for flange lumber is to raise the quality or size of the plywood webs. If, for example, Structural I C-D webs are used, the transformation required for Structural II C-D plywood is not necessary. This is so because for Structural I, E = 1,800,000 psi, the same as the lumber. Under these circumstances:

$$I_w = 2\left[\frac{0.382(15.75)^3}{12}\right] = 249 \text{ in.}^4$$

$$\text{and} \quad I_n = 729 + 249 = 978 \text{ in.}^4$$

$$f = 180,000 (7.875)/978 = 1449 \text{ psi}$$

Structural I C-D has an allowable compression stress of 1550 x 1.15 = 1785 psi, which is adequate. Also the Dense No. 1 Structural Light Framing MC15 grade which has an allowable tension stress of 1.15 x 1.17 x 1.08 x 1050 = 1525 psi is adequate. Dense No. 1 may be more readily available than the other possibility, Select Structural L.F. MC15 with F_t = 1.15 x 1.08 x 1200 = 1490 psi. Availability fluctuates with time and supplier, so it is well to have alternative grades in mind for any timber design.

In this particular example the above alternative is not necessary. Structural II C-D is adequate and is much easier to obtain. The stress it must sustain is 1584 x 1.2/1.8 = 1056 psi, transformed back to its real width. Structural II C-D per Table 25, Chapter 7, has allowable stresses of 1200 psi tension and 1100 psi compression. These are adequate even without taking the permissible 15% increase for two-month duration of load.

Let us assume we will specify *Dense Select Structural L. F. Douglas fir (F_t = 1620 psi) for the tension flange and No. 1 Structural L. F. MC15 (F_c = 1730 psi) for the compression flange, with Structural II C-D plywood* fabricated using nail pressure for gluing.

HORIZONTAL SHEAR THROUGH THE PLYWOOD THICKNESS AT THE NEUTRAL AXIS

Shear through the width of the beam enters into this design just as it would for solid beams. In the case of box beams, the width at the neutral axis is the two plywood web thicknesses. The allowable stress for shear through the thickness (F_v) of plywood is based upon the full actual thickness of the plywood as given in Tables 23 or 24, and not transformed by the plywood/lumber E-ratio.

$$f_v = \frac{VQ}{I(2t)}$$

$$V = \text{maximum shear} = 300 \times \frac{20}{2} = 3000 \text{ lbs.}$$

$$2t = 2(0.662) = 1.324 \text{ in.}$$

Q = Area moment of the beam cross-section on one side of the neutral axis, about the neutral axis (parallel plys only)

$$Q = 2.75(3.375)6.1875 + 2(0.254)(7.875)\left(\frac{7.875}{2}\right)$$

$$= 73.2 \text{ in.}^3$$

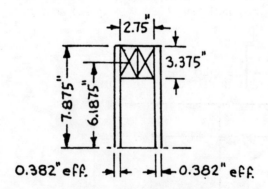

Figure 101.

$$I_n = 895 \text{ in.}^4$$

$$f_v = \frac{3000(73.2)}{895(1.324)} = 185 \text{ psi}$$

The allowable F_v (from Table 25) is 250 x 1.15 = 287 psi, which is adequate.

Shear at the Flange-Web Joint

We are dealing here with a rolling shear stress between the face and cross-band of the plywood in the region of the flange-web glue bond.

$$f_s = \frac{VQ_f}{I(2d)}$$

with V and I as in the preceding section; Q_{ff}, the statical moment of flange area about the neutral axis; and d, the depth of flange.

$$Q_f = 3.375(2.75)(6.1875) = 57.5 \text{ in.}^3$$

$$d = 3.375 \text{ in.}$$

$$f_s = \frac{3000(57.5)}{895(6.75)} = 28.4 \text{ psi}$$

The allowable F_s from Table 25, footnote 3 is 75 psi. This is reduced 50% for stress concentration at the edge (see page 66, Chapter 7) and increased 15% for two months duration of load, giving 43.2 psi for F_v. The allowable rolling shear stress is more than adequate for the imposed stress of 28.4 psi.

DEFLECTION

Plywood box beam deflections are usually computed by an approximate method and if it then seems that deflection is likely to be the governing feature of beam performance, a more refined method is used.

The approxmiate method utilizes the conventional beam deflection formulas which ignore the shear component of deflection. Shear-deflection factors from Table 74 are then applied to the result to obtain an approximation of actual deflection.

Table 74. Shear Deflection Factors

Span/Depth	Factor
10	1.5
15	1.2
20	1.0

The approximate method calculation for this beam design example follows.

$$\Delta = \frac{5}{384} \frac{w\ell^4}{EI_n}$$

$$= \frac{5}{384} \cdot \frac{300}{12} \frac{(240)^4}{1,800,000} \cdot \frac{1}{895} = 0.672 \text{ inch}$$

Span/depth = 240/15.75 = 15.2

The factor for shear deformation is 1.2

$\Delta = 0.672 \times 1.2 = 0.806$ inch.

The total load deflection by the approximate method is 0.806/240 = 1/298, which does not exceed the deflection criteria of 1/240 of the span, mentioned on page 240. The live load deflection would be 2/3 of 0.806 = 0.54 in. This is 1/446, less than the live load deflection criteria of 1/360 of span:

In this case there is no need to use the refined method of deflection computation which follows:

The deflection due to shear deformation may be determined using methods published by APA in Plywood Design Specifications, Supplement No. 2 on Design of Plywood Beams.

$$\Delta_s = \frac{P\ell Kh^2 C}{GI_g}$$

where Δ_s = shear deflection (in.)

P = total load on beam (lbs.)

ℓ = span length (in.)

K = a factor determined by the beam cross-section, and shown in Figure 102.

h = depth of beam (in.)

C = a coefficient depending on the manner of loading, also shown in Figure 102.

G = shearing modulus of the webs (psi). (From tests, G may be taken as E/20 for panels with exterior glue. Reduce 9% for panels with interior glue. Reduce an additional 16% for beams where equilibrium moisture content in service will be 16% or higher.)

I_g = Gross moment of inertia of all material in the section, using the "Effective Thickness for Shear" from Tables 23 or 24.

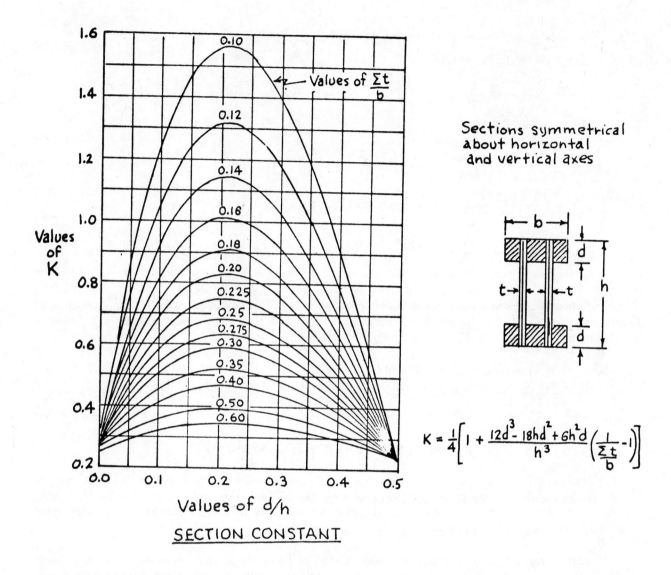

Sections symmetrical
about horizontal
and vertical axes

$$K = \frac{1}{4}\left[1 + \frac{12d^3 - 18hd^2 + 6h^2d}{h^3}\left(\frac{1}{\frac{\Sigma t}{b}} - 1\right)\right]$$

SECTION CONSTANT

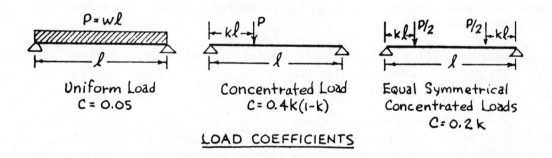

Uniform Load
C = 0.05

Concentrated Load
C = 0.4k(1-k)

Equal Symmetrical
Concentrated Loads
C = 0.2k

LOAD COEFFICIENTS

Figure 102.   Section constant and load coefficients for
shear deflection equation.
(From A.P.A. Plywood Design Spec. Suppl. #2)

For the beam in this example:

$$P = 6000 \text{ lbs.} \qquad\qquad C = 0.05$$

$$\ell = 240 \text{ inches} \qquad\qquad G = 90{,}000 \text{ psi}$$

$$h = 15.75 \text{ inches} \qquad\qquad K = 0.55$$

$$I_g = \frac{4(15.75)^3}{12} - \frac{2.75(9)^3}{12} = 1132 \text{ in.}^4$$

$$\Delta_s = \frac{6000(240)0.55(15.75)^2 0.05}{90{,}000(1132)} = 0.096 \text{ in.}$$

Total deflection is obtained by adding this shear deflection to the deflection obtained by the simple engineering formula. The value of E for plywood and lumber may be increased 10 percent in this more refined deflection calculation, thus:

$$\Delta = \frac{0.672}{1.10} + 0.096 = 0.702 \text{ in.}$$

BEARING STIFFENER SIZE & SPACING

Lumber stiffeners placed vertically between the flanges· are necessary to distribute load between the flanges at the points of support and at points of concentrated load. For uniformly loaded beams, bearing stiffeners are spaced at intervals of 48 inches or less to stabilize the webs from buckling and provide added resistance to shear through the thickness.

Bearing stiffeners at ends of beams should be sized to fill in the space between the webs. They should have sufficient cross-sections to bear the compressive load and be of sufficient size that the web-to-stiffener glue line area can transfer the compressive load to the bearing stiffener without exceeding the allowable rolling shear. While some load will be transferred from the top flange to the top of the end bearing stiffener, most of its load will come from the webs.

To satisfy the first of these requirements for the example, for which the end reaction is 3000 lbs:

$$x = \frac{R}{F_{c\perp} b} \qquad\qquad R = \text{reaction (lbs.)}$$

$$b = \text{flange width (inches)}$$

$$x = \text{stiffener dimension parallel to beam axis (in.)}$$

$$x = \frac{3000}{1.15(385)(2.75)} = 2.46 \text{ inches (use 2.5 in.)}$$

To satisfy the second requirement:

$$x = \frac{R}{F_s 2h} \qquad\qquad h = \text{depth of beam (inches)}$$

$$x = \frac{3000}{1.15(0.5)(75)(2)(15.75)} = 2.2 \text{ inches}$$

While it is not recommended that the increases in $F_{c\perp}$ described on pages 106-107, Chapter 9, be used for end bearing stiffener design, they may be used for intermediate stiffeners. The stress concentration factor of 50% on rolling shear need not be applied at intermediate stiffeners. For bearing stiffeners under applied loads let the concentrated load, P, or the portion of the uniformly distributed load contiguous to the stiffener replace R. Unlike the end bearing stiffener, all of he load does not need to be transferred through the bearing post to the lower flange and support. It would be quite conservative to estimate that half the load would be so supported. In fact, the way loads are distributed by stiffeners is indeterminate, and these design suggestions are quite conservative. Generally nominal 2-inch lumber, wide enough to fit properly between the webs, for good gluing, will provide adequate support.

In this case load per intermediate stiffener at 48-inch spacing is:

$$\frac{4 \times 300}{2} = 600 \text{ lbs.}$$

For bearing; $x = \dfrac{600}{1.15(385)(2.75)} = 0.5$ inch

For rolling shear; $x = \dfrac{600}{1.15(1.0)(75)(2)(15.75)} = 0.22$ inch

So nominal 2-inch material is entirely sufficient.

SPLICE DETAILS

Lumber Flanges

It would be highly desirable to obtain 20-ft. lengths of lumber for the flanges and ordinarily that is not difficult with a little advance planning. While 16-ft. lengths are the usual maximum common sizes, longer lumber is produced for the roof truss manufacturing consumers. These may be pieces sawn from long logs or structural end jointed lumber. Stress-rated structural end jointed lumber can be used for design at published stresses for the grade.

If shorter length lumber is used it can be *scarf jointed*. Glued scarf joints made in knot-free sections of straight-grained lumber have efficiencies per Table 75. The joint efficiency represents the reduced strength as a result of scarfing. Lumber that is end jointed by scarfing, without particular attention to location of the scarfs, must be used with tensile and compressive stresses reduced by the joint efficiencies in Table 75. If scarf joint location is confined to straight-grained, knot-free areas, the working stresses need not be reduced as long as joint efficiency exceeds strength ratio.

Table 75. Scarf Joint Efficiencies for Tension and Compression

Scarf Slope	Joint Efficiency
1 in 12	85%
1 in 10	80%
1 in 8	75%
1 in 5	60%
For dry conditions limit slope to 1 in 8 for tension and 1 in 5 for compression. For wet conditions limit slope to 1 in 10 for tension and compression.	

By permission of APA.

Table 76. Effectiveness Factors for Butt-Jointed Flange Laminations

Butt Joint Spacing (t = lamination thickness)	Effectiveness Factor
30t to 50t	90%
20t to 30t	80%
10t to 20t	60%
less than 10t	0%
Butt joints closer than 10t shall be considered as occurring in the same section.	

By permission of APA.

Butt joints may be used in flanges consisting of two or more laminations. The net section at any position is used for design if the distance to the nearest butt joint in adjacent laminations equals or exceeds 50 times the lamination thickness. For lumber flanges, i.e., flanges which are not pressure glued, the minimum spacing between butt joints in adjoining laminations is 30 t. In figuring net section for tension and compression, the area of cross section of laminations containing butt joints less than 50 lamination thicknesses from the section, shall be reduced by the Effectiveness Factors in Table 76.

In the case of clamp pressure-glued flange laminations, butt-joint spacing may be as close as 10t and still retain some effective lamination area for design per Table 76.

The application of this table can be demonstrated with an illustration using the beam in the design example of this chapter. This is a nail-pressure glued flange and the minimum butt-joint spacing is 30t or 41.25 in. If 16-foot lumber is used for the flanges, each lamination may consist of a 16-foot piece, butt-jointed to a 4-foot piece, as in Figure 103. Top and bottom flanges would be fabricated in this way.

The effective section of the butt-jointed lamination in the region of 10t (13.75 in.) on each side of the joint would be zero. In the region between 10t and 20t (13.75 in. to 27.5 in.) the effectiveness of the lamination

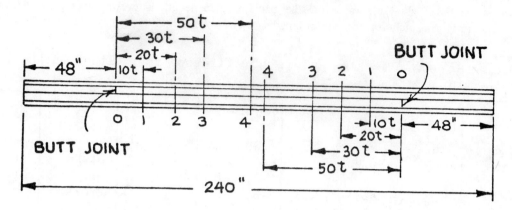

Figure 103.

will be 60%. And by the practice prescribed by Table 76 the effectiveness will be 80% between 20t and 30t, and 90% between 30t and 50t. Beyond 50t the full section may be counted upon for design.

Tension and compressive stresses for design for use with these net areas are the published value for the grade, with the exception that for tension, at the section where the butt joint occurs, $0.8 F_t$ is used.

It is necessary to determine that the section properties at the various positions are adequate to sustain the moments at those sections. This should be done after the location of web splices have been determined and their effects on section properties are established.

Plywood Webs

Scarf jointed plywood webs that are well bonded under positive pressure will have design characteristics as follows:

For tension and flexure
   100% of allowable stress if scarf slope is 1:8 or flatter
   75% of allowable stress if scarf slope is 1:5
   Scarfs steeper than 1:5 not allowed.

For compression
   100% of allowable stress if scarf slope is 1:5.

For shear
   100% of allowable stress if scarf slope is 1:8 or flatter.

Spliced butt joints in plywood webs should be well bonded with nail-pressure gluing and made with splice plates on one side, of a grade, species group, and thickness equal to the pieces being spliced. The face grain of the splice plate must be perpendicular to the line of the joint.

For tension and flexure
   Strength properties per Table 77..

For compression
   100% of allowable values for the panel at lengths given in Table 77, and proportionately less for shorter lengths.

For shear

100% of allowable value for the panel if plate length is twelve times panel thickness and proportionately less for shorter lengths.

Table 77. Allowable Tension and Flexure Stresses for Spliced Butt Joints in Plywood

Plywood Thickness (inches)	Splice Plate Length (inches)	Struct I A-A, A-C Struct I C-D	Gr. 1 A-A, A-B, A-C, A-D, B-B, B-C, B-D	Struct II	Stand. Gr. 2 Stresses	All Grades Gr. 4 Stresses
1/4 5/16 3/8 Sanded 3/8 Rough	6 8 10 12	1500	1200	1100	1000	900
1/2	14	1500	1000	1100	950	900
5/8 & 3/4	16	1200	800	850	750	700

From APA, Plywood Design Specification

Permissible alternate joints such as finger joints, lap joints, tongue and groove joints or joints backed with lumber splice plates may be used at stress levels demonstrated by acceptable tests.

All strength values are subject to duration of load and moisture content adjustments.

For the webs of the beam in this illustration, splice plates would be placed behind the webs on the interior of the beam. Such plates can only extend between the interior faces of the flanges. By making these splices 16 inches long, the maximum tensile stress will be 1.15 x 1200 = 1380 psi. The section at the splice must be calculated and checked for adequacy.

At positions where spliced butt joints occur in both webs, the moment of inertia of the webs, I_w, is reduced to

$$166 \left[\frac{9}{15.75} \right]^3 = 31 \text{ in.}^3$$

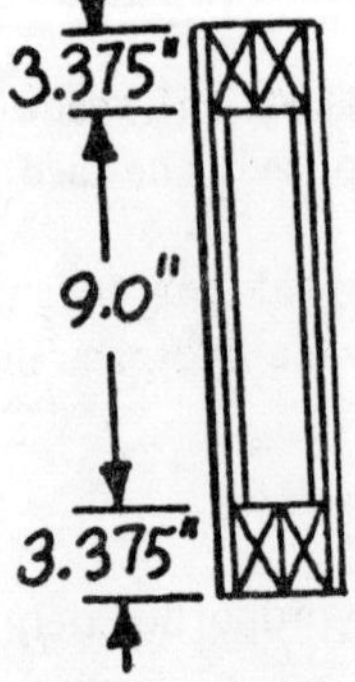

Figure 104.

The section at such points is shown in Figure 104. If these joints do not occur opposite one another, the value of

I_w is $\frac{166}{2} + 31 = 114 \text{ in.}^3$

Referring to Figure 103, the effective moment of inertia at the various positions based on the flange joints can be calculated and compared to the required moment of inertia at these locations.

The moment at a distance x from the end of the beam will be

$$M_x = \frac{w\ell x}{2} - \frac{wx^2}{2} = \frac{wx}{2}(\ell - x) = 12.5x(\ell - x)$$

The required value of moment of inertia at any position will be:

$$I = M_x c/F_t = M_x(7.875)/1620 = M_x/206$$

A tabulation of available effective moment of inertia and required moment of inertia at various positions along the beam length is shown in the following table.

Table 78. Section Property Check for Design Example

Station	X at Max. Moment in.	Maximum Moment in. lbs.	Effective I_n in.^{4}	Required I_n in^4
0	48	115,200	$0.8\left[\frac{729}{2} + 166\right] = 432$	< 599
0 to 1	61.75	137,587	$\frac{729}{2} + 166 = 531$	< 668
1 to 2	75.75	155,247	$\frac{729(1.6)}{2} + 166 = 749$	< 754
2 to 3	89.25	168,180	$\frac{729(1.8)}{2} + 166 = 822$	< 816
3 to 4	116.75	179,867	$\frac{729(1.9)}{2} + 166 = 859$	< 870
4 to center	120.00	180,000	$729 + 166 = 895$	< 873

Based on butt joints in top and bottom flanges per Figure 103.

It is evident from Table 78 that the effect of the butt-jointed chord is to reduce the value of I_n below that required between stations 0 and 2 in Figure 103 and at some places between stations 3 and 4. Therefore, either full 20-foot flange lumber or structural end-jointed or scarfed lumber must be used. Lumber scarfed in clear wood areas between allowable defects will carry the full allowable stress of the grade since the strength ratios for the flange lumber grades previously established are 37% and 31% (See Table 8), both lower than any of the scarf joint efficiencies in Table 75. Lumber with structural end joints efficiencies exceeding these strength ratios is also manufactured.

With full length, or scarfed or structural end-jointed lumber the flange areas are not reduced in net section at any location.

Two arrangements of the spliced joints in the plywood webs are shown in Figures 105 and 106, using standard eight-foot plywood. The net moment of inertia at the jointed cross-section nearest the midspan for the Figure 105 arrangement is:

$$I_n = 729 + 31 = 760 \text{ in.}^4$$

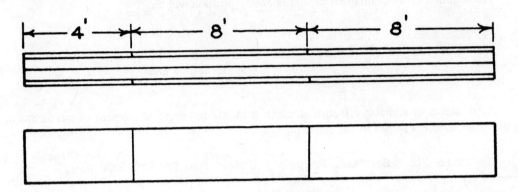

Figure 105. Web splice location at same cross section

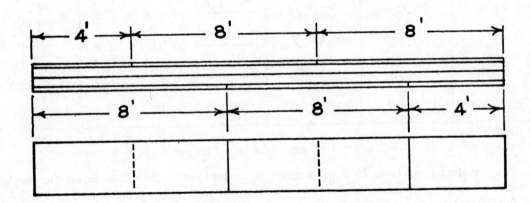

Figure 106. Web splice locations staggered to minimize
strength reduction

The moment at this location is:

$$M_x = 12.5(96)(144) = 172,800 \text{ in. lbs.}$$

$$\text{Required I} = \frac{Mx}{206} = \frac{172,800}{206} = 840 \text{ in.}^4$$

The Figure 105 arrangement has insufficient I.

The Figure 106 arrangement with only one web splice at any section gives:

$$I_n = 729 + \frac{166}{2} + 31 = 843 \text{ in.}^4$$

which meets the requirement of 840 in.^{4}

CHAPTER 18

DESIGN OF PLYWOOD STRESSED SKIN PANELS

The growing use of plywood stressed-skin panels testifies to their usefulness in building systems. Stressed-skin panel constructions are not peculiar to wood structures, but have been widely used with other materials of construction. Stressed skin designs are used in aircraft, vehicle bodies, the hulls of ships, in fact a great variety of structures in addition to buildings. They are a structurally efficient form of construction and when material is costly, or weight is important, they serve those purposes well. Costs determine the extent of their adoption in the wood building industry. Adequate wood structures for traditional uses can be constructed without using stressed-skin structures. Two factors favor their use in today's wood buildings. These are: material prices, which reflect material availability; and the stability and dimensional precision desired for factory built components that must go together without unexpected and costly field fitting. Interestingly enough, factory organized building processes which produce these requirements also best fit the economical construction of stressed-skin components.

Some builders have considerable experience with stressed-skin systems. Instances of disillusionment with stressed-skin systems arise not so much from direct cost and performance inadequacies, as from problems with regulatory agencies. As these difficulties are surmounted, the common use of stressed-skin structures should accelerate considerably. They have already found a firm place in commercial, industrial and institutional buildings of many types.

Stressed-skin structures take the form of flat and curved panels and folded plate structures of a great variety of shapes. They are built as hollow webbed components and as sandwich structures. In this chapter, attention is given to the design of simple flat panels for flexure, as in roof and floor systems, and for compression as in wall panels. Good design references for plywood stressed-skin components of other types are published by APA and are included in the Bibliography.

GENERAL

The stressed-skin concept depends upon skins and stringers fastened securely and rigidly together so the entire cross-section may function as a unit. This requires glued bonds using rigid adhesives for maximum integral action of skins and webs. Mastic adhesives which have an elastic or viscoelastic nature are of some interest for stressed-skin panel structures, because they permit some dampening of impact traffic loads, but at the sacrifice of structural efficiency and optimum material economy. Mastic-bonded panels may be well-suited to floor systems and their use for floors was mentioned in Chapter 16. However, design methods for panels made with these adhesives are not completely evolved at this point in time. Most panels made today use rigid adhesives of the casein, phenol-formaldehyde, resorcinol-formaldehyde, melamine base urea, or cross-linked polyvinyl resin emulsion types. The design methods that follow apply to panels bonded with rigid and relatively inelastic adhesives.

The size of panels is greatly affected by available sizes of plywood and lumber. Plywood and lumber can be spliced and scarfed to obtain lengths required. Manufacturers are beginning to show interest in a more versatile range of lengths for both of these products. Also, the concept of structural fiber hardboards and particleboards that already have length and width versatility superior to plywood, are on the building materials horizon today and may be available in the not-too-distant future. However, structural forms of these fiberboard products are not with us yet, (1971) while plywood and lumber have well-developed properties for engineered designs.

In addition to skins and stringers, stressed-skin panels have headers at their ends and blocking or bridging at positions within the panels. Blocking backs up splice plates for joining the skins, aligns the stringers when jigs are not used, and supports skin edges and joints to help distribute concentrated loads.

Two-sided panels do not require bridging but one-sided panels do require this for lateral support of the stringers in long panels.

While panels can be built with bottom skins as thin as 1/4" with face grain parallel to stringers, 5/16" thick plywood is preferred to avoid visible waviness of the surface on 16" stringer spacing. Stressed-skin panels are usually built with plywood face grain parallel to stringers. This is in contrast with all the tables of load and span in Chapter 16 which are predicated on face grain at right angles to joists. For this reason, special attention is given to deflection of plywood flexed on supports set parallel to face grain, the low stiffness direction of flexure.

In addition to two-sided and one-sided panels, one-sided flat panels designed with lumber flanges on the lower side is a third flat type panel. The purpose is to improve stiffness, optimize material efficiency, keep panel depth within desired limits, and provide access to space that would be concealed in two-skin panels of like depth and stiffness. These are called "T-flange" panels and may be made with nominal 1-inch or 2-inch lumber, or both, in various combinations.

Transformed Section

The reader is probably familiar with the transformed section concept. It was mentioned and used in the preceding chapter. To review this, recall that the elastic modulus of plywood differs according to species group and construction. Since these different materials will be used together in stressed-skin panels, the thickness of stringers or the width of skins and T-flanges must be transformed so the designer can consider the entire section to have the same elastic modulus.

Usually, the section is "transformed" to the elastic modulus of the skins. This is useful in computing panel deflection and the tension and compression stresses in the skins. To figure the moment of inertia of a transformed section using plywood of 1,800,000 psi elastic modulus and lumber webs of 1,600,000 psi elastic modulus, the thickness of the lumber web is considered to be reduced in the ratio of 1.6/1.8.

In calculation of rolling shear stress with this transformed section, the rolling shear stress obtained must be reduced in the ratio of 1.6/1.8 since the web thickness and rolling shear area are really larger than the transformed web thickness. Likewise, for shear at the neutral axis, and for bending stress calculated for the transformed section dimensions, the stress obtained is "restored" to its proper value for the real web thickness, with the ratio 1.6/1.8.

Effective Sections

In long panels, butt joints without splices can sometimes be allowed if distributed to low stress areas of the panel. In computing deflections butt joints may be ignored. The length of the reduced section is so small it will not affect elastic behavior.

For bending stress calculations the lumber and plywood veneers with grain parallel to the direction of stress is considered effective in resisting bending moment stresses. Unspliced butt joints render the area they cover ineffective, however. Also, the *effective width of plywood skins must be reduced* when stringer spacing exceeds certain dimensions that have been established. The degree to which the skins are effective will be described in a paragraph on page 261.

The use of splice plates and of scarf joints for beam webs was discussed, along with design information for such joints, in Chapter 17. It is also possible to splice the skins and stringers of stressed-skin panels.

Allowable Deflection

The APA suggests designing floor panels for $\ell/360$ under live load and $\ell/240$ under total load. For roofs they recommend $\ell/240$ for live load and $\ell/180$ for total load. These criteria coincide with those given in Table

39. The inclusion of an allowable deflection for creep depends on the code requirements and the designer's judgment of need. This was discussed in Chapter 8, page 90.

Camber can be built into stressed-skin panels. This possibility is not available in ordinary frame construction, except when glued-laminated beams are used. The recommended camber is 1.5 times dead load deflection. In providing camber, the designer should be very certain that the dead load and the dead load deflection are realistically computed. Ultraconservative design for camber will result in hump-backed panels that never flatten out, which is particularly undesirable in floor structures.

Added camber to provide drainage pitch and prevent ponding (Chapter 9, page 114) may be wanted in roof panels.

Continuous and Cantilevered Spans

Long panels that are continuous over three or more supports, and panels with projecting overhangs are not uncommon. In the case of two-span continuous floor panels, designing to take full credit for the inherent stiffness increase of uniformly loaded two-span continuous formulas over that of single span formulas (a gain of about 2.4 to 1) is not advisable. Floors are rarely actually loaded equally on both spans at one time. Footnote 1 of Table 28 suggests designing for 50% of the live load on one span and 100% on the other. Be sure to consider the reversal of moment over supports of continuous panels and provide adequate skin material on both sides of panels.

When designing cantilevered overhangs, bear in mind that snow loads will remain on overhangs after they have melted from the surfaces over heated spaces. In addition, ice can form on overhangs when snow melt from the interior spans refreezes on the overhangs.

Connections

Design panelized structures for uplift loads and connect adjoining panels to prevent differential deflection of loaded and unloaded panels when concentrated load is a factor. Usually this can be done with suitable nesting edge joint details. Consider also that moisture differential between inner and outer faces of stressed-skin panels can create problems in a finished structure in service. Provide strong anchorage to prevent long panels from lifting off interior supports. This moisture content problem deserves special attention.

To prevent interferences as a result of panel expansion, allow at least 1/16-inch between edges of 4-foot wide panels and 1/4-inch for 20-foot long panels, with proportional expansion spacing for other dimensions. Nailedconnections between panels will permit the yielding necessary to accommodate this come-and-go.

DESIGN OF FLEXURAL PANELS

Flexural panels are usually roof and floor panels. A particular feature of stress-skin panels is the shallow depth of the section compared to framed joist or rafter construction. Deflection criteria are more likely to govern design than strength properties, so a good starting point for design is the deflection consideration.

At the outset, it is necessary to estimate a trial panel section size. This may need to be revised as the design proceeds. Panel cross-sections take the forms generally shown in Figure 107.

The design procedure can be illustrated by an example.

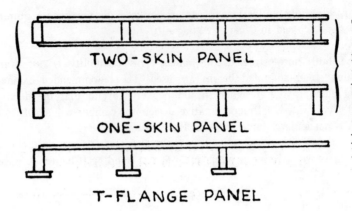

This stringer sometimes increased in thickness to provide adequate rolling shear area and nailing surface for connection.

This stringer sometimes reduced in thickness because stringer in mating panel carries a sizable portion of the load.

Figure 107. Typical Panel Sections.

PROBLEM: Design a floor panel for a 14-foot span.
Live load: 40 PSF Dead Load: 10 PSF
Deflection under live load not to exceed
$\ell/360$. Deflection under total load not
to exceed $\ell/240$.

Note that if the live load deflection is $\ell/360$ at 40 PSF,
total load deflection will be $\frac{50}{40} \cdot \frac{\ell}{360} = \frac{\ell}{288}$

This is less than $\ell/240$. Even allowing one-half of dead load
deflection for creep, the total load deflection of $\frac{55}{40} \cdot \frac{\ell}{360} = \frac{\ell}{260}$

is less than $\ell/240$. The design can be made on the basis of $\ell/360$
at 40 PSF for deflection.

Floor panels often require access underneath for pipes. Wiring can be pulled through two-sided panels with reasonable planning. Piping and underfloor heating ducts are not so easily installed in two-skin panels. Therefore, this design will be for a one-skin panel, arbitrarily without flanges.

References to span-load tables for floor joists indicates that a conventional framed floor for these conditions requires 2" x 8" joists on 16" centers when the E of the joist is 1,500,000 or higher. Also, Table 68 for field glued 5/8" plywood over 2" x 8" joist, 16" on center, will span 13'-7". Since stressed-skin panels with rigid glue should be considerably stiffer than panels made with field applied mastics, it seems likely that 2" x 6" stringers might be assumed for trial.

ASSUMED PANEL MATERIAL:

Lumber: 2" x 6" Hem-fir, No. 1 Structural J&P
E = 1,500,000 psi
F_t = 800 psi F_c = 1,000 psi
F_t = 75 x 1.66 for reduced end split = 125 psi
$F_{c\perp}^v$ = 245 psi

Plywood: 5/8 Group 1, Underlayment, INT,
$E = 1,800,000$ psi $F_b = 1,650$ psi
$F_t = 1,650$ psi $F_c = 1,550$ psi
$F_v = 230$ psi $F_s \cong 48$ psi
$F_{c\perp} = 340$ psi

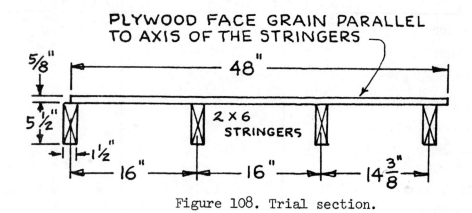

PLYWOOD FACE GRAIN PARALLEL TO AXIS OF THE STRINGERS

Figure 108. Trial section.

Trial Section

The section properties of the trial section must be established. Since the elastic modulus of the plywood and lumber are not the same, the section dimensions must be adjusted or transformed so the entire section can be treated as though all the material in it has the same value of E.

The values of E for plywood and lumber as usually published are based on the assumption that the materials are to be used in flexure about their individual neutral axes. To account for shear deformation, these values have been reduced from their real values in pure tension or compression, by a factor of 1/1.1. Since, in stressed-skin panels, they will not be flexing about their own neutral axes, but about a new neutral axis for the composite section the published E properties should be increased by 10 percent. Therefore:

Plywood E is 1.1 x 1,800,000 = 1,980,000 psi

Lumber E is 1.1 x 1,500,000 = 1,650,000 psi

It is customary to transform the lumber width, the dimension parallel to the neutral axis of the panel, so the design can be carried out using the plywood E. The 1.5-inch dimension of the lumber stringers is transformed to:

$$1.5 \times 1.65/_{1.98} = 1.25\text{-inch}$$

If the spacing between stringers is extremely wide, the plywood skin can distort under stress. Instead of supporting the bending stress, the skins will "dish" toward the neutral axis to escape load. Because of this the portion of the skin between the stringer is limited to the "b-value" or basic spacing of the plywood. Basic spacing varies with plywood thickness. Table 79 gives the basic spacing for various common plywood thicknesses. This applies to panels which are 3 inches or more in thickness. If panels are less than 3 inches thick, the practice is to use one-half of the basic spacing.

This limitation on effective width of plywood between stringers applies only to the determination of section properties *for use in bending stress calculations.* For deflection and shear design calculations, all of the plywood skin is included in the section property calculations. *As a general policy, stringer spacing should never exceed twice the basic spacing.*

Table 79. Basic spacing, b, for Various Plywood Thicknesses.
(For panels 3-inches or thicker. If panels are less than 3-inches
thick basic spacing is 50% of these values.)

Plywood Thickness	Basic Spacing, b, in inches	
	Face Grain // to Stringers	Face Grain ⊥ to Stringers
1/4" Sanded	10.3	11.6
5/16" Sanded	11.9	16.8
3/8" Unsanded (3-ply)	14.2	20.1
3/8" Sanded (3-ply)	16.4	16.4
3/8" Sanded (5-ply)	18.1	20.2
1/2" Unsanded or Sanded (5-ply)	23.2	28.5
5/8" Unsanded or Sanded (5-ply)	29.1	35.6
3/4" Unsanded or Sanded (5-ply or 7-ply)	38.2	38.2
7/8" Unsanded or Sanded	41.6	48.1
1" Unsanded	45.5	58.9
1" Sanded	54.5	47.9
1 1/8" 2-4-1	53.4	57.3

The basic spacing for 5/8" Underlayment, which is a sanded product, is 29.1". This well exceeds the actual spacing of 14.5-inches, so all of the skin is effective for the illustrative example. [If we were using 5/16" Sanded plywood, with a basic spacing of 11.9 inches, we would need to omit 14.5 - 11.9 = 2.6 inches of skin in two of the plywood spans and 12.875 - 11.9 = 0.975 inches from the other, shorter span. This totals 6.175 inches leaving an effective width of skin of 42.825 inches.]

The *location of the neutral axis* of our section is obtained by the conventional area-moment method, using the transformed stringer width.

$$A_{plywood}\left(y_{plywood}\right) + A_{lumber}\left(y_{lumber}\right) = (A_p + A_\ell)\,\bar{y}$$

$\bar{y}$ = distance, neutral axis to top face of panel.

From Table 24, A_p = 2.407 x 4' = 9.628 sq. in.

Transformed A_ℓ = 1.25 x 5.5 x 4 = 27.5 sq. in.

y_p = 0.625/2 = 0.3125 in.

y_ℓ = 0.625 + 5.5/2 = 3.375 in.

$$\bar{y} = \frac{9.628(0.3125) + 27.5(3.375)}{9.628 + 27.5} = 2.58 \text{ in.}$$

The *moment of inertia* of the section is determined by conventional methods using appropriate dimensions as follows:

$$I_g = [I_o + Ax^2]_{plywood} + [I_o + Ax^2]_{lumber}$$

x = distance, neutral axis to center of gravity of skin and of stringer

From Table 24, plywood I_o = 0.133(4) = 0.532 in.^{4}

x for plywood = 2.58 - 0.625/2 = 2.2675 in.

From Table A8, lumber I_o = $20.8\left(\dfrac{1.25}{1.5}\right)$ 4 = 69.4 in.^{4}

x for lumber = 5.5/2 + 0.625 - 2.58 = 0.795 in.

I_g = 0.532 + 9.628 $(2.2675)^2$ + 69.4 + 27.5 $(0.795)^2$ = 136.912 in.^{4}

The *allowable live load based on deflection* is determined from the deflection equation that includes both bending and shear deformation elements of deflection.

Pure bending $\Delta_b = \dfrac{5w\ell^4}{384EI_g}$

Shear deformation $\Delta_s = \dfrac{0.15w\ell^2}{AG}$

A = cross-sectional area of <u>all stringers</u>

G = E/16.6 for Hem-fir (E/10 for Southern pine).

= 119,000 psi

$$\Delta_T = \frac{5}{384} \frac{w\ell^4}{EI_g} + \frac{0.15w\ell^2}{AG} = \frac{\ell}{360}$$

$$w = \frac{1}{360\left[\frac{5\ell^3}{384EI_g} + \frac{0.15\ell}{AG}\right]} \quad \text{all units inches and lbs.}$$

$$w = \frac{1}{360\left[\frac{5(168)^3}{384(1,980,000)136.9} + \frac{0.15(168)}{27.5(119,000)}\right]}$$

$$= \frac{1}{360(0.000227 + 0.0000077)} = 11.84 \text{ lbs./inch (4' width)}$$

$$= 11.84 \times \frac{12}{4} = 35.5 \text{ PSF} < 40 \text{ PSF}$$

This is inadequate for the live load required.

To alter the trial section, consider changing the depth of the stringers or adding a stringer. Adding a 2 x 6 stringer would involve less additional lumber than changing the stringers to 2 x 8's. However, it would involve more adhesive and more fabricating labor. An alternative would be using 2 x 8 stringers and 1/2-inch plywood. Going through the same process of design it will be found that this alternatives gives:

$$A_p = 9.6 \text{ sq. in.} \qquad\qquad I_p = 0.32 \text{ in}^4$$

$$A_\ell = 36.2 \text{ sq. in.} \qquad\qquad I_\ell = 158.3 \text{ in}^4$$

$$\bar{y} = 3.3 \text{ in. from top of panel}$$

$$X_p = 3.05 \qquad\qquad x_\ell = 0.825$$

$$I_g = 272.7 \text{ in}^4$$

The *allowable live load based on deflection* for this new trial section is:

$$w = \cfrac{1}{360\left[\cfrac{5\,(168)^3}{384(1,980,000)272.7} + \cfrac{0.15\,(168)}{36.2(119,000)}\right]}$$

$$= \frac{1}{360(0.000114 + 0.00000583)} = 23.2 \text{ lbs/in (4' width)}$$

$$= 23.2 \times \frac{12}{4} = 69.6 \quad \text{PSF} > 40\text{PSF} \cdot \text{Ok.}$$

(The designer might wish to alter the stringer spacing to perhaps 24-inches, for economy. That has not been done in this example.)

Top Skin Deflection.—In addition to computing the deflection of the whole panel acting as a unit, the designer must also check the deflection of the top skin between stringers. It is usually only necessary to check the deflection, but for unusually heavy loading or wide stringer spacing the bending and shear strengths may also require checking.

For *one-skin panels* with four stringers the skin will act like a 3-span beam with the following equation:

$$\Delta = \frac{w\ell^4}{145EI} \quad \text{all units in inches and lbs.}$$

I for a one-foot wide plywood section, stressed perpendicular to the face grain, from Table 24, is 0.040 in^4

$\ell = 16$ inches

E is the Group I plywood value, 1,800,000 psi, not increased 10 percent, in this case.

$$\Delta = \frac{3.33\,(16)^4}{145(1,800,000)(0.040)} + 0.0208 \text{ inch}$$

$\ell/360 = 0.0444 \gg 0.0208"$ OK.

For *two-skin panels* it is assumed that the skins are uniformly loaded beams with fixed-end conditions for which:

$$\Delta = \frac{w\ell^4}{384EI} \quad \text{with } \ell = \text{distance between stringers}$$

Bending Moment

As mentioned on page 261, for bending stress only, it is sometimes necessary to figure on the reduced section based on the b-distance. In that case a different neutral axis location and section moment of inertia must be calculated. That moment of inertia is designated, I_n. The sample problem used here does not require figuring a new I_n as the spacing of stringers is well within the b-distance.

When non-stress-graded lumber is used for stringers in two-sided panels, the stringers are ignored in bending stress calculations. Stress-graded stringers must be used for one-sided panels. Actually, practically all nominal 2-inch lumber manufactured in the United States today is stress rated. Nominal 1-inch lumber is less often readily available in the stress-rated form, but provisions for stress-rating this size are in the rule books of the principal grading agencies and it can be obtained from some mills on special order.

Allowable stresses for plywood used in stressed-skin panels *must be reduced if the b-distance is exceeded,* according to the graph, Figure 109. This reduction is to insure against effect of skin buckling, and applies to both tension and compression stresses, but not to rolling-shear stresses.

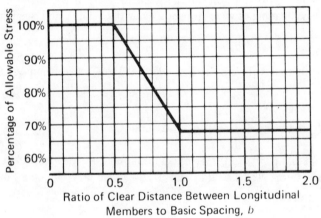

Stress Reduction Factor for Framing Member Spacing

Percentage of Allowable Stress

Ratio of Clear Distance Between Longitudinal Members to Basic Spacing, b

Figure 109.

For the sample problem with 1/2" plywood the ratio is 14.5/23.2 = 0.625, so the reduction factor is 0.916. For plywood, F_c = 0.916 x 1550 = 1425 psi. For lumber, F_t = 800 psi.

Because most stressed skin panels are not symmetrical about their neutral axis, and because the materials at the upper and lower extremes may have different allowable stresses, it is usually necessary to figure stresses at both extremes.

Using the general equation for uniformly distributed load on a simple span:

$$f = \frac{Mc}{I_g} = \frac{w\ell^3}{8} \frac{c}{I_g} \quad \text{all units in lbs. and inches.}$$

w = total load in lbs./inch (4' width)

$$f = \frac{50 \times 4}{12} \cdot \frac{(168)^2 c}{(8)272.7} = 216\ c$$

For top skin, c = 3.3 and f_c = 712 psi $<F_c$ = 1425 psi

For bottom of stringer, c = 4.45 and f_t = 960 psi

Referring back to page 319, since actual stringer width is 1.5 inches.

$F_t = \dfrac{1.25}{1.5}$ x 960 = 800 psi. F_t for the stringer is 800 psi, so the strength of the stringer is adequate.

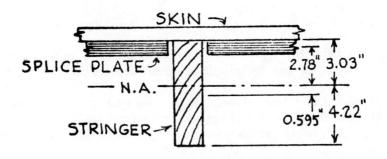

Figure 110. Section of splice plate.

Splice Plate Design

To design the splice between plywood sheets the moment of inertia at the splice plate must be calculated. The splice plate is not continuous across the stringers. Assuming 1/2-inch difference between clear distance between stringers and splice plate width, and no splice plate outside the right hand stringer (Figs. 108 & 110), splice plate widths total 40.375 inches.

A_p = 9.6(40.375)/48 = 8.05 sq. in. I_p = 0.32(40.375)/48 = 0.269 in^4

$\bar{y}$ = $\dfrac{8.05(0.25) + 36.2(7.25/2)}{8.05 + 36.2}$ = 3.03 inches from inner face of skin

x_p = 3.03 - 0.25 = 2.78 inches

x_ℓ = 3.625 - 3.03 = 0.595 inches

I_s = 0.269 + 8.05$(2.78)^2$ + 158.3 + 36.2$(0.595)^2$

= 233.6 in^4

f = $\dfrac{50 \times 4}{12} \cdot \dfrac{(168)^2}{(8)\,233.6} c$ = 251 c

For top skin splice plate with c = 3.03 inches, f_c = 760 psi $<F_c$ = 1425 psi.

For the bottom stringer with c = 4.22 inches, f_t = 1060 psi. This is reduced in the ratio 1.25/1.5, and f_t = 883 psi. As this exceeds the allowable value, it will be necessary to change the stringer specification to a stronger grade and/or species of lumber, or avoid splicing at the location of maximum moment.

The moment the spliced section can carry will be 800/883 = 0.905 of the maximum.

The position where moment is 0.905 of mid-span moment can be obtained determined

$$\frac{w\ell x}{2} - \frac{wx^2}{2} = 0.905 \frac{w\ell^2}{2}$$

Solving this for x gives 0.346. The splice must be at least 0.5 - 0.346 from mid-span. This is 0.154 x 14 = 2.16 feet from the mid-point of the span. By observing this limitation, the panel splice can carry the load.

The splice plate must be 1/2-inch plywood of the same kind as the panel. Its length, by reference to Table 77 must be 14-inches to develop full compression strength of the skin. The required skin compression strength is 760/1550 or 49% of its capacity, so splice plate length can be 0.49 x 14, or 7 inches.

For a two-skin panel, the splice on the tension side would also need to be designed.

Rolling Shear

The allowable shear load on a stressed-skin panel may be limited to the shearing strength of the plywood in the region of the glue bond to the webs, or of the lumber web at the neutral axis. This is explained in Chapter 7. It is necessary to check the shear stress at each of these locations. Shear in the plywood is rolling shear.

The equation for rolling shear is:

$$f_s = VQ/Ib$$

For an unsymmetrical two-skin panel, there are two values of Q, the statical moment of the parallel to span wood fibers of the veneers outside of the plane where stress is being checked. Q for the thicker skin is usually larger than for the thinner skin and it is generally necessary only to compute rolling shear for the thicker skin. Only some experience in designing a variety of panels will enable the designer to know when this is true. Until that experience has been acquired, it is advisable to check rolling shear stress in both skins.

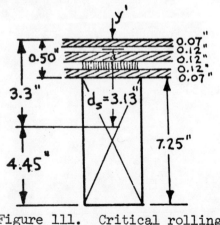

Figure 111.   Critical rolling
shear area.

When the face grain is parallel to the stringers, the critical rolling shear area is in the plane between the inner face veneer and the adjacent cross-bend. It is between the stringer and the face veneer when the face grain is perpendicular to the stringer.

For the sample problem, the critical rolling shear area lies between the inner face veneer and the cross-band. (Vertical shading in Figure 111). The area of veneer parallel to the stringer outside this plane for sanded 1/2-inch veneer can be obtained using dimensions from Table 26. Face veneers are 0.07-in. and the centers and cross-bands are 0.12-inch. For a four-foot panel width, the area of parallel plies outside the critical plane is (0.70 + 0.12) 48 = 9.12 sq. in. The centroid of these two veneers is

$$y' = \frac{0.07(0.07/2) + 0.12(0.19 + 0.12/2)}{0.07 + 0.12} = 0.171 \text{ inch. With the area}$$

and y' known, it is a simple calculation to obtain $Q_s = Ad_s$

$$\text{where } d_s = c - y'$$

This explanation has assumed that Group I underlayment is all of Group 1 species. Actually, it is not. Inner plys may be of other groups. This fact makes it necessary to transform the veneer layers to an equal E basis, a rather tedious task that has been done for us by the APA with results presented in Table 80.

Table 80. Area C.G. of Plys Outside Rolling Shear Plane (A and y' for Computing Q_s) Four Foot Panel Width Basis.

Plywood Thickness (in.)	Structural I, or any Group 4 Panel				All Other Panels			
	Face Grain Parallel		Face Grain Perpendicular		Face Grain Parallel		Face Grain Perpendicular	
	A	y'	A	y'	A	y'	A	y'
Unsanded								
5/16	4.800	0.050	4.800	0.150	4.800	0.050	2.400	0.150
3/8	4.800	.050	6.000	.188	4.800	.050	3.000	.188
1/2	9.600	.150	9.600	.250	7.200	.117	4.800	.250
5/8	13.543	.219	12.000	.312	9.171	.175	6.000	.312
3/4	13.600	.260	18.000	.375	9.200	.205	9.000	.375
Sanded								
1/4	3.360	0.035	4.800	0.120	3.360	0.035	2.400	0.120
3/8	3.360	.035	8.400	.188	3.360	.035	4.200	.188
1/2	9.120	.171	9.600	.250	6.240	.134	4.800	.250
5/8	9.180	.211	11.657	.312	6.270	.164	5.829	.312
3/4	12.144	.281	17.600	.375	7.752	.228	8.800	.375
2-4-1	---	---	---	---	20.553	.476	26.916	.562

The section of this table headed "Structural I or any Group 4 Panel" is for plywood that has all veneers of one species. The values of A and y' computed in the preceding illustration are in this section of Table 80 in the Sanded, 1/2-in., row.

As Group I Underlayment may have other species in the center, the proper values of A and y' are 6.24 sq. in. and 0.134-in. Using these, $d_s = 3.3 - 0.134 = 3.166$-inches.

$$Q_s = 6.24(3.166) = 19.8 \text{ in}^3$$

The shear stress in the critical area above each stringer is:

$$f_s = V Q_s/Ib = \frac{50(4)14}{2} (19.8)/272.7(5.25) = 19.4 \text{ psi}$$

Note: "b" is taken as 3.5 times the full stringer width, since that is the sum of the stringer plywood contact areas.

The *allowable rolling shear stress* Table 25, is 48 psi over interior stringers and 24 psi over edge stringers. They are not exceeded.

Horizontal Shear

For a single skin panel, the simplest way to obtain Q for shear at the neutral axis is to figure it for the stringer area below the axis. The Q is, of course, equal to that which would be obtained by figuring it for the stringer and plywood above the neutral axis. For two-sided panels, consideration of plywood cannot be avoided. Q will be figured both ways for purposes of illustration.

The cross-sectional area of the parallel plys from Table 24 is: 2.4 x 4 = 9.6 sq. in.

The distance from the skin centroid to the neutral axis is: 3.3 - 0.25 = 3.05 inches.

Q for the plywood is: 9.6 x 3.05 = 29.3 in^3

The area of the stringers above the neutral axis (transformed) is: 1.25(2.8)4 = 14.0 sq. in.

The distance of its centroid from the neutral axis is: 2.8/2 = 1.4 in.

Q for the lumber stringers is: 14 x 1.4 = 19.6 in^3

Total Q is: 29.3 + 19.6 = 48.9 in^3

By the alternative method, Q of the stringers below the neutral axis is:

4[1.15 x 4.45 x 4.45/2] = 49.5 in^4

The small difference, 49.5 - 48.9, is the effect of rounding errors in computing.

$$f_v = VQ/Ib = \frac{50(4)14}{2} \ (49.5)/272.7(6.0) = 42.4 \ \text{psi}$$

Note: "b" has been taken as the sum of the untransformed stringer thickness.

The actual shear stress at the neutral axis, 42.4 psi, is well below the *allowable F_v = 125 psi.*

The maximum loads this panel could carry based on the various principal criteria are:

ℓ/360 deflection	69.6 PSF
ℓ/360 skin deflection	85.5 PSF
Bending stress	50 PSF
Rolling shear stress	61.8 PSF
Horizontal shear stress	147 PSF

The 50 PSF, of course, governs the allowable load. A panel with five 2 x 6 stringers and 1/2-inch plywood might be worth investigating. The use of fairly high grade lumber is often more economical than the use of low grades, in engineering panel structures.

The use of nominal 1-inch lumber, which can be secured in stress-rated grades should be considered for stringers and the flanges of T-flange panels. Used on 12-inch center-to-center spacing, thin plywood skins have been shown to produce effective economies in floor and roof constructions.

The design of curved panels and folded plates is described in other literature found in the reference section.

CHAPTER 19

SHEAR WALLS & DIAPHRAGMS

Well built wood structures have a good record of performance under the influence of wind and earthquake forces. Wood itself has great resilience and a high damping capacity. Its ability to sustain short term and shock loads that produce stresses nearby double the normal strength properties is largely responsible for this situation. Additionally, the repetitive nature of principal elements in framed structures distributes load to the stronger members and the average allowable strength properties of commonly used grades of lumber and plywood are usually at least 50 percent above the imposed stresses. Detailed studies made in the aftermath of hurricanes and seismic disasters reveal that resilient wood structures acquit themselves well. Weaknesses which occur generally are in the form of poorly made connections and anchorage. With reasonably conscientious attention to these details, secure structures can be consistently built.

Plywood is an ideal material for shear walls and diaphragms. The proportions of length to breadth of plywood panels produce large moment resistance to forces that rack and twist a structure. To obtain similar results with lumber-sheathed structures requires diagonal alignment of the sheathing boards or the use of well-designed moment resisting bracing as a part of the frame.

Engineering design methods have been developed for plywood-sheathed structures. American Plywood Association's publication, "Plywood Diaphragm Construction," 70-310, presents the basic information for these designs, which are not difficult to master. Engineers in Oregon, California and Washington have given close attention to research and testing on this subject. The recommended practices of the International Conference of Building Officials, described in the Uniform Building Code are basic to the design of earthquake resistant structures, while building officials in Florida, the Gulf Coast and some of the Prairie States, notably Kansas, have developed extensive background on wind and hurricane resistant designs.

This chapter will present design methods suggested by A.P.A. out of a consideration of the work of these many engineers and APA's own research on wood structural diaphragms and shear walls.

A diaphragm is a large flat structure such as a roof deck or a floor system, acting in response to lateral loads. As such, it functions as a thin deep beam in flexure. The two opposing surfaces of a pitched roof, or the curved surface of a roof over bowstring trusses, also act as diaphragms. Steeply pitched gabled roofs are materially strengthened to resist ordinary gravity loads by the diaphragm action of well-designed plywood sheathing. Folded plate roofs are essentially diaphragms acting to resist vertical loads.

Shear walls are designed for definite resistance to racking under the sheathing effect of horizontal loads carried from the top of the walls to the foundations.

Wind forces acting on the vertical projection of a structure, produce both diaphragm and shear wall loads as indicated in Figure 112. The force at the eave line is considered to be the sum of all the forces acting on the roof projection and upon the upper half of the walls. The wind forces on the lower half of the walls is considered to be transmitted directly to the footings at the walls. The eave line forces are carried to the foundation via the shear walls, as a racking load.

In the case of *earthquake forces,* the lateral loading is based upon the dead weight of the structure. For a building of the type shown in Figure 112, the dead weight of all of the structure above the mid-height of the side walls is considered to act at the eave line, and the dead weight below the mid-height is regarded as acting at the footings.

One can visualize seismic action as the effect of a sudden movement of the ground upon which the structure rests. The structure tends to remain at rest while the footings move. This produces an acceleration of the structure with reference to the ground, with lateral forces dependent upon the mass of the structure and the

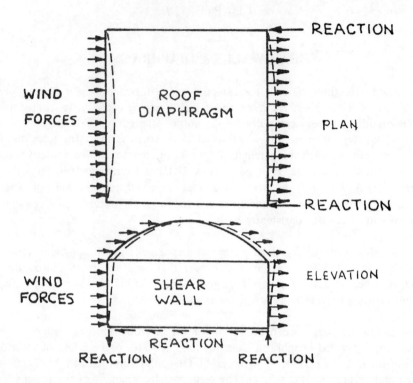

Figure 112. Wind forces acting on a structure.

intensity of the earthquake. For a given earthquake intensity, light structures are subject to lower forces than heavy structures. These relationships are described in Chapter 8. For Zone 3 on the Seismic Zone Map (Figure 23), the lateral load is 0.133 times the weight for this type of structure. For lower seismic intensity, such as Zones 2, 1 or 0, the multipliers for this type of structure are: 0.0665, 0.03325 and 0.0, respectively.

Diaphragm design for either seismic or wind loads follows identical procedure once the loads have been established.

A plywood diaphragm, then, acts like a deep beam, with the plywood skin functioning as a web, resisting shear. The lumber edge members behave like flanges or chords, resisting the compression and tension forces produced by bending.

The shear stresses in the web, according to studies of nailed diaphragm performance, are *not* parabolically distributed from zero at the edges to a maximum at the center, as in a relatively shallow I or box beams. Shear stress is essentially uniform across the depth of the web.

The chords behave as compression and tension members, and are not considered to share these stresses with the webs. This is different from the conception of stress in I and box beams discussed in Chapter 17.

In the design of diaphragams, attention must be given to bearing stiffeners, continuity of both webs and chords, and possible buckling of the webs.

While diaphragms may be constructed with plywood connected only to the supporting rafters, purlins, or floor joists, the inclusion of blocking at plywood panel edges, perpendicular to these members, adds measurably to the load-carrying ability of the diaphragm. Blocking (Figure 113) consists of lightweight nailers, usually 2 x 4's framed between these members. Blocking connects the plywood panels to one another and functions to transfer shear stress between these panels.

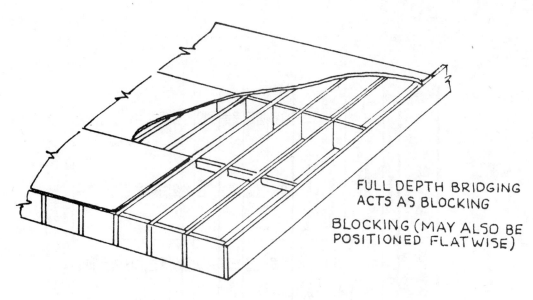

FULL DEPTH BRIDGING
ACTS AS BLOCKING

BLOCKING (MAY ALSO BE
POSITIONED FLATWISE)

Figure 113. Blocking

The load-carrying capacity of unblocked diaphragms is limited by the buckling of panels at the unblocked edges. This means that diaphragm strength cannot be raised by using additional nails in the supporting members, beyond those necessary to sustain the stresses at which buckling becomes a factor.

For a given nail spacing, blocked diaphragms have 1.5 to 2 times the design load capability of unblocked diaphragms. This can be seen by reference to Table 81, for the 6-inch nail spacing loads of blocked and unblocked diaphragms (Cases 2, 3, and 4). Furthermore, allowable shear can be raised effectively to much higher values by closer nail spacing in blocked diaphragm designs.

Since all of the load on a diaphragm must be transferred from the origin of the forces, to the many pieces that constitute the diaphragm structure (joists, rafters, purlins, trusses, stiffeners, panels and chords) and finally via the shear walls to the foundations, the design of all connections is even more important than for structures acting primarily under gravity loads.

The design procedure given here is taken from the A.P.A. publication mentioned on page 273, based on a paper by J. M. Carney, Head, Engineering Service, A.P.A. and presented at the A.S.C.E. Structural Engineering Conference January 31-February 4, 1966.

DESIGN METHOD FOR PLYWOOD DIAPHRAGMS

A conventional frame roof, floor or wall, with only slight modifications, will function as a structural diaphragm. The steps necessary to design a diaphragm are relatively few and uncomplicated.

Plywood panel nailing can be taken from Table 81 for most horizontal applications. Table 82 covers vertical-diaphragm (shear wall) nailing. If design shears are higher than those shown in the table, required nailing may still be calculated by reference to allowable nailing values and appropriate adjustments for time under load, width of framing members, and nail spacing. Other steps are identical for any load level. These steps follow, and will be illustrated and discussed in connection with a design example.

Table 81. **Recommended shear in pounds per foot for horizontal plywood diaphragms for wind or seismic loading** (Plywood and framing assumed already designed for perpendicular loads)

Plywood grade	Common nail size	Minimum nail penetration in framing (in.)	Minimum nominal plywood thickness (in.)	Minimum nominal width of framing member (in.)	Blocked diaphragms — Nail spacing at diaphragm boundaries (all Cases) and continuous panel edges parallel to load (Cases 3 and 4) (a) 6 / Nail spacing at other plywood panel edges (in.) 6	4 / 6	2½ / 4	2 / 3	Unblocked diaphragms — Nails spaced 6" max. at supported edges (a) Load perpendicular to unblocked edges and continuous panel joints (Case 1)	All other configurations (Cases 2, 3 & 4)
STRUCTURAL I C-D INT-DFPA or C-C EXT-DFPA	6d	1-1/4	5/16	2	185	250	375	420	165	125
				3	210	280	420	475	185	140
	8d	1-1/2	3/8	2	270	360	530	600	240	180
				3	300	400	600	675	265	200
	10d	1-5/8	1/2	2	320	425	640(b)	730(b)	285	215
				3	360	480	720	820	320	240
C-C EXT-DFPA, STANDARD C-D INT-DFPA sheathing, and other DFPA grades except Species Group 5	6d	1-1/4	5/16	2	170	225	335	380	150	110
				3	190	250	380	430	170	125
	6d	1-1/4	3/8	2	185	250	375	420	165	125
				3	210	280	420	475	185	140
	8d	1-1/2	3/8	2	240	320	480	545	215	160
				3	270	360	540	610	240	180
	8d	1-1/2	1/2	2	270	360	530	600	240	180
				3	300	400	600	675	265	200
	10d	1-5/8	1/2	2	290	385	575(b)	655(b)	255	190
				3	325	430	650	735	290	215
	10d	1-5/8	5/8	2	320	425	640(b)	730(b)	285	215
				3	360	480	720	820	320	240

(a) Space nails 12 in. on center along intermediate framing members.
(b) Reduce tabulated allowable shears 10 percent when boundary members consist of a single 2" lumber piece.
(c) All recommendations based on the use of DFPA grade-trademarked plywood.
(d) When installing roof panels, leave ⅛" spacing between panel ends and ¼" between panel edges. Where wet or humid conditions prevail, double these spacings.

Table 81. (continued)

Notes: Design for diaphragm stresses depends on direction of continuous panel joints with reference to load, not on direction of long dimensions of a plywood sheet. Continuous framing may be in either direction for blocked diaphragms.

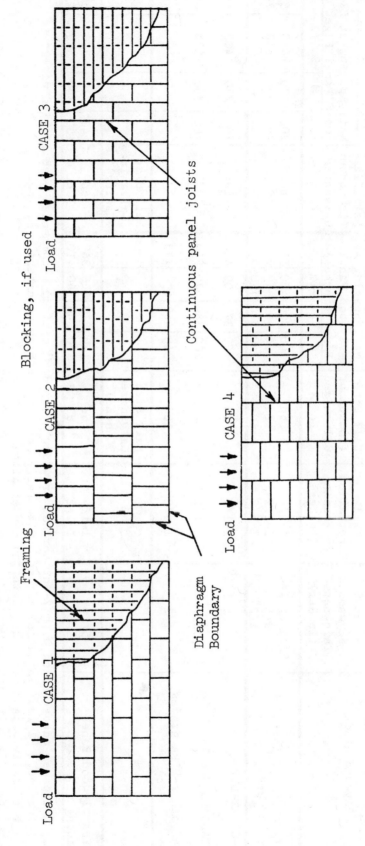

Courtesy of American Plywood Assn.

Table 82. Recommended Shear in Pounds Per Foot for Plywood Shear Walls for wind or seismic loading (a).

Plywood Grade	Minimum Nominal Plywood Thickness (inches)	Minimum Nail Penetration in Framing (inches)	PLYWOOD APPLIED DIRECT TO FRAMING						PLYWOOD APPLIED OVER 1/2" GYPSUM SHEATHING					
			Nail Size (Common or Galvanized Box)	Nail Spacing at Plywood Panel Edges (inches)					Nail Size (Common or Galvanized Box)	Nail Spacing at Plywood Panel Edges			
				6	4	2-1/2	2			6	4	2 1/2	2
STRUCTURAL I INT-DFPA or EXT-DFPA	5/16 or 1/4	1-1/4	6d	200	300	450	510		8d	200	300	450	510
	3/8	1-1/2	8d	280	430	640	730		10d	280	430	640	730
	1/2	1-5/8	10d	340	510	770	870		-	-	-	-	-
C-C EXT-DFPA	5/16 or 1/4[b]	1-1/4	6d	180	270	400	450		8d	180	270	400	450
STANDARD C-D INT-DFPA	3/8	1-1/2	8d	260	380	570	640		10d	260	380	570	640
and other DFPA grades (c)	1/2	1-5/8	10d	310	460	690	770		-	-	-	-	-
			Nail Size (Galvanized Casing)						Nail Size (Galvanized Casing)				
DFPA Plywood Panel Siding (c)	5/16[b]	1-1/4	6d	140	210	320	360		8d	140	210	320	360
	3/8	1-1/2	8d	160	240	360	410		10d	160	240	360	410

(a) All panel edges backed with 2-in. nominal or wider framing. Plywood installed either horizontally or vertically. Space nails at 12 in. on center along intermediate framing members.

(b) 3/8" minimum recommended when applied direct to framing as exterior siding.

(c) Except Group 5 species.

Steps in Plywood Diaphragm Design

1. Calculate loads applied to diaphragm.

2. Calculate diaphragm shears.

3. Determine plywood panel layout.

4. Find plywood nailing schedule from appropriate table (or calculate).

5. Determine required chord size.

6. Check deflection.

7. Check anchorages at edges, particularly hold-down at bases of shear walls.

Design Assumptions

The following design example assumes that size and spacing of framing members, and plywood sheathing thickness, have already been designed to resist gravity loads, and that location of supports, such as shear walls, has been chosen to comply with permissible length-width ratios. (The U.B.C., specifies maximum diaphragm dimension ratios for plywood nailed at all edges to span/width of 4 for horizontal diaphragms and 3.5 for vertical diaphragms. For plywood diaphragms with blocking omitted, the ratios are 4 for horizontal diaphragms and 2 for vertical diaphragms.) The example also assumes that wind uplift design has been, or will be performed.

DESIGN EXAMPLE

Calculate roof and wall diaphragms for the wood-framed warehouse in Figure 114.

Note that although the diaphragm is not actually flat, it is still capable of resisting shears. As in any "beam", adequate web stiffeners are required. Thus, the bowstring trusses must be sufficiently stiff (or braced) to function as compression stiffeners.

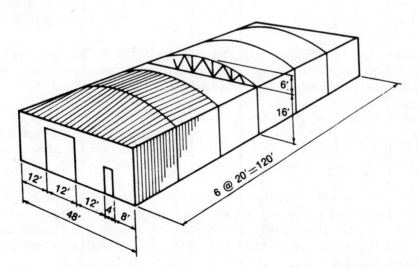

Courtesy of American Plywood Assn.

Figure 114.

Assume the warehouse is in a hurricane area, with Zone 0 seismic probability. Lateral load design, in that case, must consider wind load but need not consider earthquake forces. Design wind pressure is 25 psf.

In this building, roof joists on trusses are Douglas fir 2 x 12's, spaced 24 inches on center and solidly blocked at their ends (Figs. 115, 116 and 117). End-bay joists are sloped down from the truss to the end wall (Figs. 117, 118). Wall studs are 2 x 8's spaced 16 inches on center. All rod, knee, and diagonal bracing, except vertical X-bracing between trusses, is eliminated because of the diaphragm action of the plywood roof and wall sheathing.

Roof

1.   Calculate loads applied to diaphragms.

Wind loads are calculated from design wind pressure on "tributary" areas. Thus, loads to a roof diaphragm for a single story building may most simply be considered to come from the top half of the windward wall. (When considering connections, it must be remembered that, actually, part of this load comes in as suction on the top half of the leeward wall.) Note that though wind can blow from any direction, it is evident from inspection that *in this building*, wind on the long wall will produce the highest stresses.

$$\text{Wind force at eave line on horizontal projection of side.} = 25 \text{ psf} \left(\underset{\text{from wall}}{6' + \overset{\text{from roof}}{\frac{16'}{2}}} \right) = 350 \text{ lbs. per ft. of building length}$$

2.   Calculate diaphragm shears.

Maximum total shear at each wall $= 350 \text{ lbs. per ft.} \left(\frac{120'}{2} \right) = 21{,}000 \text{ lbs.}$

Maximum unit shear in roof sheathing $= \frac{21{,}000 \text{ lbs.}}{48 \text{ ft.}} = 438 \text{ plf}$

3.   Determine plywood panel layout

The various Cases shown below Table 81 are simply illustrations of the rule expressed in the note on that table. Design for diaphragm stresses in all diaphragms depends on direction of continuous panel joints with reference to load. In *unblocked* diaphragms, the direction of unblocked edges is also significant.

Observation of building shape and allowable load figures from Table 81, indicates that 3/8-inch Structural I plywood, with face grain perpendicular to joists, can easily carry the panel shears, if blocked and that it will be best for continuous panel joints to run in the long direction of the building. Since framing and continuous panel joints are in the same direction, this layout is classed as Case 2 in Table 81.

Three-eighths inch plywood with its face grain perpendicular to joists will adequately carry vertical load, but requires blocking at 4-foot centers. (Figure 115) An alternate would be use of 1/2-inch plywood with its face grain parallel to the joists, requiring blocking only at panel ends (8-foot centers). An analysis of blocking and labor costs for Alternate 1 (Figure 115) versus Alternate 2 (Figure 116) will indicate which is desirable. Note that either layout is Case 2, Table 81.

4.   Find plywood nailing schedule.

Table 81 lists allowable loads for a number of different combinations of nailing; plywood species and thickness; and framing lumber width; as well as for both blocked and unblocked diaphragms. As an example of

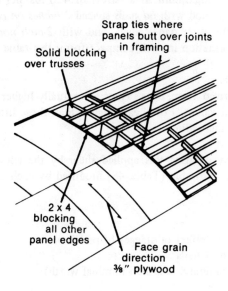

Figure 115.   **Panel Layout Alternate 1.**

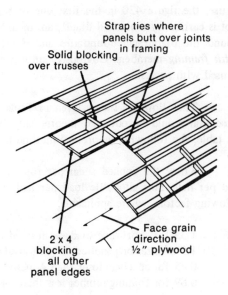

Figure 116.   **Panel Layout Alternate 2**

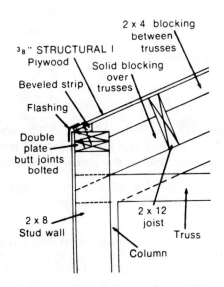

Figure 117.   **Chord Detail at Side Wall.**

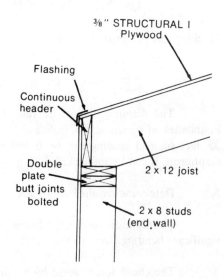

Figure 118.   **Chord Detail at End Wall.**

its use, the figure 420 in the first line of the table signifies that a maximum shear stress of 420 lbs. per lineal foot is carried by a blocked diaphgram of 5/16-inch Structural I plywood with *6d* nails spaced *2 inches on center* around the diaphragm boundaries and *3 inches on center* on the other panel edges, and with *2-inch nominal width framing* members. Obviously, since it contains so much information in such compact form, this table must be used with precision.

The allowable shears given in Table 81 have all been derived from tests. They are actually higher than those that would be obtained theoretically from the standard nail values. For shears higher than those listed in the table, the following theoretical method may be used to determine nailing.

Know the applied shear per foot, find the nail spacing by dividing this applied shear by the allowable load per nail. This allowable load per nail is equal to the normal allowable (Table 48) modified by each of the following factors, where applicable.

    1.33 for short-time load, as in wind or earthquake
    1.5 at interior panel edges (not at diaphragm boundaries) for effect of stagger of panels
    0.85 for spacing closer than 4-inches on center *in each* line of nails
    0.89 for framing lumber less than 3-inch nominal width (minimum is 2-inch nominal width)

Screwed cleats may be designed by a similar procedure for use in place of blocking, figuring load in pounds per joist space and dividing by allowable load per screw, to arrive at the required number of screws each side of the cleat.

Returning to the example, interpolation in Table 81 indicates that nailing at 3.5 inches and 5 inches will carry the 438 plf maximum shears in the diaphragm under consideration, using 3/8-inch Structural I plywood and *8d* nails.

Nail spacing could be increased to 6 inches at both panel edges where the shear becomes 270 plf or less. Since shear varies linearly along the span from zero at the center to a maximum at the ends, this point occurs at

$$\frac{270}{438} \times 60 = 37 \text{ feet from the center}$$

Blocking can be omitted where shear is 180 plf and less, occurring at a point:

$$\frac{180}{438} \times 60 = 25 \text{ feet from center}$$

The diaphragm must be fully blocked for 35 feet in from each end with nails spaced 3.5 inches at boundaries of panels and 5 inches on intermediate members for 23 feet in from each end. Between 23 feet and 35 feet in, nail spacing can be 6 inches at boundaries and intermediates, and in the central 50 feet of the diaphragm, it can be unblocked with 6-inch nail spacing.

5.   Determine required chord size

Chords must resist axial forces only, since the action of plywood panels in resisting shear does not apply significant bending stress to the chords.

The chord force caused by bending moment in the roof diaphragm is

$$\frac{\text{Moment}}{\text{depth } b} = \frac{w\ell^2}{8b} = \frac{350 \text{ plf } (120 \text{ ft})^2}{8 (48 \text{ ft})} = 13,100 \text{ lbs.}$$

Top plate for the wall is a double 2 x 8. If this is bolted together with butt joints staggered, one 2 x 8 less bolt hole area, will constitute the net section. A one-inch bolt in single shear in Douglas fir may be loaded to 1895 lbs. x 1.333 = 2520 lbs. Six 1-inch bolts at mid-span with fewer bolts at joints closer to ends will form adequate chord connections. If bolts are in two rows and staggered at least four diameters, net section of the 2 x 8 will be 9.4 sq. in. Required allowable stress is 13,100/9.4 = 1410 psi. No. 1 Structural J&P Douglas fir, F_t = 1000 psi, F_c = 1250 psi, with the one-third short-term load increase will be adequate if MC15 lumber is specified. (1.333 x 1.08 x 1000 = 1440 psi)

6.   Check deflection.

Codes do not usually require deflection calculations if diaphragm length/width ratios are restricted to the values specified by the code (see page 279.) In this example roof length width ratio (2.5) is less than the maximum of 4 specified for blocked or unblocked horizontal diaphragms. Deflection will be computed, however, to illustrate the method.

Maximum lateral deflection at the center of the long wall of the building, caused by a hurricane design load of 25 psf, assuming all panels blocked can be calculated from the formula:

$$d = \frac{5vL^3}{8EAb} + \frac{vL}{4Gt} + 0.094 \, Le_n + \frac{\Delta_c X}{2b}$$

where d =   deflection, inches

v =   shear, plf

L =   diaphragm length, feet

b =   diaphragm width, feet

A =   area of chord cross-section, sq. in.

E =   elastic modulus of chords, psi

G =   shearing modulus of the webs, psi. (From tests, G may be taken as E/20 for panels with exterior glue. Reduce 9 percent for beams where equilibrium moisture content in service will be 16 percent or higher. For example, G for Structural I plywood in a dry location is 90,000 psi.)

t =   effective plywood thickness for shear, in.

e_n =   nail deformation from Figure 116 at calculated load per nail, based on shear per foot divided by number of nails per foot.

$(\Delta_c X)$ =   sum of individual chord-splice slip values, each multiplied by its distance to nearest support.

The first part of this equation comes from the simple bending deflection; the second fraction represents the shear deflection; the third gives deflection due to nail slip; and the fourth yields deflection due to slip in chord splices. In case end-wall deflection is significant, it should be added.

In the example, assume 20-foot chord units. Assume splice design such that there might be 1/16-inch slip in each of five splices.

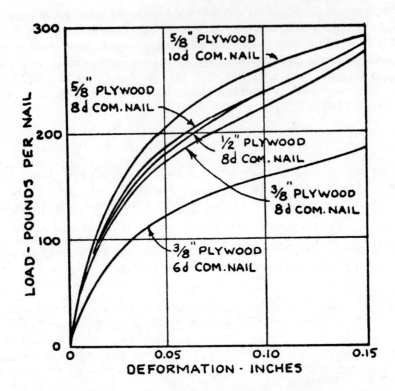

Douglas fir or Southern Pine lumber; green
when nailed; tested after seasoning to 13%
moisture content; average sp. gr. = 0.48

Figure 119. Lateral bearing strength of
plywood joints.

Courtesy American Plywood Association

$$\frac{5vL^3}{8EAb} = \frac{5(438)(120)^3}{8(1,800,000 \times 1.1)\,(21.76)(48)} = 0.229 \text{ in.}$$

$$\frac{vL}{4Gt} = \frac{438(120)}{4(90,000 \times 1.1)(0.375)} = 0.354 \text{ in.}$$

$$0.094 \, Le_n = 0.094\,(120)(0.0025) = 0.282 \text{ in.}$$

$$\frac{(\Delta_c X)}{2b} = \frac{2(.0625)20 + 2(.0625)40 + 0.0625(60)}{2(48)} = 0.117 \text{ in.}$$

For a total deflection of:

$$d = 0.229 + 0.354 + 0.282 + 0.117 = 0.982 \text{ inch}$$

[NOTE: The diaphragm in this example has all panel edges blocked where this is necessary to develop the shear
values required. APA does not suggest a deflection equation for a diaphragm without blocking. Presumably, the
deflection of the diaphragm without blocking would be somewhat larger, probably affecting the second term of
the equation, the shear deflection. With over half of this diaphragm blocked, and the unblocked edges half the

length of the blocked edges, an increase of less than 25% of the second term seems likely. An estimate of d for this example diaphragm would be 1.071 inch. (This note inserted by author, not by A.P.A.)]

The above deflection calculation illustrates that although a diaphragm does behave in a manner *analogous* to a beam, the engineer must consider the differences as well as the similarities. Shear deflection and connector slip are the major differences.

The wood-framed wall, 16-foot high, can easily tolerate a total deflection at its top equal to 0.982 (or 1.071) inch. (Masonry block walls are permitted to deflect 1/16-inch per foot of height.) To use this roof diaphragm with a masonry wall having a smaller allowable deflection, the most effective measures for stiffening would be to increase plywood thickness and/or nailing, or to use an additional shear wall somewhere within the building. Increase in plywood thickness can be accompanied by an increase in joist size and spacing, if the vertical load remains the same. A possibility to consider would be 1/2-inch plywood over 3 x 12 joists on 32-inch centers. Such a combination would require less erection time than the original 3/8-inch plywood over joists on 24-inch centers. Board footage of joists would be the same in either case.

7.   Anchorages

Anchorages for roof diaphragms in wood construction seldom present a problem. They require only that the shear stresses from the plywood be transferred to the chord members, which may not be in the plane of the sheathing itself. For this particular building, only a beveled strip will be required at the long edges of the building. (See Fig. 117) At the ends, a continuous header may be used to transfer loads to the doubled plate, as in Figure 118. In many cases, such as where an overhang is desired, cut-in blocking will accomplish the same result.

For masonry walls, the perimeter detail for the roof could be handled in either of two ways. Chords could be of lumber, bolted to the masonry walls; or the plywood web could be attached to a bond beam at the top of the wall. The bond beam would then have to function as the chord. Because of the ease of nailing plywood to a lumber chord, and of bolting this chord to the masonry, lumber chords are standard.

DESIGN METHOD FOR SHEAR WALL

Walls with openings may be designed as rigid bents by using statically indeterminate analysis, where required. In order to simplify, in the case illustrated, calculate loads on the end wall assuming it functions as three separate shear walls; 12-foot, 12-foot, and 8-foot wide, respectively. (See. Fig. 114.)

1. and 2.   Forces and shears

Tests and analysis indicate that shear walls carry load in direct proportion to their width (even when varying in height).

$$\text{End wall shear} = \frac{21,000 \text{ lbs}}{12 \text{ ft} + 12 \text{ ft} + 8 \text{ ft}} = 656 \text{ plf}$$

3.   Panel layout

Detailing must be executed so that the three portions of the end wall shown in Figure 114 will act as separate shear walls. In other words, doubled verticals must be carried full height and "filler panels" (over doors) nailed less heavily than "shear wall" panels.

4.   Plywood nailing

Table 82 shows that with 3/8-inch Structural I plywood sheathing-siding, nailing at plywood boundaries must be 8d galvanized box nails at 2 1/4 inches. Since a shear wall acts essentially as a cantilever loaded at its top end, shears and nailing are not reduced toward the center as in a roof diaphragm.

5.   Chord size

Each individual shear wall must be designed separately. Ordinarily building corners will use at least three members. Framing around wall openings, however, would normally require only a doubled member, and would therefore control design.

For the 8-foot wide wall, maximum chord force is:

$$Ph/b = \frac{656 \text{ plf x 8 ft x 16 ft}}{8 \text{ ft}} = 10,500 \text{ lbs.}$$

P = load at top, lb.
h = wall height, ft.
b = width of shear wall, ft.

For the 12-foot wide wall, maximum chord force is:

$$Ph/b = \frac{656 \text{ plf x 12 ft x 16 ft}}{12 \text{ ft}} = 10,500 \text{ lbs.}$$

[NOTE: In this particular example, wall heights are uniform, and chord requirements are alike. With a curved or gabled end wall panel top, the chord requirements could vary.]

A 2 x 8, area being 10.9 sq. in., must be of a grade with tension and compression allowable stress of 10,500/10.9 = 960 psi. With the one-third short-term load increase, No. 2 Structural Joist and Plank of Douglas fir has F_t = 825 x 1.33 = 1100 psi; and F_c = 1050 x 1.33 = 1400 psi. The grade is adequate if at least one 2 x 8 at each chord is full length lumber. The compression chord should be checked for buckling in the 7.25-wide direction.

$$F'_c = \frac{0.3E}{(\ell/d)^2} = \frac{0.3 \text{ x } 1,700,000}{(26.5)^2} = 725 \text{ psi}$$

Increased for wind load to 725 x 1.33 = 965 psi.

This stress grade will be adequate, in fact with doubled chords, even if one is jointed, it will provide considerable reserve.

6.   Deflection

If height width ratio is one or greater, the deflection should be calculated. The formula for deflection at the top of a wall is:

$$d = \frac{8vh^3}{EAb} + \frac{vh}{Gt} + 0.376he_n + da$$

where v = shear load at top of wall, plf
        h = wall height, feet
        b = wall width, feet
       da = deflection due to anchorage details (rotation and
              slip at tie-down bolts

Other symbols as for diaphragm deflection formula.

For 8-foot wall: $e_n = 0.025$ based on 2 1/4-in. nail spacing

da is estimated at 1/8 inch.

$$d = \frac{8(656)(16)^3}{(1,700,000 \times 1.1)(21.76)(8)} + \frac{656(16)}{(85,000 \times 1.1)(0.375)} + 0.376(16)0.025 + 0.125$$

$$= 0.066 + 0.299 + 0.151 + 0.125 = 0.641\text{-inch}$$

For 12-foot wall: d = 0.619-inch

Since these end wall sections are tied together, they must deflect together. It is estimated that the deflection would be:

$$\frac{24}{32}(0.619) + \frac{8}{32}(0.641) = 0.623\text{-inch}$$

7.   Anchorages

A force of 10,500 lbs. must be resisted at each edge of each opening, and at the corners. A steel bracket can handle this load. It should be connected to the doubled lumber chord members with the 1-inch-diameter bolts, and anchored to the foundation with one 1-inch-diameter bolt. The shear force along the bottom 3 x 8 sill in this 8-foot panel will be resisted by five 5/8-inch diameter bolts. In the 12-foot panels, place 5/8-inch bolts on 18-inch centers, well anchored to concrete footings.

Side Walls

Calculation of wind on the end wall shows that shear along the side walls is so low (70 plf) that even the minimum nailing for 3/8-inch plywood will be more than ample, i.e., 8d nails 6-inches on centers.

DESIGN CONCLUSION

The building just designed is now adequate to withstand the horizontal forces of hurricanes, using essentially the same materials as would have been required for the least expensive construction satisfactory for vertical loads only. The only additions are some nails and additional foundation bolting along the ends. Uplift wind forces do not affect diaphragm design, although they must also be considered for proper anchorage. Thus, the engineer has been able to supply his client with a hurricane-resistant building at the cost of additional fasteners, application labor, and a few hours of professional time.

OTHER MATERIALS FOR DIAPHRAGMS AND SHEAR WALLS

Although plywood has virtually displaced lumber for roof and wall sheathing, *lumber* can be used for constructing diaphragms. The sheathing boards are laid diagonally to joists, studs, or rafters at a 45-degree angle. Design methods for lumber diaphragms have not been developed as well as those for plywood. U.B.C. describes minimum nailing requirements and other detail (1970 U.B.C. Vol. I, Section 2514). The designer must analyze the stresses and determine chord and sheathing size requirements. Maximum shears for diagonally sheathed lumber diaphragms are 300 plf per U.B.C. for single sheathing. Two layers of lumber sheathing placed diagonally at 45 degrees to stringers, and at 90 degrees to one another may be designed for shears up to 600 plf.

Diaphragm dimension ratios for horizontal diagonally sheathed lumber diaphragms are limited to 3 for single layer and 4 for double layer sheathing. For vertical diaphragms, i.e., shear walls, the ratios are 2 for single layer and 3.5 for double layer.

Fiberboard sheathed diaphragms are permitted by the U.B.C. for vertical diaphragms. Panels are 4' x 8' over nominal 2-inch wood studs not more than 16-inches on center. Blocking of all horizontal joints is required. Nailing is 3-inches on center, and 3/8" from edges of panels. Height-width ratio must not exceed 1.5. Nailing and allowable shears are given in Table 83..

Table 83.   Allowable Shears for Wind or Seismic Loading on Vertical Diaphragms of Fiberboard Sheathing Board Construction.[1]

Fiberboard Panels	Nail Size	Shear Value 3-inch Nail Spacing Around Perimeter and 6-inch at Intermediate Points
7/16" x 4' x 8'	11 gage galv. roofing nail, 1 1/2" long, 7/16" head	125 plf
1/2" x 4' x 8'		175 plf
25/32" x 4' x 8'	11 gage galv. roofing nail, 1 3/4" long, 7/16" head	175 plf
[1] May not be used to brace concrete or masonry walls.		

By permission of APA.

CHAPTER 20

DESIGN OF LUMBER DECKS

The use of lumber for floor and roof decks supported by beams and stringers is fairly common for spans of four feet and longer. In bridge structures with heavy moving concentrated loads, it is often used on shorter spans. Heavy wood decking is a common material for railroad car floors also.

Spans greater than four feet are generally beyond the capacity of plywood, even in the 1 1/8-inch thickness. Lumber decking has been used effectively for walls and partitions.

Solid Sawn Decking

Sawn decking is basically nominal 2, 3 and 4-inch in thickness. Widths are nominal 6 through 12-inches. Widths of 6-inch and 8-inch are most common. Decking of greater width should be exceptionally well-seasoned, otherwise the shrinkage after installation will open gaps that harm the effectiveness of the tongues and grooves as well as the general appearance for exposed applications. Differential moisture conditions on opposite sides of wide deck can induce a cupping effect that may be objectionable.

Decking grades are described in Chapter 4 where it is mentioned that standard practice is to season decking to 15 percent maximum moisture content. Higher moisture content decking is often unsatisfactory in dry service, so many manufacturers have adopted this practice. The design properties of decking are mentioned in Chapter 4, and listed in Table A7 of the appendices. Strength and elastic modulus adjustment factors are given in Table 15, Chapter 5, for use at moisture equilibriums above 15 percent.

Two-inch, Sawn, T&G Heavy Timber Decking is generally purchased *random length* for large jobs continuous over several spans. It is put in place with the abutting ends of pieces randomly located. Even though this is called "random," certain limitations are placed on end joint location to insure that an excessive concentration of such abutting ends in any localized area will not occur. These rules are simple and not difficult to follow. Contractors accustomed to building wood decks become acquainted with these rules. They provide that:

(a)   The end-joints in adjacent courses must be at least 2-feet apart.

(b)   The end-joints in every second course may not be closer than 6-inches in the direction of the span.

(c)   End-joints that are within 6-inches of alignment perpendicular to the span must be separated by at least two courses without end-joints in that area.

(d)   All pieces must rest on at least one support (no floaters).

(e)   If the decking used is predominantly short lengths special attention must be given to providing a continuous tie between the beams at intervals of six or seven courses.

(f)   All pieces must be nailed to all supports which they cross. Nailing shall be designed for forces anticipated. Provision should be made for expansion due to wetting if that is a factor. On pitched roofs, install with tongue edge up.

Table 84. Nominal Two and Three-inch, Sawn Deck, Single T & G.

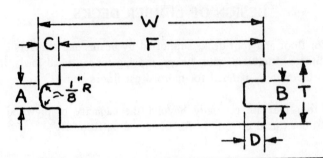

	Nominal 2-in.		Nominal 3-in.	
	Seasoned (in.)	Unseasoned (in.)	Seasoned (in.)	Unseasoned (in.)
Thickness, T	1 1/2	1 9/16	2 1/2	2 9/16
Overall width W	5 3/8 7 1/8 9 1/8	5 1/2 7 3/8 9 3/8	widths same as for nominal 2"	
Face width, F	5 6 3/4 8 3/4 10 3/4	5 1/8 7 9 11	widths same as for nominal 2"	
A B C D	7/16 1/2 3/8 7/16	7/16 1/2 3/8 7/16	3/4 13/16 3/8 7/16	3/4 13/16 3/8 7/16

Tongues and grooves are centered with respect to thickness of the deck.

A chamfer of 1/4" x 1/4" is a standard V-joint pattern which may be specified on one face.

Striated-face with 1/8" wide x 1/4" deep sawn grooves equally spaced at intervals specified, may be obtained.

Decking may be end-matched, i.e., have T & G ends; or slotted for metal splices.

When the deck system involves less than four support beams, the random arrangement of end joints for decks with loads and deflections calculated by the formulas given in this Chapter is not recommended. Instead full length decking to span two or three supports should be specified.

Minimum length of pieces should not be less than 75 percent of span. Despite the presence of end joints, the deflection of random length decks is less than that for simple span decks without joints between supports.

Two-inch decking is usually secured with at least two nails (three for nominal 6" or wider deck) with one nail driven slant-wise just above the tongue. This nail is driven first and draws the adjacent courses together.

The first two courses on each edge of a deck should contain lengths such that the joints can be distributed to positively fix the beam spacing. The two courses at the bottom of Figure 120 satisfy this condition.

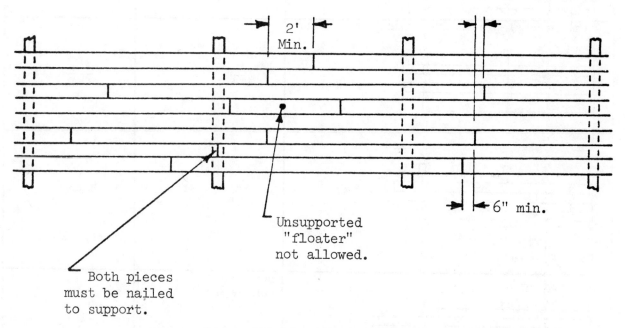

Figure 120.   Illustration of "random length rule" for 2" sawn decking.

Other end joint arrangements are given in Table 85, together with stress and deflection formulas for design. Theoretically, perfectly abutted offset end joints and perfectly fitting tongues and grooves would make decks that would deflect exactly like unjointed decks. This is unrealistic, and the deflection formulas in Table 85 for the last three decks were developed from tests. The deflection for the first two arrangements follow theory and both deflection and stress equations are mathematically derived.

Bending stress formulas for the last three end-joint types in Table 85, are theoretically derived with the reduction in cross-section due to end joints taken into consideration.

Table 85. Design Formulas for Decking.

TYPE	DEFLECTION	BENDING STRESS
Simple Span	inches $$\frac{5w\ell^4}{384EI}$$	psi $$\frac{w\ell^2 c}{8I}$$
Two-span, continuous	$$\frac{w\ell^4}{185EI}$$	$$\frac{w\ell^2 c}{8I}$$
Combined, simple and two-span, continuous	$$\frac{w\ell^4}{109EI}$$	$$\frac{w\ell^2 c}{8I}$$
Cantilevered pieces intermixed	$$\frac{w\ell^4}{105EI}$$	$$\frac{w\ell^2 c}{6.66I}$$
Random Rule:	Nom. 2 & 3-inch Center matched: $$\frac{w\ell^4}{100EI}$$ Nom. 3 & 4-inch Double T & G, Horizontal Spiked: $$\frac{w\ell^4}{116EI}$$ All glu-lam sizes Slant nailed courses $$\frac{w\ell^4}{130EI}$$	$$\frac{w\ell^2 c}{6.66I}$$

In the Cantilevered pieces intermixed diagram: $\frac{\ell}{3}$ to $\frac{\ell}{4}$

ℓ = span in inches
c = half deck thickness, inches
I = moment of inertia of a one-foot wide section of deck, in.^{4}
w = maximum load, lbs. per lineal inch of deck

The combined simple and two-span continuous stress equation has been developed analytically. The derivation shows moments of $w\ell^2/10.5$ at a point 0.48ℓ from the end support, and $w\ell^2/16$ at the interior support. At the 0.48ℓ position there are no joints and the stress is $w\ell^2 c/10.5I$, whereas at the interior support there is a joint and all the moment must be carried by half the cross section of deck present elsewhere in the system. At the interior support, where the derived moment is $w\ell^2/16$ and moment of inertia is the full deck $I \div 2$, bending stress is $w\ell^2 c/8I$. A similar analysis for any interior span shows maximum stress occurring over the supports with a value $w\ell^2/8I$.

Design properties for decking given in Table A7 include a stress increase for repetitive member arrangement. The stress can, of course, be further increased for the usual duration of load effects. Allowable stress for decking can also be increased for depth effect; by 10 percent for nominal 2-inch, 4 percent for nominal 3-inch, with no increase for nominal 4-inch.

Shear stress in decking is rarely critical. It can be computed with the conventional formulas for shear stress in flexural members. Moisture content adjustments for MC-15 decking used above 15% M.C. are 0.79 for bending stress and 0.92 for E. For decking manufactured either dry or green, the usual property adjustments for wet use would apply.

Three and Four-inch, Sawn, T&G, Heavy Timber Decking.—These heavier decking sizes are commonly purchased random length and installed with certain limitations on location of abutting ends. This is described in detail in AITC Timber Construction Standard 112-65, found in the Timber Construction Manual. It places the following limits on end joints:

(a)   All pieces shall be nailed to at least one support.

(b)   Minimum distance between end-joints in adjacent courses is four feet.

(c)   Minimum longitudinal distance between joints in every second course shall be six inches.

(d)   End joints that are within six inches of one another, measured longitudinally, must be separated laterally by two courses without end joints in that area.

(e)   For 3-inch decking the mixture of lengths must be 40% or more to be 14 ft. or longer, with a minimum of 10% less than 10 ft., and no "floaters." For 4-inch decking, the mixture must be 25% or more to be 16 ft. or longer, 50% or more to be 14 ft. and longer, not more than 10% in the 5 to 10 ft. range, and no "floaters." A maximum of 1% of pieces may be in the 4 to 5 ft. range for both sizes. These percentages are percentages of the total board foot measure of the material in the deck.

To compute deflections, spans, loads, sizes or required elastic modulus, use the formulas in Table 85. The random length formula for deflection of 3-inch and 4-inch decking gives less deflection than the one for 2-inch decking. This is due to the improved T&G, the dryness required for this thicker decking, and the fact that the courses of 3-inch and 4-inch decking are spiked together horizontally at intervals of 30 inches or less. This is usually done with 1/4" spikes in predrilled holes.

Overhangs

The effect of overhangs should receive consideration. Overhangs reduce deflection of the interior spans, and seldom raise the bending stresses, unless the overhangs are very long. The deflection of the overhang should be checked if it exceeds 0.35ℓ in length. A comprehensive set of charts for figuring overhang deflections and stresses are given in the AITC Timber Construction Manual.

Table 86. Three and Four-inch, Sawn Decking, Double T & G.

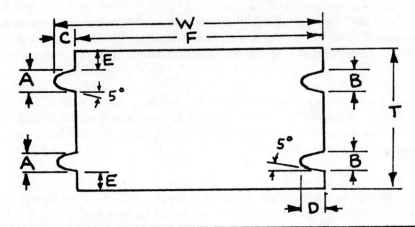

	Nominal 3-in.	Nominal 4-in.
	Seasoned	Seasoned
Thickness, T	2 1/2	3 1/2
Overall width, W	5 3/8 7 1/8 9 1/8 11 1/8	5 3/8 7 1/8 9 1/8 11 1/8
Face width, F	5 6 3/4 8 3/4 10 3/4	5 6 3/4 8 3/4 10 3/4
A B C D E	3/8 7/16 3/8 7/16 1/2	3/8 7/16 3/8 7/16 41/64

Standard V-joint bevel is 1/4" wide x 3/16" deep.

Grooved pattern is 3/8" wide x 3/16" deep, spaced on 1" centers.

Striated pattern is 1/8" wide x 3/16" deep, spaced on 1" centers.

Eased joint patterns is 3/16" Radius.

Decking may be end-notched, i.e., have T & G ends; or slotted for metal splice plates.

Nailed (Mechanically) Laminated Decking

This is an old and rather common arrangement of planks, often rough sawn and unseasoned, used primarily for highway bridges and wet mill decks. The planks are placed on edge on supports and nailed or bolted together horizontally. Nails must penetrate 2 1/2 laminations. Concrete is sometimes poured on top of such decks. For details refer to the Timber Construction Manual.

Glued Laminated Decking

When jobs call for deck thicknesses over nominal two-inches, a number of kinds of glued laminated decking are available. This product is made from nominal 1-inch to 2-inch laminations. It is usually exceptionally well-seasoned, bonded with entirely durable adhesives, and with a much thicker and wider tongue and groove than sawn decking. Glued laminated decking costs more than sawn deck, but straightness and quality features due to good seasoning make it economical to install. High quality faces or special species on faces for appearance can be placed over the more common structural quality center and back laminations.

Glued laminated decking sizes naturally differ from standard lumber sizes because standard lumber is the starting point in the construction of this decking. The decking is of three to five laminations. Typical finished thicknesses are 2 1/4, 2 5/8, 3 1/16 and 3 3/4 inches. Typical face widths are 5 1/4, 7, 9 and 11 inches. The need to lose face width to form tongues and grooves, as for sawn decking, is avoided in these products, by offsetting the laminations during manufacture.

Glued-laminated decking is usually seasoned to a maximum moisture content of 12 percent. If this decking is to be used in wet locations, some provision must be made to prevent it from spreading and bulging. This can be done by providing gaps of 1/16 to 1/8-inch between courses, subject to the width of courses, the moisture content when installed, and the swelling factors of the species (See Chapter 2).

Random length, continuous over three or more spans, is the most widely used end-joint arrangement. Specific rules recommended by a principal manufacturer and the major building codes are:

(a)   Distance between joints in adjacent courses must be at least two feet.

(b)   Joints in courses not directly adjacent, must be separated by one foot longitudinally, or two courses.

(c)   In any section of deck less than one foot in length, the number of end joints must not exceed one-third the number of courses.

(d)   All pieces must rest on at least one supporting beam, with not more than one end joint between supports in any row. A joint on a support shall be considered a joint in one of the adjacent rows.

(e)   Joints must be end-matched (T&G).

(f)   Courses must be slant nailed laterally within one foot of all end joints.

(g)   In end-spans, one-third of courses must be free of end joints.

Structurally glued end joints in the laminations are sometimes present in this decking. They are not considered end-joints in the context of the above random length layup rules.

The deflection formula for glued-laminated decking, given in Table 85, results in less deflection than the random-length formula for sawn solid wood decking.

Typical strength properties and section properties are given in Tables 87 and 88.

Roof deck is insulated with rigid fiber insulation board placed above the deck. Attention should be given to proper placement of the vapor barrier to maintain minimum vapor barrier temperature above the dew point temperature of the air on each side of the decking. Insulation factors for laminated decking are given in Table 89.

Table 87. Allowable Stresses, Glued-laminated Decking

	E	F_b		F_v
		Roof	Floor	
	psi	psi	psi	psi
Inland Red Cedar	1,200,000	1590	1380	150
Redwood	1,200,000	1590	1380	130
Idaho White Pine	1,500,000	1850	1610	150
Inland White Fir	1,500,000	1850	1610	130
Douglas Fir/Larch	1,800,000	2640	2300	165
Southern Pine	1,800,000	2640	2300	200
Douglas Fir	1,800,000	2640	2300	165

Courtesy of Potlatch Forests, Inc.

Table 88. Properties of A One-Foot Section of Glued-laminated Decking

Nominal Thickness	Actual Thickness inches	Area sq. in.	Moment of Inertia in.^{4}	Section Modulus in.^{3}
3	2 1/4	26.4	11.06	9.74
3 Super	2 5/8	30.8	17.76	13.44
4	3 1/16	35.9	27.99	18.22
5	3 13/16	45.0	53.80	28.20

Courtesy of Potlatch Forests, Inc.

Table 89. Weight and Insulation Factors (U).
BTU/hr., sq. ft. degree F

Species	Weight PSF	Nominal Decking Thickness	U Values for Insulation Thickness				
			0	1/2	1	1 1/2	2
Inland Red Cedar	4.5	3"	0.24	0.18	0.14	0.12	0.10
(all Laminations)	5.3	3" Super	.22	.16	.13	.12	.10
Redwood	6.0	4"	.19	.15	.12	.11	.09
	7.5	5"	.15	.13	.11	.09	.08
Southern Pine	6.5	3"	0.30	0.21	0.16	0.13	0.11
Douglas Fir	7.5	3" Super	.27	.20	.15	.12	.10
Larch	8.5	4"	.24	.18	.14	.12	.10
	10.5	5"	.20	.15	.13	.11	.10
White Fir	5.0	3"	0.27	0.19	0.15	0.12	0.11
Idaho White Pine	5.8	3" Super	.24	.18	.14	.12	.11
	7.6	4"	.21	.16	.13	.11	.10
	9.5	5"	.17	.14	.12	.10	.09

Courtesy of Potlatch Forests, Inc.

CHAPTER 21

WOOD TRUSSES

The structural mechanics of trusses is included in many textbooks on structural design. The analysis of stresses in wood trusses follows much the same processes found in such references. The particular properties of wood, the time-dependent nature of its allowable stresses, the influence of moisture on all its properties, and the practices recommended for the design of joints made with bolts, shear plates, split-ring connectors, nails, and adhesives contain the elements of difference between truss design in wood and in other materials.

Several successful combinations of wood and metal members have become quite common. Trusses made with metal gusset plates with punched teeth have, during the past twenty years, become the most common form of wood truss. During the period of 1960 to 1970, the use of these metal-plate-connected wood trusses has virtually displaced conventional residential roof framing in the United States, and is rapidly having a similar influence on construction practices in many other countries. Trusses constructed in this fashion are largely pitched or parallel chord (flat) trusses in the span range of 20 to 50 feet, and on spacings of two to four feet.

Trusses with tubular steel web members are another example of the effective combination of two materials. Timber chords have the necessary large cross-sectional dimensions for lateral and compressive stiffness, both important features of a truss, while steel tubes minimize joint slip and provide strength and a high degree of manufacturing economy in producing the connections. Steel is well-suited to tension web members, as it is sometimes difficult to develop full tensile strength of wood members with bolted connections. Material and labor economies combine with structural attributes in this sort of marriage of two materials.

Plywood gusseted roof trusses may be of the nailed or glued type. Nailed plywood gusset trusses perform much like metal plate connected trusses, to a degree depending on the care used in their construction. Glued plywood gusset trusses are exceptionally stiff and rugged, and are adaptable to long spans with little creep from the yielding of the joints.

Heavy timber roof trusses constructed with bolts, split rings and shear plates, using steel gusset plates and tension tie rods, are used on spans of 50 to 100 feet. The design of such structures has been practiced for hundreds of years, although the development of modern connectors, glued laminated material, and treated wood has lent a new dimension to these styles of construction. Some of the older designs required highly skilled artisans for their execution. The newer technology has permitted the use of less-specialized people. Many evidences of the old crafts are visible in heavy timber structures constructed up to about 1960 and going back as far as 500 years or more, in other instances.

Type of Timber Truss Configuration

The basic types of truss are pitched, flat, and bowstring. The *pitched truss* is the most efficient type for center point loading. Under that type of load, the chords are in pure tension and compression, with no secondary bending stresses in the members, if they are pin-connected. Pitched trusses are commonly used to support uniformly distributed loads, loads placed at numerous panel points, and moving concentrated loads.

The *parallel chord truss* would be the least efficient type were it not possible to reduce the size of members in locations of low stress. By proper choice of sizes, flat or cambered parallel chord trusses can be reasonably efficient. This style of truss, with camber and a moderate top chord pitch to permit drainage, fits into many architectural plans. Parallel chord trusses function well as floor trusses when manufactured with joints that are not susceptible to creep as a result of joint yielding over time. Glued plywood gussets and tightly fitted bolted or pinned connections are best for wood trusses for this purpose. One feature of parallel chord trusses that may be of some importance for certain designs is that columns, attached to both top and bottom chords have top end fixity. This automatically reduces the need for knee bracing between columns and trusses and reduces column dimensions. Knee braces are usually considered undesirable by building owners and can be

TRUSSES

omitted through the use of roof diaphragm structure and/or parallel chord trusses. Actually, in parallel chord trusses, the knee-bracing exists in the space between the chords, so actually, the function is provided at greater cost than for pitched trusses. Strictest economy would favor pitched trusses or bowstring trusses, with knee braces. If wind and earthquake loads require diaphragm structure, knee-bracing becomes unnecessary except on exceptionally long buildings.

The *bowstring truss* is considered the most efficient truss in terms of material utilization when the load is uniformly distributed. Architecturally, it has limitations. However, bowstring trusses are very widely used in a number of forms which, while not developing the full efficiency of the bowstring concept, take sufficient advantage of it to produce some worthwhile structural and cost benefits.

The bowstring truss design principle rests on the idea that truss height is proportioned so that a uniform chord force (chord stress x chord area) multiplied by the height would equal the moment at any station along the length. The equation for required truss depth is rather complex and may be simplified by considering the upper and lower chord forces to be parallel at all stations. See Figure 121. In that case:

$$M_x = \frac{w\ell x}{2} - \frac{wx^2}{2} = F_{yx}$$

$$y_x = \frac{w}{2F}(\ell x - x^2)$$

At various stations:

$$x = \ell/8 \qquad y = \frac{7}{16} \cdot \frac{w\ell^2}{8F}$$

$$x = \ell/4 \qquad y = \frac{12}{16} \cdot \frac{w\ell^2}{8F}$$

$$x = 3\ell/8 \qquad y = \frac{15}{16} \cdot \frac{w\ell^2}{8F}$$

$$x = \ell/2 \qquad y = 1 \cdot \frac{w\ell^2}{8F}$$

This describes a top chord that is very close to a parabola. The vertical component of top chord force in a theoretically designed bowstring truss, under uniformly distributed load, will equal the vertically applied load or vertical shear at any station. Under those conditions, no web members are required. In practice, loads are not always uniformly distributed so web members are necessary. Bowstring trusses are not actually manufactured to a parabolic shape, but usually have top chords in the form of a circular arc proportioned so the radius of curvature is equal to the span, or to give a mid-span depth suited to the allowable stress, chord area and bending moment. Although these fabricating practices deviate from the purely developed curvature, the form does minimize web member requirements.

The AITC Timber Construction Manual and AITC Timber Construction Standard 102-65 contain detailed discussion of bowstring truss design practice, to which the reader is referred. The Timber Design and Construction Handbook, by the Timber Engineering Company (F. W. Dodge Corporation, publisher) is another good reference.

Upper chords may be glued laminated, mechanically laminated, or comprised of segments with the top edge sawn to the curvature required.

The upper chord is designed as a free end column between panel points with axial load and bending moment due to loads applied through joists or purlins, plus the eccentricity of the line of force and the center line of the segment. Chord continuity is not generally assumed in design, but end joints are assumed to act in full bearing in compression. For this reason the secondary bending moment given in Figure 123 is PS/4 - Fe instead of PS/8 - Fe.

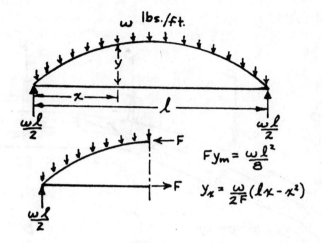

Figure 121. Bowstring truss principle.

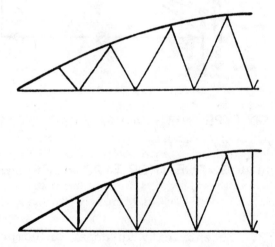

Figure 122. Bowstring truss web arrangements.

302

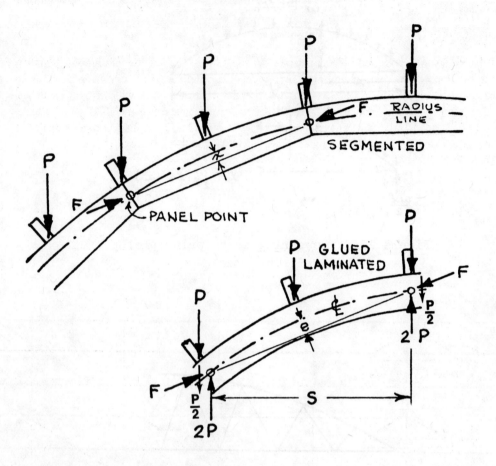

FOR SEGMENTED TYPE WITH PANEL POINT AT MID-DEPTH

ECCENTRICITY = $\nu/2.= e$

SECONDARY MOMENT, EITHER TYPE = $\dfrac{PS}{4} - Fe$

Figure 123.   Eccentricity in upper or compression chord.

Lower chords, unless they carry directly applied vertical loads, are tension members. If loads are directly applied, design must consider the secondary bending stresses that occur. Methods described in Chapter 10, with allowable tension stress replacing allowable compression stress are used. Buckling is not a consideration.

Deflection and Camber

All trusses may be cambered to compensate for deflection. In the case of trusses, camber is built-in to compensate for full load deflection, rather than simply dead load deflection as for beams. For bowstring trusses, camber is especially important to insure that changes in panel point geometry will not materially alter the stress analysis. Should that occur, the stress in some of the more lightly loaded web members could change, or reverse direction, leading to a substantial shift in member loading. Camber requirements for trusses made with split-rings and shear plate connected trusses, as developed from tests by the Timber Engineering Company, are given in Figure 124. These curves are plots of:

$$\text{camber} = K_1 \frac{L^3}{H} + K_2 \frac{L^2}{H}$$

where $K_1 = 32 \times 10^{-6}$ and K_2 is 63×10^{-5} for bowstring trusses and 28×10^{-5} for pitched and flat trusses

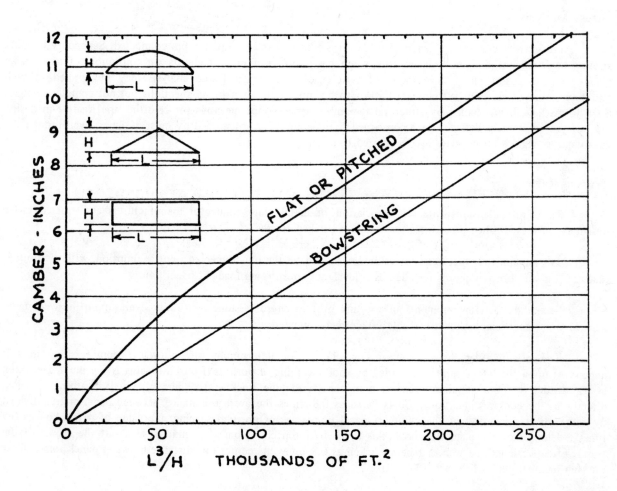

Figure 124. Camber for full load deflection of split-ring connected trusses. (Courtesy Timber Engineering Co.)

For other types of joint connection, deflection can be estimated with reasonable accuracy by calculating the deformation of all the individual members and determining the change of truss shape from the change in loaded member lengths. Dead load creep should be included in this estimate, based on criteria given in Chapter 8, which suggests allowing one-half the dead load deflection for creep of seasoned wood and the full dead load deflection for creep of unseasoned wood. A graphical solution is probably most convenient.

The Timber Engineering Design Handbook by Pearson, Kloot and Boyd of the Australian Council for Scientific and Industrial Research (CSIRO) suggests creep be considered equal to dead load deformation at a 15% wood moisture content and twice dead load deflection when moisture content exceeds 15% at the time of truss fabrication.

Slip at joints should also be considered. *Joint slip* can be established by tests of the particular joints when facilities and time are available. A recommendation for split ring connectors is to increase deflection calculated without considering slip by a factor of 1.5 to 2.0. The above Australian reference suggests slip in split-ring and shear plate connector joints should be 0.08-inch in unseasoned wood, 0.05-inch in seasoned wood, if the joint is fully loaded. If not fully loaded, slip is proportional to percentage of full loading.

For bolted joints slip is taken as the amount (above) for connector joints plus the bolt hole clearance values.

Stress Analysis

Truss stress analyses are generally made on the basis that all joints are pin connected. Secondary bending stresses in chords of flat and pitched trusses are based on continuity, if chords are continuous. Trusses using glued plywood gusset plates have joints of high rigidity and rigid frame analysis may be applied to such structures. Many truss joint systems are known to be more rigid than pin-connections yet not completely rigid. Such joints have been studied by structural research engineers, but methods for crediting the rigidity in design are not yet completely defined. As a consequence, pin-connection is assumed by most designers even though the advantages of rigid joint behavior are recognized to exist.

Trussed Rafters

The Truss Plate Institute, an association of metal plate connector manufacturers and trussed rafter designers, have established procedures for design of pitched trusses.

TPI recommends that axial forces be determined on the pin-connected joint assumption, with distributed loads on top and bottom chords regarded as equivalent concentrated loads at panel points.

Secondary bending moments in top and bottom chords assume continuity over supporting web members. Moment coefficients shown in Table 90 are recommended.

The effective lengths of compression chords for determining the allowable compression stress is dependent upon the lateral support afforded by roof sheathing or purlins. If purlin spacing is ℓ_p, the ℓ/d is taken as ℓ_p divided by the minimum dimension of the chord (the thickness). Where plywood sheathing is nailed directly to the compression chord, ℓ/d is taken as 0.8 times the average distance between panel points, divided by the vertical dimension of the chord. If panel points are of unequal spacing, the value of ℓ is taken as 0.9 times the longer of the panel distances (this is for four top chord panels, symmetrical about the crown of the truss). Effective length of web members is taken as 0.8 times the center line distance between panel points along the web member center line. See Table 90.

As an alternative to these methods of analysis, the method described in Purdue University Agricultural Experiment Station, Research Bulletin 783, "Digital Computer Program for Analysis of Member Stresses in Symmetric W Trusses" may be used.

Table 90. Formula for chord bending moments for trussed rafters under uniform loading. Courtesy Truss Plate Institute.

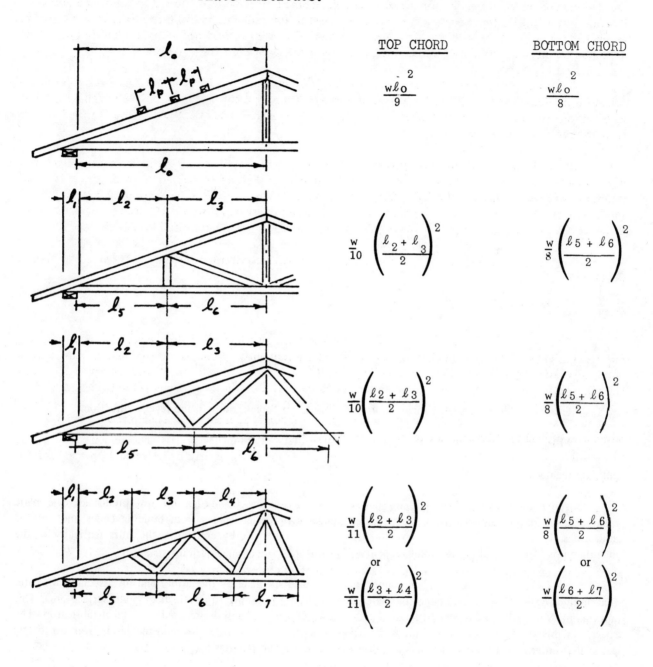

TOP CHORD | BOTTOM CHORD

$$\frac{w\ell_o^2}{9}$$ $$\frac{w\ell_o^2}{8}$$

$$\frac{w}{10}\left(\frac{\ell_2 + \ell_3}{2}\right)^2$$ $$\frac{w}{8}\left(\frac{\ell_5 + \ell_6}{2}\right)^2$$

$$\frac{w}{10}\left(\frac{\ell_2 + \ell_3}{2}\right)^2$$ $$\frac{w}{8}\left(\frac{\ell_5 + \ell_6}{2}\right)^2$$

$$\frac{w}{11}\left(\frac{\ell_2 + \ell_3}{2}\right)^2$$ $$\frac{w}{8}\left(\frac{\ell_5 + \ell_6}{2}\right)^2$$

or   or

$$\frac{w}{11}\left(\frac{\ell_3 + \ell_4}{2}\right)^2$$ $$\frac{w}{8}\left(\frac{\ell_6 + \ell_7}{2}\right)^2$$

Formulas for computing member stresses are:

Axial tension only: $P/A \leq F_t$

Axial compression only: $P/A \leq 0.3E/(\ell/d)^2$

or F_c, whichever is less

Bending only: $\dfrac{M}{S} \leq F_b$

Combined tension and bending:

$$\frac{P/A}{F_t} + \frac{M/S}{F_b} \leq 1$$

Combined compression and bending:

$$\frac{P/A}{[0.3E/(\ell/d)^2]^*} + \frac{M/S}{F_b} \leq 1$$

* or F_c, whichever is least.

Maximum ℓ/d is 50 in compression and 80 in tension.

Trusses should be designed for one-third of all member forces acting in the reverse direction.

When more than two trusses are spaced on centers of 24-inches or less and are joined by a load distributing deck system, allowable bending stresses for single member use may be increased 15 percent for this multiple member use.

Connector plates are proprietary devices and load values for design are not published. The plate manufacturers have conducted tests and secured approval of design values from building codes and housing authorities. Usually, the designer may obtain truss plans for his use by contacting the truss fabricator or the manufacturer of the metal plates used by the truss fabricator.

An independent study of plate connector load capacities made by the author and his associates indicates that normal design values for connector plates are 80 to 100 lbs. per square inch of plate surface area. This information will enable a designer to estimate a design which can probably be secured from most fabricators. The species in this study included white fir, western hemlock and Douglas fir, with values increasing from 80 to 100 psi in that order. Southern pine would give performance values like Douglas fir.

Connector plates are installed on both sides of the trusses at each panel point.

Heel joints are designed to resist the axial force of the top and bottom chords with reductions in allowable design values of plates for pitch per Table 91.

The plates at the peak or crown should resist 50 percent of top chord compression force. The other 50 percent is taken in direct bearing.

Tight-fitting compression joints are credited with 50 percent of compression in direct bearing. They must also resist one-third of the total design force in tension.

Table 91.   Toothed Plate Design Value Reduction Factors

Slope of Top Chord	Factor
Less than 3:12	0.85
3:12 to 4:12	0.80
4:12 to 5:12	0.75
5:12 to and including 5.5:12	0.70
Over 5.5:12	0.65

By permission of Truss Plate Institute.

Plate area within 1/2-inch of ends of members, measured parallel to grain is considered inactive. Plate area within 1/4-inch of edges measured perpendicular to grain is considered inactive. These limitations do not apply to heel joints. Plates must have sufficient strength to carry tensile and shear loads. Steel used is ASTM A446-67 grade A with allowable tensile strength of 20,000 psi and allowable shear strength of 13,500 psi. Punched out void areas must be subtracted from plate area to obtain net plate cross-section for design. Punched out area is about 40 to 50 percent of gross plate area.

All trussed-rafter joints must be capable of 375 lbs. axial force to withstand handling and erection loads.

The usual duration of load adjustments apply to allowable stresses for wood and to connector plate tooth load values. They do not apply to allowable stresses for steel, except that steel stresses can be increased one-third for wind and seismic loading.

When fire retardant chemical treatments are used, reduce allowable stresses 10 percent if lumber is kiln-dried after treatment, and 20 percent if not kiln-dried.

Trussed-rafter deflections are difficult to calculate. They are usually determined by the plate manufacturer on the basis of tests.

Live load deflections are limited to 1/360 of span when plaster ceilings are used, and 1/240 of span when dry-wall (gypsum board) or no ceiling is used. Cantilever overhangs are limited to 1/180 and 1/120 of the length of overhang for plaster and drywall ceilings, respectively.

Lower chords are cambered for dead load deflection.

An approximation of deflection for pitched trussed-rafters joined with toothed metal plates, in the slope range of 3:12 to 5:12, for spans up to 32 feet, developed from test information may be made with the following equation:

$$\Delta = \frac{10.5 \; w\ell^4}{Eh^3} \quad \text{For trusses constructed of Nom. 2-in. lumber.}$$

where Δ = deflection in inches
w = load in lbs. per lineal foot of horizontal projection
ℓ = span in feet
h = distance between top and bottom chord center lines at mid-span (crown or peak), feet
E = elastic modulus, psi

Properties for Trusses

The ratio of depth to span generally recommended for various truss configurations are:

Bowstring	1:6 to 1:8
Pitched	1:5 to 1:6
Flat	1:8 to 1:10

Deeper trusses will deflect less and use smaller chord members. Shallower trusses will deflect more and require larger chords. The use of as few splices as possible, and as few panels as possible will contribute to truss stiffness. Closely fitted bolts and connectors also contribute to stiffness as do large member sizes. It is often more desirable to produce a design with an intermediate to low grade of member with correspondingly large cross-sectional area, than to use extremely high grade material of small cross-section.

Some of the specialty trusses using very well-fitted connector pins with steel web members and glued chord splices or structural finger joints perform well with high strength chord members. Glued plywood gussets also produce exceptionally stiff trusses. Recent research on trusses with plywood gussets and other rigid connection systems show stiffness to be about three times as great as metal plate connected trusses of the same proportions. This added stiffness is not always necessary and if it is achieved at greater fabricating cost, the metal plate connected trusses may be entirely adequate and economically advantageous.

Minimizing the number of panels reduces fabricating costs, both in terms of labor and hardware. Many trusses are made with nominal 2-inch to 4-inch lumber in which case panel lengths in the order of 5 to 10 feet, depending on compression member size, and lateral support provided for upper and lower chords.

Lateral symmetry is a desirable feature in trusses from a structural point of view, to improve end fixity and to avoid eccentric loading of chords.

CHAPTER 22

POLE BUILDING DESIGN

Pole type structures in the modern sense enjoyed their initial acceptance in the farm building field and their use has expanded to a wide range of industrial and commercial structures. They have been used in residential designs on the basis of their performance record in these other types of structures. Moderate cost and unique suitability to certain types of building sites account for this growing range of applications.

The success of pole type structures is a consequence of the availability of good preservative treatment methods developed for the use of timber piling, electric utility structures, and lumber treatment for durable performance in contact with soils and moist environments.

Pole structures commonly carry the load of roof decks and wind loading on vertical projections of roofs and of walls. Floor loads usually are not supported by the pole structure itself, but go to the ground directly as concrete slab floor systems. Pole type structures have as much permanence as any structures, if correctly designed using the right kind of treatment and foundation design.

Foundations

Foundation engineering essential to pole-type structural design involves investigation of soil properties, a subject of considerably wider scope than can be covered adequately in this chapter. This topic as it applies to lateral forces on pole-type structures is covered by a publication of the American Wood Preservers Institute by Donald Patterson, entitled *Pole Building Design.*

Direct bearing under vertical load is dependent on the bearing capacity of the soil against the end of the pole and the frictional resistance between the pole and the soil, together with the shear strength of the soil in which the post is embedded. In the case of pole-type buildings, the amount of embedment necessary to resist the lateral force of wind loads, to resist the moment on the supporting poles, provides more than sufficient skin friction to bear the vertical weight of the structure. Vertical forces are carried to the soil by skin friction between the soil and the upper portions of the embedded length of the pole, without producing much end-bearing pressure at the butt-end. Interestingly, it has been determined that firm backfilling of the hole with compacted soil, sand, soil concrete or concrete is a more effective way to increase vertical force resistance, than placing mats or footings of concrete beneath the butt-ends. Concrete encasement of the pole in the ground contact area enlarges the frictional surface, and can generally be credited with a wood to concrete bond strength of 30 psi.

With these few comments about foundations and those which will follow about lateral resistance of embedded poles to pressure, this chapter will concentrate attention upon design features of pole-type buildings.

General Features of Pole Building Structure

Pole buildings take the form of cantilevers fixed at the lower ends, and carrying the wind or earthquake loads perpendicular to the pole axis. The dead and live loads are carried by the poles acting as columns.

The pole building is a grid-like structure of more or less uniform bays whose dimensions are chosen to utilize standard lengths of lumber for rafters, purlins and plates. Trusses permit long span designs with spacing between trusses linked to the lengths of available lumber. Commonly, 16-foot lengths are the longest readily available lumber sizes. Pieces longer than 16 feet are in demand for trusses and command a premium price that tends to exclude their economical use for the rafters and purlins required in great quantity for pole-type structures. In recent years, structural end-jointed lumber has become more common, but is not yet sufficiently plentiful to reduce the price premium on lengths greater than 16-feet. Lumber lengths of 12 and 14 feet are frequently a more economical material than 16-foot lumber. The designer, therefore, should acquaint himself with price versus length relationships at the outset of a design for a large structure that will consume much lumber. Some balance between cost of poles, cost of trusses, and cost of rafter lengths or purlin lengths must be examined in determining the true economies to be achieved via pole-type structures. Designs that permit the use of standard lengths, without further cutting for length are important to achieving construction economy.

When it is possible, designing the structure so the poles act as fixed-end columns at top as well as bottom will reduce required pole size and embedment length. Such fixed top end conditions can be obtained by truss-bracing or by the use of knee-braces between poles and roof structure.

Some pole frame structures are constructed with heavy timber plates extending horizontally between poles at the upper ends, supporting in turn the rafters. (See Figure 125) These plates are bolted to the poles or bear on wood cleats connected by bolts, nails or lag screws. This type of structure may not have the upper end fixity previously described, or it may be secured with knee-braces from rafters and plates to produce fixity.

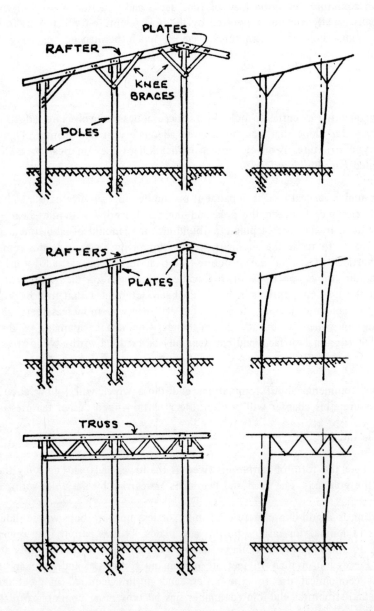

Figure 125. Types of pole building structure.

Provision for resistance to wind forces on the end walls of the structure is, of course, necessary. When building length greatly exceeds width, longitudinal forces may be distributed among a great many poles making it possible to omit longitudinal knee-bracing. The poles, in this case, act as simple cantilevers, with the plates or the roof structure distributing the wind load among the poles.

Where a roof diaphragm is used, such as plywood, the walls can be designed with either bracing, or as plywood sheathed shear walls to carry the lateral forces to the pole footings.

Pole buildings with light metal sheathed walls and roofs may not have effective roof and wall diaphragms. In that case the lateral loads tributary to the roof will be carried by the poles acting as cantilevers, with or without fixity at the upper end, as the design warrants.

Properties of Poles

Standard pole sizes as set forth by the American National Standards Institute, for the range of interest in most pole building designs are given in Table 92. Pole size standards are based on pole breaking loads. There

Table 92. Dimensions of Douglas Fir and Southern Pine Poles. (a)

Class		1	2	3	4	5	6	7
Minimum Circumference at Top (inches)		27	25	23	21	19	17	15
Minimum Diameter at Top (inches)		8.6	8.0	7.3	6.7	6.0	5.4	4.9
Breaking Load (Approximate) (lbs.)		4500	3700	3000	2400	1900	1500	1200
Length of Pole (ft.)	Groundline Distance from butt (ft.)*	Minimum Circumference at 6 ft. from Butt inches						
20	4	31.0	29.0	27.0	25.0	23.0	21.0	19.5
25	5	33.5	31.5	29.5	27.5	25.5	23.0	21.5
30	5.5	36.5	34.0	32.0	29.5	27.5	25.0	23.5
35	6	39.0	36.5	34.0	31.5	29.0	27.0	25.0
40	6	41.0	38.5	36.0	33.5	31.0	28.5	26.5
45	6.5	43.0	40.5	37.5	**35.0**	32.5	30.0	28.0
50	7	45.0	42.0	39.0	36.5	34.0	31.5	29.0
55	7.5	46.5	43.5	40.5	38.0	35.0	32.5	--
60	8	48.0	45.0	42.0	39.0	36.0	33.5	--

*For use only in establishing pole grades. Actual length of embedment depends on application.

From the Timber Construction Manual by permission of AITC. (Minimum top diameters have been added.)

are ten of these strength classes. Seven of the more commonly used classes are given in Table 92, along with the standard breaking loads. Do not use these loads as a basis for design. They are used for pole acceptance testing purposes. Table 92 is for Douglas fir and southern pine poles, which have an ultimate bending stress at failure of 8000 psi. The top dimension of each pole class is a standard, and applies to any species. The dimension at six feet from the butt differs from species to species, and is related to the ultimate bending stresses. Southern pine and Douglas fir have an ultimate bending stress of approximately 8000 psi (Table 93). Thus, for a 20-foot long Class 2 pole, for a 3700 lb. load applied two feet below the top, the bending stress at the arbitrary gound line, must not exceed 8000 psi.

$$f_b = \frac{32M}{\pi d^3} = \frac{32\,(14)(12)(3700)}{\pi d^3} = 8000$$

$$d = 9.25\text{-in. at } 4'$$

This would be 9.1" at 6 feet and the circumference at 6 feet from the butt would be 28.6 inches. The table shows 29 inches, which is reasonably close, probably having been rounded up. A 20-foot, Class 2 pole of another species, for example jack pine, common in Canada has an ultimate bending stress of about 6600 psi (Table 93). This gives a calculated diameter at ground line of 9.86-inches, which is 9.6-inches at 6 ft., for a circumference of 30.5-inches. Tables similar to Table 92 published for jack pine will show a diameter of 31-inches at six feet from the butt for this class and length of pole.

Formulas for Designing Poles

The stress at the point of maximum bending moment is computed using the formula, which incorporates a form factor for round poles.

$$f_b = 32M/\pi d^3 \leq F_b$$

Table 93.   Properties for Treated Poles   (Normal Duration of Load)

Species	Breaking Strength in Bending-psi	Allowable Bending Stress F_b - psi	Modulus of Elasticity E - psi
Cedar, western red	6,000	1,620	1,000,000
Douglas fir	8,000	2,160	1,600,000
Hemlock, western	7,400	2,000	1,400,000
Larch, western	8,400	2,270	1,500,000
Pine, jack	6,600	1,780	1,100,000
Pine, lodgepole	6,600	1,780	1,000,000
Pine, ponderosa	6,000	1,620	1,000,000
Pine, red (Norway)	6,600	1,780	1,200,000
Pine, southern	8,000	2,160	1,600,000

From the Timber Construction Manual by permission of AITC.

where   M   =   the maximum bending moment, inch-lbs.

            d   =   diameter at point of maximum bending moment, inches

            F_b =   allowable bending stress, psi, adjusted for load duration

The point of maximum bending moment is assumed to occur at one-fourth the depth of embedment below the ground line, unless special restraint at ground level, such as a poured concrete slab is used. For poles with roof bracing, the moment should be checked at the connection to knee braces or the bottom of the roof truss.

When poles are loaded as simple cantilevers, with no top end moment the distance h is taken as the distance from actual ground to the point of loading, usually the top. For poles with fixity at the top end, the distance, h, is taken as the point of inflection, which, for round tapered poles is two-thirds of the distance from the ground line to the point of restraint (knee-brace or lower chord of truss).

The maximum compression stress in the pole may be computed using the formula:

$$f_c = P/A \leq F'_c$$

where   P   =   direct compressive load, lbs.

            A   =   area of top of pole, or at level where stress is greatest, sq. in.

F'_c is the allowable compressive stress based on ℓ/d and elastic modulus.

$$F'_c = \frac{0.225E}{(\ell/d)^2}$$

where ℓ =   unsupported length of pole, inches

            d   =   diameter of pole at one-third of total length from the top, inches.

The ℓ/d ratio shall not exceed 43. The weight of the pole shall be considered in compression stress analyses. F'_c shall not exceed 60 percent of F_b given in Table 93.

Combined axial load and bending load based on lateral force and dead load should be checked. Usually maximum live load and lateral load do not occur simultaneously. See Chapter 10 for combined stress formulae.

The depth of embedment for a pole may be calculated using the allowable lateral passive soil pressure determined by a soil investigation or other source. *A typical value for preliminary design of 250 psf per foot of depth is reasonable*

$$D = \sqrt[3]{\frac{12hP}{Bp}}$$

where   D   =   depth of embedment, ft.
            P   =   horizontal force, lbs.
            h   =   height from ground line to point of application of force, ft.
            B   =   butt diameter of pole or diameter of concrete casing, ft.
            p   =   allowable lateral passive soil pressure psf per ft. of depth

Using this formula to obtain a value for D, which is regarded as approximate, D is recalculated by the equation:

$$D = \frac{A}{2} \left(1 + \sqrt{1 + \frac{4.36h}{A}} \right)$$

where $\quad$ A $\quad = \quad$ $2.34P/S_1B$

$\qquad\quad$ S_1 $\quad = \quad$ $pD/3$

Many pole structures are built so the poles project through a concrete floor slab. This alters the computation of embedment which is approximated by the formula:

$$D = \sqrt{\frac{4.25Ph}{S_3B}}$$

where $\quad$ S_3 $\quad = \quad$ pD

Lumber Portions

The lumber and plywood portions of a pole building are designed using the methods and stresses described in earlier chapters.

Bolt Strength

Bolt capacities can be calculated as explained in Chapter 12. For bolts connecting lumber members to poles, the side members, which are the lumber members, will usually be less than one-half the pole thickness. In that case, for bolts in double shear, base the calculation of bolt capacity on twice the side member thickness. For single shear, use one-half that value.

Choose perpendicular to grain values where they apply, the usual case for the plates or the lateral force of wind on the poles. Make appropriate adjustments for moisture content and reduce values 40 percent if lumber is installed unseasoned with more than one bolt per connection. These details are all discussed in Chapter 12.

CHAPTER 23

WOOD DURABILITY AND PROTECTION

Dry wood is as durable as any structural material. Old timber which has not been mechanically damaged shows little if any degradation of its properties. Surface weathering can erode unpainted wood, but this proceeds very slowly (about 1/4-inch per century). Flat-grained surfaces of some species, particularly those with strong springwood to summerwood density variation, tend to exhibit separation of springwood and summerwood near the surface upon weathering. This is why woods used for siding and fascia are preferably even-textured species such as western red cedar, white pine, luaun, etc., and quarter or vertically-grained boards of other species.

Sunlight and oxygen turn unpainted wood gray, or brown. With moisture wood surfaces may blacken. Paint protects wood from these discolorations and erosion. Clear transparent finishes are reliable protection in interior and protected areas, but for exposed exterior use such finishes are not always effective, and considerable refinishing is necessary to preserve a bright appearance. Much research has been devoted to transparent wood finishes and some fairly durable ones are offered. They must be chosen carefully, based on adequate evidence of performance. Pigmented stains, on the other hand, protect wood almost as well as paint and generally, if of the penetrating type, will not peel as they allow the wood to remain permeable.

Wood placed in the ground does not decay, as air is excluded. Thus, the portions of piles well below the ground line will remain free of degradation. The same may be said for underwater piling in fresh water. Salt water has some preservative effect, but marine borers flourish on unprotected wood in salt water, so usually it must be heavily treated with creosote for such exposure.

Butt ends of piling taken from the ground after 150 years, even when made of normally non-durable species, have been found in perfect condition.

High temperatures degrade wood structurally, a factor that is considered in the application of hot preservatives and in the kiln drying process. The strength loss is not severe, usually not more than ten percent. Carried to extremes, temperature elevation culminates in combustion, but there are preservatives that prevent and retard high speed oxidation of woods.

Natural Durability

Heartwood of some species is naturally durable; cedar, redwood, cypress, locust are examples. Sapwood is not durable. However, sapwood receives treatment well and species with wide sapwood rings can be treated extremely well. Southern pine is such a species, as are many hardwoods. Poles and timbers are often incised to make them more penetrable by preservatives.

Causes of Deterioration

Decay, insects, marine borers, fire and strong *alkaline* liquids are the principal causes of deterioration.

Decay is caused by micro-organisms. These are *fungi of the wood-destroying* type, a form of parasitic plant life to which unprotected wood is the host and the food supply. Wood-destroying fungi feed on cellulose or lignin, or both. The so-called brown rot fungi feed on cellulose leaving the brown lignin as residue, while the white rot fungi feed upon the lignin.

Another type are the *wood-staining fungi*, which discolor the sapwood, cause moldy growths, but do not harm the wood, structurally. Wood-staining fungi feed on the nutrients in the liquid sap rather than the cellulose and lignin. It is useful to note that the conditions which permit one type to flourish are favorable to the other.

DURABILITY

For decay to occur in wood the fungi must have *moisture, air* and a *temperature* range 40 to 105° F. (70 to 95°F, for really active decay.)

Above 20 percent moisture content, either continuously or intermittently, wood is susceptible to decay. Close proximity to soil exposes wood to decay by the so-called "dry-rot" fungi. Although all fungi need moisture to be active, "dry-rot" fungi can build water conducting strands to conduct moisture from the soil. (See Figure 126) For most uses, wood will be too dry to support decay. The fungi in infected wood can lie dormant during periods of dryness or cold, and become active whenever these conditions reach suitable levels. The designer can reduce the prospects for decay by avoiding joints that can become water traps, and surfaces then cannot drain. When these steps are impractical, preservative treatment is necessary.

Fungi require oxygen from the air. Wood which is submerged becomes completely saturated to the exclusion of air, hence cannot decay. Twenty percent by volume of the wood occupied by air is sufficient to support fungal activity. For wood in the specifc gravity range of 0.35 to 0.55, air sufficient for decay is present up to moisture contents of 162 to 80 percent, respectively. (This covers the important commercial species for building in North America.) So decay can occur in wood at moisture levels well above fiber saturation (25 - 30 percent).

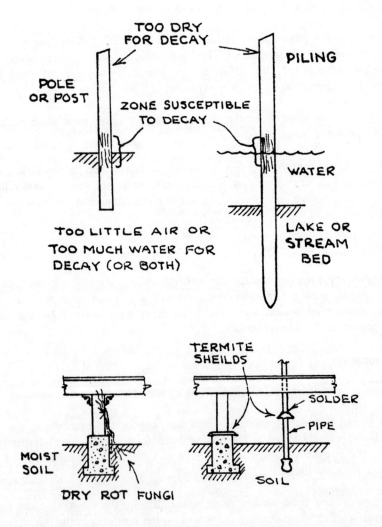

Figure 126. Decay and termite situations.

Posts in the ground exhibit all of these conditions. At the lower end, there is insufficient air and excessive moisture. (See Figure 126) At the top there is insufficient moisture. For some distance above and below the ground line, conditions usually favor decay. Dry-rot fungi will transport their own moisture to the above-ground portion of posts and poles. It is not uncommon to treat poles and posts from the lower end to a point sufficiently far above ground level to discourage fungi. Likewise, untreated timber piling in marine use shows decay in the region near the water line.

From the bottoms of rivers like the Columbia and the Willamette, the St. Lawrence and the Au Sable (Michigan) and of Lake Ontario, timber has been recovered after many years of submersion, found in perfectly good condition, and converted to normal usage, for construction and furniture purposes.

Fungi are sensitive to temperature and thrive in the 70-95°F range. Above and below this range their activity is retarded. Below 40°F, decay practically ceases. Exposing wood to a temperature of 120°F for 24 hours will kill fungi and at 150°F sterilization occurs in 75 minutes. Conventional kiln-drying schedules kill the fungi in most instances. If kiln-dried wood is exposed to the right moisture conditions, it can become reinfected by contact with the air-bourne spores of living fungi.

Termites and carpenter ants consume wood substance. *Subterranean termites* cause the most termite damage to wood in the U.S., particularly in the South, but not unknown practically to the Canadian border except at higher elevations. They feed on moist wood and will enter a structure and devour it internally leaving a thin shell of sound wood on the outside. Their access can be impeded with metal termite shields. Untreated wood should be kept well away from the ground (18-inches). Soil poisoning near foundations is effective, but may need to be renewed in areas of severe termite activity. Treatments effective against termites are usually also effective against decay.

Non-subterranean or dry-wood termites live in the wood and do not require as much moisture. They occur in the dry southern U.S., and the southeastern coastal plain, and account for only a small portion of termite damage in the U.S. They produce galleries and tunnels in the timber, much like the subterranean varities. Because they do not require as much moisture, they often operate undetected. They enter wood when it is exposed and unpainted. Infested wood should be replaced. Termite nests can be poisoned by dry powder or liquid treatments of various kinds, and by fumigation.

Carpenter ants do not live on the wood, as food, but merely build galleries for shelter. They inhabit soft or decayed wood, and can introduce wood decaying fungi into moist timber.

Various kinds of *beetles and boring insects* infest logs and freshly cut lumber, particularly hardwoods. Softwood logs are attacked by *sawflys*. Dip treatments, poisons and fumigation are all used to eradicate these harmful pests.

A variety of *marine borers* (mollusks and crustaceans) attack wood in salt water. The only real protection lies in heavy treatment with creosote. Boats are best protected by a well maintained anti-fouling paint and copper containing preservatives. Practically all marine piling is treated against marine borer attack.

Non-Pressure Treatment

Solutions of toxic chemicals in oil or water are often applied by dipping, soaking, brush, or spray treatments. These are primarily useful against wood-staining fungi, and to protect lumber during distribution. They usually contain water repellents. Some species take up preservatives into their end grain faces quite well, and while the life expectancy is more limited than pressure treatement preservatives, brush, soak and dip treatments have considerable value. Effectiveness is a function of the penetration and retention of the preservative. Without pressure these are usually limited and seasoning will open up and expose untreated wood to attack.

Vacuum treatments are really very mild pressure processes. By evacuating the chamber containing the treating charge, then admitting the toxic chemical liquid at atmospheric pressure, a treating pressure of about 15 psi is achieved. While better than dipping and brushing, it doesn't produce the results of pressure treatment with cold or hot solutions.

Hot and cold soak processes for poles and piling of certain hard-to-penetrate species, are about as effective as pressure treatment, but slower. Usually only sapwood can be penetrated. Wood like southern pine, with a thick sapwood band, treats very well by pressure treatment as compared to hot and cold soaking, boiling in oil, or vacuum treatment. Douglas fir and cedar, with narrow sapwood is more difficult to penetrate and the advantage of full pressure treating over some non-pressure processes is less distinct.

The variety of chemicals used is too lengthy to discuss in this chapter. Reference to appropriate standards will follow.

Pressure Treatment

The two common pressure processes are the: (a) full-cell process and the (b) empty-cell process. The *full-cell process* leaves the cell cavities in the portion of the wood which has been penetrated, essentially filled with treating solution. This process provides greatest retention of chemical. It is used for the treatment of marine piling with creosote. Water-borne preservatives are also applied by this process. The water then is evaporated off in dry kilns or by air drying in service, to leave a heavy concentration of toxic chemical. Water-borne chemicals are used for mine timbers, structural lumber and plywood for dry use, (wet use with higher concentrations of toxic ingredient), and roof decking for moist mills where condensation may be a problem.

Full-cell process creosote treatments produce a product that is not paintable, exudes oil when heated and is dirty. However, this is the most durable treatment and offers protection against both decay, weathering and moisture penetration.

The *empty-cell process* leaves the cell cavities empty of solution, but to the extent of the penetration, the cell wall material is effectively treated. Retention is much lower than in the full-cell process. This process is used with the solutions of pentachlorophenol or copper napthenate in petroleum oil.

Preservative retentions are usually specified in terms of weight of preservative per cubic foot of wood treated. This can be determined by measuring the amount of chemical consumed for a given volume of material treated, or by the analysis of borings taken from the treated pieces. Retention requirements vary with size of timber. Typical retentions are given in Table 94, which also indicates principal uses of various chemical treatments.

Complete penetration of sapwood is a goal. Heartwood is difficult to treat. As some lumber contains no sapwood, penetration may not be very deep. Incising the timber with knives is often a practical way to improve penetration.

Oil-borne treatments such as 5 percent penta or 0.75 percent copper napthenate in petroleum oil, are relatively clean treatments, and much preferred to the creosotes where contact with the public or odor problems are likely to prevail. Applied with the empty cell process, they are paintable.

Water-borne salts are relatively inexpensive and are excellent for dry use. They are also paintable. The use of water-borne salts on dry laminated timber is not recommended unless done by real experts who appreciate the possible damage to the product by swelling, or on dry-use adhesives. In general, they are not likely to produce satisfactory results unless applied before laminating. Laminating firms are not all equipped to glue lumber treated with water-borne salts.

Information on preservation treating standards, location of treating plants and recommended treatments can be obtained from the American Wood Preservers Institute at 1021 Yeon Building, Portland, Oregon, 97204; 1651 Old Meadow Road, McLean Va. 22101, or 1499 Bayshore Highway, Burlingame, Calif. 94010.

Table 94. Minimum Net Retentions of Preservatives, lbs./cu.ft.[1]

	Coal-tar Creosote, and Creosote-Coal--Tar Solutions	5% Penta 0.75% Cu Napthenate In Oil	Various Water-borne Salts to AWPA Specifications
TIES	8	--	--
Lumber & Structural Timber: For Coastal Waters:			
Douglas fir	14	--	--
Southern pine	20	--	--
For fresh water, ground contact, important members for dry use	10	10	--
For moderate leaching conditions	--	--	0.50-1.15
For dry use	--	--	0.30-0.75
PILES			
For Coastal waters:			
Douglas fir	14	--	--
Southern pine	20	--	--
For land or fresh water use	12	--	--
POLES	8	8	--
POSTS	6	6	0.5-1.15

[1] Retentions are lbs. of solution per cubic foot for columns 2 and 3 and lbs. of dry salt per cubic foot for column 4. Retentions for plywood may be considerably higher owing to the large surface to volume ratio.

By permission of American Wood Preserves Inst.

Fire Retardant Treatments

Fire consumes wood at a rate of about 0.05 inch per minute during the first 30 minutes of exposure, and 0.02 inch per minute thereafter. Large timbers build a protective coating of char (carbon). Small size timbers do not have enough volume to do this before they are, to all practical purposes, consumed.

Fire-retardant chemical *pressure* treatments act by reducing flame spread, giving off gases that extinguish flame. *Fire-retardants* are water-borne solutions of ammonium phosphate, diammonium phosphate, ammonium sulphate, borax, boric acid and zinc chloride. Use approved specifications of AWPI, mentioned above. As they are water-borne and often applied to dry wood, swelling distortion problems require recognition and careful attention by the treater. Treatment of laminations prior to gluing is a preferred procedure when it can be obtained. Fire retardant treated framing is becoming common for use in commercial buildings and institutions.

Coatings to protect against fire are also available. They reduce flame spread, but haven't the resistance to intense fire over time shown by pressure treatments. They prevent the rapid spread of fire and are used primarily in old existing structures where added protection is wanted, usually due to a change in the type of occupancy (as when a residence becomes a dormitory or commercial office or apartment house). Examples are borax, sodium silicate, monoammonium phosphate and intumescent paints.

Heavy Timber Construction for Fire Durability

Heavy Timber Construction (HTC) is accorded a fire rating similar to one-hour resistive. Many codes place HTC in a special category, better than frame construction, but not equivalent to one-hour resistive.

Columns:

(1) Wood columns may be sawn or glued-laminated and shall not be less than 8-inch nominal width and depth when supporting floor loads; 6-inch nominal width by 8-inch nominal depth when supporting roof and ceiling loads only.

(2) Columns shall be continuous, or superimposed through all stories by means of reinforced concrete or metal caps with brackets, or connected by properly designed steel or iron caps, with pintles and base plates, or by timber splice plates affixed to columns with metal connectors housed within the contact faces.

Floor Framing:

(1) Beams and girders of sawn or glued-laminated wood shall be 6-in. x 10-in. nominal or larger.

(2) Framed or glued-laminated arches which are supported at the floor line and support floor loads, shall be 8-in. nominal minimum dimension.

(3) Members of framed timber trusses supporting floor loads shall be not less than 8-in. nominal width or depth.

Roof Framing:

(1) Framed or glued-laminated arches for roof construction which start at the floor level and do not support floor loads shall be 6-inch nominal minimum width by 8-inch nominal minimum depth in the lower half of the height, and 6-inch nominal minimum width or depth for the upper portion.

(2) Framed or glued-laminated arches for roof construction which start from the tops of walls or abutments, framed timber trusses and other roof framing which do not support floor loads, shall have members not less than 4-inch nominal width by 6-inch nominal depth. Spaced members may be composed of two or more pieces not less than 3-inch nominal thickness when solidly blocked throughout their intervening spaces or when constructed with a continuous wood cover plate of 2-inch nominal minimum thickness secured to the underside of such spaced members. Splice plates shall be at least 3-inch nominal thickness. When protected by approved automatic sprinkler systems under the roof deck, such framing members may be 3-inch nominal width.

Floors shall be of sawn or glued-laminated: (1) Spliced to T & G plank not less than 3-inch nominal thickness covered with 1-inch nominal Spliced T & G flooring laid crosswise or diagonally to the plank, or with other approved wearing surface, or (2) planks not less than 4-inch nominal width set on edge close together well spiked and covered as above. The planks shall be laid so there is no continuous line of end joints except at points of support. Floors shall not extend closer than 1/2-inch to walls to provide for expansion, with the expansion space covered to prevent flue action.

Roof Decks shall be of sawn or glued-laminated spliced or T & G plank not less than 2-inch nominal thickness, or of planks not less than 3-inch nominal width set on edge close together and laid as for floors, above. Other wood or wood-fiber based decking are available and may be used upon presentation of evidence of satisfactory fire resistive performance.

These definitions are taken from AITC 108-65, "Standard for Heavy Timber Construction." Other pertinent information on wall construction and construction details is found in this AITC Timber Construction Standard. Reference is also made to National Forest Products Association's "Wood Construction Data No. 5" and applicable building codes.

The above described features are illustrated in Figure 127.

Chemical Agents

Wood is unaffected by chemicals present in the atmosphere, as far as structural degradation is concerned. Wood resists the effects of acids better than many materials and is often used for acid storage tanks, being more durable than steel. Mild alkalies do little harm to wood, but strong alkalies will destroy wood fairly rapidly. Organic liquids and petroleum oils and solvents are generally harmless to wood.

The U.S. Department of Agriculture's "Wood Handbook" No. 72, contains a discussion of chemical degradation of wood, with several references.

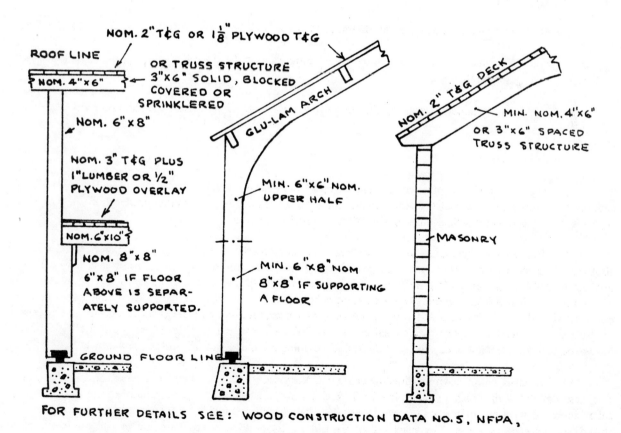

Figure 127.   Heavy timber construction.

Cost of Treatments (1971)

Treating costs vary widely depending upon the amount and kind of preservative the equipment, time and labor involved in effecting the treatment, and the material being treated. Some of the water-borne salt treatments can be obtained for $30 and $40 per thousand board feet. The penta and copper napthenate in oil, empty-cell treatments may cost $60 to $80 per thousand board feet. Creosote treatment (full-cell) of poles and piling is about $75 per thousand, while fire retardant treatments vary considerably, up to $90 per thousand. These figures are very rough estimates based on a rather limited variety of experience. The principal point in noting these costs is to indicate that treating costs may represent a 50 to 100 percent increase in material value and cost. Accordingly, treatment should not be specified unless essential, and then only if economically justifiable. By far the major portion of wood construction are used untreated, in applications where treatment is not necessary.

CHAPTER 24

ADHESIVES IN CONSTRUCTION

Many wood products depend on adhesive systems for their form and strength. For wood, adhesives serve a function somewhat like that of welded joints in metallic materials. While the use of adhesives is not new, their acceptance in structural wood members has, during the period since 1940, become increasingly widespread. A number of adhesive types are firmly established in the building construction business and others are rapidly finding their place as builders, designers, and research engineers develop means of applying them and effectively controlling the quality of the resulting adhesive bonds.

Table 96 is a list of adhesives used in bonding wood to wood and other materials. Animal, soybean, blood and casein glues are protein adhesives. Experience with their use extends far back into the past, and although they have limitations they have served well within these limits. Most are capable of developing bond strengths between side grain surfaces fully equal to the normal strength of solid wood, at wood moisture content levels below about 16%.

Animal glues are applied hot and develop bonds as they cool and lose moisture to the wood and the surrounding atmosphere. This type of adhesive is not used for structural building products. *Starch* glues are applied cold and form bonds by the evaporation of water. Less sensitive to heat than animal glues, they are principally used in making low cost plywood for products where only temporary durability is needed, such as packing cases not intended for re-use.

Soybean adhesives can be hot-pressed to accelerate their cure. Where environmental moisture is low, they are fairly durable, and are used by some producers of decorative interior paneling and furniture parts.

Blood glues are more tolerant of moisture than those previously mentioned, but are far from waterproof. Their use for sheathing plywood has been extensive. As long as they are not exposed to direct wetting for extended periods of time, performance may be good. Low cost and the ability to cure by heat in a few minutes permits the use of heated multiple-opening presses to achieve economic production rates. By blending blood adhesives with moderate amounts of phenolic resin materials, durability can be improved. However, phenolic resins have been continuously reduced in price to a point where this economy is less important than it formerly has been.

Casein adhesives are products of the dairy industry. They have rather good moisture tolerance if the joints are well-made, but cannot stand continuous immersion or extremely humid atmospheres. Casein adhesives can be applied at temperatures down to around 40°F. This has permitted their use in unheated work areas. Many curved arches and beams have been field fabricated with casein glues. Casein adhesives have reasonably good gap-filling properties and are more tolerant of imperfect pressure uniformity than are most other structural adhesives.

Adhesive Bonding Technique

At this juncture some of the basic requirements for good glued-joint fabrication should be mentioned.

The surfaces to be joined should be well-mated, whether curved or flat. They should be clean, free of dirt, oil, oxides, resinous deposits, and generally well-seasoned.

The moisture content of wood parts in a glued assembly should not differ more than 5% if high shrinkage stresses are to be avoided.

ADHESIVES

Table 96. Adhesives Used in Wood Products Manufacture & Construction

Type	Method of Cure	Water Resistance	Uses
Animal	Cooling & loss of water	Low	Furniture & cabinetry
Starch	Loss of water	Low	Low grade plywood, paper
			Not for construction
Soybean	Heat & loss of water	Low	Interior plywood
Blood	Heat & loss of water	Moderate	Sheathing, plywood, an extender for phenol
Casein	Chemical reaction & loss of water	Good	Dry use laminating, lumber-plywood components
Urea	Polymerization, hot or cold	Poor when hot High when cold	Furniture, cabinetry, interior plywood, laminating*, particle-board
Melamine	Polymerization, hot	Waterproof, all temp.	Laminated timber
Phenol	Polymerization, hot	Waterproof, all temp.	Exterior plywood, laminated timber, hardboard
Resorcinol	Polymerization, hot or cold	Waterproof, all temp.	Exterior plywood, laminated timber

*Used for laminated timber, in Europe; Not used for that purpose in U.S.A.

Table 96. Continued

Type	Method of Cure	Water Resistance	Uses
Polyvinyl Acetate	Chemical reaction, cold water loss	Varies with formulation, low to quite high	Furniture, cabinetry, trim, and specialties
Polyurethane	Chemical reaction, hot or cold	High	Specialties
Polyester	Loss of solvent, cold	High	Specialties with fiberglas
Epoxy Resin	Chemical reaction, hot or cold	Good, sometimes high	Specialties (expensive)
Rubber Base Mastic	Loss of solvent, cold	High	Field gluing semi-structural and sealant
Contact Cements	Loss of solvent, cold	High	Field gluing of overlays
Hot Melts	Cooling, phase change	High	Specialties, lumber, plywood, particleboard overlays
Elastomerics	Loss of solvent, reaction with water	High	Field gluing semi structural and sealants

The adhesive should be spread evenly and uniformly over the entire surface. Usually the manufacturer recommends a definite weight of adhesive for a given surface area. Spreads run from 24 pounds per thousand square feet of glue bond to 80 pounds, depending upon the type of pressing equipment used. Facilities to apply uniform pressure up to the ability of the wood to withstand surface crushing under process moisture and heat, allow use of the lower rates of glue spread.

Pressure is important for several reasons. Adequate uniform pressure improves the mating of surfaces. For the more common structural adhesives, thin glue lines are stronger than thick ones. The idea that the adhesive can form a thick connection is a misconception. Most adhesive bonds must be around 0.005 inches thick for structural work. This requires hydraulic pressure presses, or screw jack presses with closely spaced jacks and short thick pressure plates, usually tightened systematically with calibrated torque wrenches and hydraulic compressometers.

Excessive pressure can squeeze so much glue from the joint that a poor bond results. Thus, good results depend on experienced attention, a knowledge of adhesive technology, and good customer service on the part of the adhesive manufacturer. Quality control inspection and testing during production is essential to structural gluing. Most building codes accept glued products on the basis that some form of regular and formal quality control be practiced and certified by a seal or inspectors stamp, backed by test records and service marking of the product.

Glued members must remain clamped until the glue bond strength is reasonably well developed. The time depends upon the adhesive and the curing system. Cold curing systems require more time than hot curing systems, a point that will be mentioned again. Heat accelerates both chemical reactions and water or solvent evaporation. Where, as noted in Table 96, these methods of cure apply, the effect of heat is generally similar.

For certain adhesives, such as polyvinyl resin emulsions, animal glue and hot melts, heat cannot be used as it merely softens, or melts the adhesive.

Pressure release is also a factor in successful gluing. For adhesives mixed with water or volatile solvents, the release of pressure from a hot press charge permits formation of vapor between the parts. As this cannot escape readily it may produce blisters or "blows" at the glue line and explode the assembly.

Structural Adhesives

The most commonly used structural adhesives are the synthetic resin glues: urea, melamine, phenol, resorcinol and certain blends of these adhesives. The urea resin and melamine adhesives are nearly colorless and their glue lines are indistinct. Phenol and resorcinol glues are reddish brown and fairly dark. Urea-melamine blended 60% melamine or greater is used structurally where glue line stresses are not highly critical as in roof-decking. Phenol-resorcinol blends provide the economic advantage of low cost phenol and the curing properties of resorcinol. Without being too highly technical, a word of explanation is offered here.

These synthetic resin adhesives cure by polymerization, the formation of a new compound of higher molecular weight. For melamine and phenol adhesives, this is accomplished by heating to some specific temperature level. If that temperature level is not reached, the adhesive will never completely cure or become fully strong. Urea resin and resorcinol resin adhesives will polymerize cold, given adequate time. For such bonds, pressure may be released before development of full strength, as they will continue to cure and gain full strength with time.

The phenol and melamine adhesives are rather critical inasmuch as a specific polymerization temperature must be achieved during manufacture, usually in the vicinity of 325°F. Blends of these with resorcinol or urea resin modifies the polymerization requirements, making them less critical and able to develop full cure with time.

The most common laminating adhesives used in North America are the phenol-resorcinol resins. Casein is still used by some plants but its use appears to be diminishing somewhat.

In Europe, urea resin glues has been successfully used for many years, although this practice appears to be yielding to phenol-resorcinol.

From a manufacturers point of view, the economic advantages of either casein or urea resin glues are slight and the freedom from delamination due to wet conditions of service, provides a strong incentive to the trend toward use of phenol-resorcinol. Similar trends are also evident in plywood manufacturing practice. As it is most impossible to control the misuse of interior glue bonds in exterior environments, use of waterproof types removes that source of glued wood product performance failures, which often through no fault of the producer arise to discredit him. Still there will probably always be some use of non-waterproof adhesives in structural work.

Design Properties of Structural Adhesives

Because structural adhesives have high shear moduli, and are applied in thin layers, wood products joined by these glues are designed as though the wood was continuous through the bond.

The shear parallel-to-grain strength of a laminated beam is equal to the allowable shear stress for the species and grade of wood used.

Section properties for design are also computed on the basis that the wood is continuous through the joint. No special transformed section or allowance for area occupied by adhesive is necessary.

Glued joints are immeasurably more rigid than nailed, bolted, or metal plate connected joints of most types. Trusses made with glued plywood gussets are more rigid than simple nailed gusset types. Rotation of glued plywood gusset joints is negligible by comparison.

It is interesting to note that one square inch of glue line has more lateral load strength than almost any type of nail, and considerably greater rigidity.

Good glued *butt-joints*, end-grain to end-grain, remain an unreached objective with most of the structural adhesives. However, scarfed and finger jointed splices can be highly successful. These are discussed briefly in Chapter 16 of this book, in the Uniform Building Code, and in "Fabrication and Design of Glued Laminated Wood Structural Members" by Freas and Selbo.

Some of the polymeric adhesives, such as polyurethane and certain hot melts show some promise of good end-joint strength. However, their use of this purpose is still under development.

Semi or Non-Structural Adhesives

The remaining adhesives in Table 96 (excepting epoxies) have shear moduli below that of wood. This means that they permit shear-slip between connected members. The amount of this slip greatly affects their utility as structural adhesives. Some are nearly as rigid as the "structural adhesives" and others flow and creep to the point that they are virtually useless in developing connection rigidity. They will, however, bond wall panels to framing and subflooring to joists.

Research to define techniques for structural design of assemblies bonded with these adhesives is currently active. In the near future rational approaches to designs with such adhesives should emerge. A proper formulation by adhesive manufacturers, with specified shear strength, shear modulus of elasticity and creep properties, will probably permit their effective use. Meanwhile, they are finding considerable acceptance in modular and mobile home construction for their value as sealants and for securing panels to frames. They may serve as well as, or better than, conventional nailing, particularly in providing rigidity during the delivery of factory-built structures to the consumer's site.

Epoxy resins tend to be rather costly, but have some remarkable properties in bonding dissimilar materials where shrinkage and thermal stresses do not develop in excess of adhesive strength. They have been used to advantage for field repair work and grouting of checked or delaminated timber.

Future developments in adhesives will produce some highly utilitarian fastening techniques. Gluing technology is not bound or limited by tradition and new claims should be accorded fair consideration. One must use care in entrusting crucial structures to untried adhesive compounds. However, means of establishing the utility of new adhesives are available in the various standard tests for strength, creep, aging, and durability found in the ASTM Standards on wood and adhesives.

BIBLIOGRAPHY

American Association of State Highway Officials. "Standard Specifications for Highway Bridges."

American Institute of Timber Construction. 1970. "Standard Specifications for Structural Glued Laminated Timber of Douglas Fir, Western Larch, Southern Pine and California Redwood." AITC 203-70.

American Institute of Timber Construction. 1966. *Timber Construction Manual.* John Wiley & Sons, Inc.

American Plywood Association. 1966. "Plywood Design Specification."

American Plywood Association. 1968. "Design of Curved Plywood Panels." P.D.S. Supp. No. 1.

American Plywood Association. 1968. "Design of Plywood Beams." P.D.S. Supp. No. 2.

American Plywood Association. 1970. "Design of Flat Plywood Stressed Skin Panels." P.D.S. Supp. No. 3.

American Plywood Association. 1970. "Design of Flat Plywood Sandwich Panels." P.D.S. Supp. No. 4.

American Plywood Association. "Plywood Diaphragm Construction." Form 70-310.

American Plywood Association. 1970. "Guide to Plywood Sheathing for Floors, Walls & Roofs. Form S70-30.

American Plywood Association. 1970. "Guide to Plywood Grades." Form 66-390.

American Plywood Association. 1969. "Guide to Plywood Components." Form S69-60.

American Plywood Association. 1970. "Guide to Plywood for Siding." Form S70-40.

American Plywood Association. 1969. "Plywood Sidings."

American Plywood Association. "Plywood Components for Church Architecture.

American Plywood Association. "Plywood Construction Systems for Commercial and Industrial Buildings." Form 65-310.

American Plywood Association. "Qualified Coatings for Plywood." Form 68-910.

American Plywood Association. "Finishing Softwood Plywood." Form 63-60.

American Plywood Association. 1969. "2-4-1 Plywood Design and Installation Data." Form 69-375.

American Plywood Association. 1967. "Plywood Specification Guide." Form 67-820.

American Plywood Association. 1968. "Glued Plywood Floor System, Concpets No. 114."

American Plywood Association. "Fire Retardant Treated Plywood Roofs." Form 65-250A.

American Plywood Association. "Pressure Preserved Plywood." Form 66-220.

American National Standards Institute. "Properties of Treated Poles." A05.1-1963.

American National Standards Institute. "Minimum Design Loads in Buildings and Other Structures." A58.1-1955.

American Society for Testing & Materials. 1969. "Establishing Structural Grades for Visually Graded Lumber." ASTM-D245.

American Society for Testing & Materials. 1965. "Testing Small Clear Specimens of Timber." ASTM-D143.

American Society for Testing & Materials. 1970. "Establishing Clear Wood Strength Values." ASTM-D2555.

American Society for Testing & Materials. "Testing Metal Fasteners for Wood." ASTM-D1761.

American Wood Preservers Institute. "Pressure Treating Plants Throughout the West."

Anderson, L.O., T.B. Heebrink and A.E. Oviatt. 1971. Construction Guide for Exposed Wood Decks, U.S.D.A. Forest Service (Pacific Northwest Forest and Range Experiment Station, Portland, Oregon).

Anon., "Digital Computer Program for Analysis of Member Stresses in Symmetric W Trusses." 1964. Res. Bull. 783. Wood Research Lab., Purdue Univ., Agricultural Exp. Sta.

Anon., "Properties of Wood Related to Drying." 1951. U.S. Forest Products Laboratory Report 1900-1.

Bonnickson, Leroy W. 1968. "Pole Type Structures." PNW 100. Pacific Northwest Cooperative Extension Publication. Oregon State University, Washington State University or University of Idaho.

Booth, L.G. and Reece, P.O. 1967. *The Structural Use of Timber* SPON (London).

Boyd, Donald W. 1962. "Snow Loads on Roofs in Canada." National Research Council of Canada." *Forest Prod. J.*, 12(8)

Brown, Panshin and Forsaith. *Textbook of Wood Technology*. Vol. II, 1952. McGraw-Hill Book Co.

Federal Housing Administration. 1963. "Minimum Property Standards for One and Two Living Units." FHA No. 300.

Federal Housing Administration. 1964. Report No. 750, *Guide to Impact Noise Control in Multi-family Dwellings*. Sup't of Documents.

Freas, A.D. and Selbo, M.L. 1954. "Fabrication and Design of Glued Laminated Wood Structural Members." USDA Tech. Bull. 1069.

Grantham, J.B. and T.B. Heebink. 1971, Insuring Noise Control in Wood-Framed Buildings, *Forest Prod. J.*, V. 22, n. 5, pp. 36-43. (Pacific Northwest Forest & Range Exp. Sta., Wood Construction Unit)

Harlow, William M. 1970. *Inside Wood, Masterpiece of Nature*. American Forestry Association.

Hoyle, R.J., Jr. 1968. "Background to Machine Stress Grading." *Forest Prod. J.*, 18(4).

International Conference of Building Officials. 1967. *Uniform Building Code*. Vol. I.

International Conference of Building Officials. 1970. *Uniform Building Code Standards*.

Let's Get Sophisticated with Timber Piles. 1968. Wood Preserving, 46(8).

Midwest Plan Service. 1965. "Designs for Glued Trusses." MWPS-9. Iowa State University.

Midwest Plan Service. 1965. "Designs for Nailed Trusses." MWPS-11. Iowa State University.

National Forest Products Association. 1971. *National Design Standard for Stress Grade Lumber and its Fastenings.*

National Forest Products Association. "Wood Construction Data No. 5."

National Forest Products Association. 1970. "Working Stresses for Joists and Rafters."

National Forest Products Association. 1970. "Wood Structural Design Data."

Nemeth, L.J. 1967. "Determination of Allowable Working Stresses for Vertically Laminated Beams." *Forest Prod. J.,* 17(4).

Nemeth, L.J. 1964. "Evaluation of Fifteen Truss Plate Connectors with E.M.S.R. Lumber of Three Species." Potlatch Forests, Inc.

Newlin, J.A. 1934. "Shear in Checked Beams," *Proceedings of the American Railway Engineering Association,* Vol. 35.

Orosz, Ivan. 1970. "Simplified Method for Calculating Shear Deflection of Beams." USDA Forest Service Res. Note FPL-0210.

Owens-Corning Fiberglass Corp. *Solutions to Noise Control Problems in the Construction of Apartments, Motels, and Hotels.*

Patterson, Donald. 1969. "Pole Building Design." American Wood Preservers Institute, 6th Edition.

Payne, R.J. 1969. *Plywood Construction Manual.* Council of The Forest Industries of British Columbia.

Pearson, R.G., Kloot, N.H., and Boyd, J.D. 1958. *Timber Engineering Design Handbook.* (Melbourne).

Peck. E.C. 1955. "Moisture Content of Wood in Use." U.S. Forest Products Laboratory Report 1655.

Schein, Edward W. 1968. "The Influence of Design on Exposed Wood in Buildings in the Puget Sound Area." Pacific Northwest Forest & Range Experiment Station. USDA Forest Service.

Scofield, W.L. and O'Brien, W.H. *Modern Timber Enginering.*

Seely, F.B. and Smith, J.O. 1962. *Advanced Mechanics of Materials.* John Wiley & Sons.

Southern Pine Association. 1970. "How to Build Storm Resistant Structures."

Southern Pine Inspection Burea. 1970. "1970 Standard Grading Rules for Southern Pine Lumber."

Timber Engineering Company. 1962. "Design Manual for Timber Connector Construction."

Timber Engineering Company. 1956. *Timber Design and Construction Handbook.* F.W. Dodge Corporation.

Timoshenko, S. and Young, D.H. 1968. *Elements of Strength of Materials.* Fifth Edition. D. Van Nostrand and Company.

Timoshenko, S. 1968. *Strength of Materials, Part I, Elementary Theory & Problems*. Third Edition. D. Van Nostrand and Company.

Truss Plate Institute. 1970. "Design Specifications for Light Metal Plate Connected Wood Trusses. TPI-70.

U.S. Department of Commerce. 1970. American Softwood Lumber Standard. Product Standard PS 20-70.

U.S. Department of Commerce. 1966. "Softwood Plywood–Construction and Industrial." Product Standard PS 1-66.

U.S. Department of Commerce. 1963. "Structural Glued Laminated Timber." Commercial Standard CS 253-63.

United States Steel Corporation. "Pressure-Treated Wood for Lasting Construction." ADUSS 83-1821.

West Coast Lumber Inspection Bureau. 1970. "Standard Grading Rules for West Coast Lumber." No. 16.

Western Wood Preservers Institute. "An Architect's Guide Covering Pressure Treated Wood (Protected from Insects, Decay and Fire).

Western Wood Products Association. 1970. "1970 Standard Grading Rules for Western Lumber."

Western Wood Products Association. 1970. "Determination of Recommended Design Values for Western Softwood Lumber."

Wood Handbook. 1955. U.S. Forest Products Laboratory, USDA, Agriculture Handbook No. 72.

Wood, Lyman W. 1956. "Formulas for Columns with Side Loads and Eccentricity." FPL Report 1782, U.S. Forest Products Laboratory.

APPENDIX A

LUMBER PROPERTIES
FOR DESIGN

Tables A1 through A6 are from the grading rules of the Western Wood Products Association, and are used in this text primarily to simplify the presentation. The insert following Table A11 lists the design properties and grades of all U.S. lumber grade rule agencies.

Table A1

LIGHT FRAMING and STUDS—2″ to 4″ Thick, 2″ to 4″ Wide
Recommended Design Values in Pounds Per Square Inch[1]

Species or Group	Grade	Extreme Fiber Stress in Bending "Fb"		Tension Parallel to Grain "Ft"	Horizontal Shear "Fv"	Compression		Modulus of Elasticity "E"
		Single	Repetitive			Perpendicular "Fc⊥"	Parallel to Grain "Fc"	
Douglas Fir-Larch	Construction[2]	1050	1200	625	95	385	1150	1,500,000
	Standard[2]	600	675	350	95	385	925	1,500,000
	Utility[2]	275	325	175	95	385	600	1,500,000
	Studs	800	925	475	95	385	600	1,500,000
Douglas Fir South	Construction[2]	1000	1150	600	90	335	1000	1,100,000
	Standard[2]	550	650	325	90	335	850	1,100,000
	Utility[2]	275	300	150	90	335	550	1,100,000
	Studs	775	875	450	90	335	550	1,100,000
Hem-Fir	Construction[2]	825	975	475	75	245	925	1,200,000
	Standard[2]	450	525	275	75	245	750	1,200,000
	Utility[2]	225	250	125	75	245	500	1,200,000
	Studs	625	725	375	75	245	500	1,200,000
Mountain Hemlock	Construction[2]	875	1000	525	95	370	900	1,000,000
	Standard[2]	500	575	275	95	370	725	1,000,000
	Utility[2]	225	275	125	95	370	475	1,000,000
	Studs	675	775	400	95	370	475	1,000,000
Mountain Hemlock— Hem-Fir	Construction[2]	825	975	475	75	245	900	1,000,000
	Standard[2]	450	525	275	75	245	725	1,000,000
	Utility[2]	225	250	125	75	245	475	1,000,000
	Studs	625	725	375	75	245	475	1,000,000
Subalpine Fir (White Woods) (Mixed Species)	Construction[2]	625	725	375	60	195	650	800,000
	Standard[2]	350	400	200	60	195	525	800,000
	Utility[2]	175	200	100	60	195	350	800,000
	Studs	475	550	275	60	195	350	800,000
Engelmann Spruce (Engelmann Spruce- Lodgepole Pine)	Construction[2]	675	775	400	70	195	650	1,000,000
	Standard[2]	375	425	225	70	195	525	1,000,000
	Utility[2]	175	200	100	70	195	350	1,000,000
	Studs	525	600	300	70	195	350	1,000,000
Lodgepole Pine	Construction[2]	775	875	450	70	250	800	1,000,000
	Standard[2]	425	500	250	70	250	675	1,000,000
	Utility[2]	200	225	125	70	250	425	1,000,000
	Studs	600	675	350	70	250	425	1,000,000
Ponderosa Pine- Sugar Pine (Ponderosa Pine- Lodgepole Pine)	Construction[2]	725	825	425	70	250	775	1,000,000
	Standard[2]	400	450	225	70	250	625	1,000,000
	Utility[2]	200	225	100	70	250	400	1,000,000
	Studs	550	625	325	70	250	400	1,000,000
Idaho White Pine	Construction[2]	725	850	425	65	240	825	1,100,000
	Standard[2]	400	475	250	65	240	675	1,100,000
	Utility[2]	200	225	125	65	240	450	1,100,000
	Studs	550	650	325	65	240	450	1,100,000
Western Cedars	Construction[2]	750	850	425	75	295	875	900,000
	Standard[2]	425	475	250	75	295	725	900,000
	Utility[2]	200	225	125	75	295	475	900,000
	Studs	575	650	325	75	295	475	900,000

[1]These design values apply to lumber when used at a maximum moisture content of 19% such as in most covered structures. For other conditions of use, see Table 15.
[2]Fb, Ft and Fc recommended design values apply only to 4″ widths of these grades.

Courtesy Western Wood Products Assn.

Table A2

STRUCTURAL LIGHT FRAMING and APPEARANCE—2″ to 4″ Thick, 2″ to 4″ Wide

Recommended Design Values in Pounds Per Square Inch[1]

Species or Group	Grade	Extreme Fiber Stress in Bending "Fb"		Tension Parallel to Grain "Ft"	Horizontal Shear "Fv"	Compression		Modulus of Elasticity "E"
		Single	Repetitive			Perpendicular "Fc⊥"	Parallel to Grain "Fc"	
Douglas Fir-Larch	Select Structural	2100	2400	1200	95	385	1600	1,800,000
	No. 1 & Appearance	1750	2050	1050	95	385	1250	1,800,000
	No. 2	1450	1650	850	95	385	1000	1,700,000
	No. 3	800	925	475	95	385	600	1,500,000
Douglas Fir South	Select Structural	2000	2300	1150	90	335	1400	1,400,000
	No. 1 & Appearance	1700	1950	975	90	335	1150	1,400,000
	No. 2	1400	1600	825	90	335	900	1,300,000
	No. 3	775	875	450	90	335	550	1,100,000
Hem-Fir	Select Structural	1650	1900	975	75	245	1300	1,500,000
	No. 1 & Appearance	1400	1600	825	75	245	1000	1,500,000
	No. 2	1150	1300	675	75	245	800	1,400,000
	No. 3	625	725	375	75	245	500	1,200,000
Mountain Hemlock	Select Structural	1750	2000	1000	95	370	1250	1,300,000
	No. 1 & Appearance	1450	1700	850	95	370	1000	1,300,000
	No. 2	1200	1400	700	95	370	775	1,100,000
	No. 3	675	775	400	95	370	475	1,000,000
Mountain Hemlock— Hem-Fir	Select Structural	1650	1900	975	75	245	1250	1,300,000
	No. 1 & Appearance	1400	1600	825	75	245	1000	1,300,000
	No. 2	1150	1300	675	75	245	775	1,100,000
	No. 3	625	725	375	75	245	475	1,000,000
Subalpine Fir (White Woods) (Mixed Species)	Select Structural	1250	1400	725	60	195	900	900,000
	No. 1 & Appearance	1050	1200	600	60	195	700	900,000
	No. 2	850	1000	500	60	195	550	900,000
	No. 3	475	550	275	60	195	350	800,000
Engelmann Spruce (Engelmann Spruce- Lodgepole Pine)	Select Structural	1350	1550	775	70	195	900	1,200,000
	No. 1 & Appearance	1150	1300	675	70	195	725	1,200,000
	No. 2	950	1100	550	70	195	575	1,100,000
	No. 3	525	600	300	70	195	350	1,000,000
Lodgepole Pine	Select Structural	1500	1750	875	70	250	1150	1,300,000
	No. 1 & Appearance	1300	1500	750	70	250	900	1,300,000
	No. 2	1050	1200	625	70	250	700	1,200,000
	No. 3	600	675	350	70	250	425	1,000,000
Ponderosa Pine- Sugar Pine (Ponderosa Pine- Lodgepole Pine)	Select Structural	1400	1650	825	70	250	1050	1,200,000
	No. 1 & Appearance	1200	1400	700	70	250	850	1,200,000
	No. 2	1000	1150	575	70	250	675	1,100,000
	No. 3	550	625	325	70	250	400	1,000,000
Idaho White Pine	Select Structural	1450	1650	850	65	240	1150	1,400,000
	No. 1 & Appearance	1250	1400	725	65	240	925	1,400,000
	No. 2	1000	1150	600	65	240	725	1,300,000
	No. 3	550	650	325	65	240	450	1,100,000
Western Cedars	Select Structural	1450	1700	850	75	295	1250	1,100,000
	No. 1 & Appearance	1250	1450	725	75	295	975	1,100,000
	No. 2	1000	1200	600	75	295	775	1,000,000
	No. 3	575	650	325	75	295	475	900,000

[1]These design values apply to lumber when used at a maximum moisture content of 19% such as in most covered structures. For other conditions of use, see **Table 15**.

Courtesy Western Wood Products Assn.

Table A3

STRUCTURAL JOISTS and PLANKS and APPEARANCE
2″ to 4″ Thick, 6″ and Wider
Recommended Design Values in Pounds Per Square Inch[1]

Species or Group	Grade	Extreme Fiber Stress in Bending "Fb"		Tension Parallel to Grain "Ft"	Horizontal Shear "Fv"	Compression		Modulus of Elasticity "E"
		Single	Repetitive			Perpendicular "Fc⊥"	Parallel to Grain "Fc"	
Douglas Fir-Larch	Select Structural	1800	2050	1200	95	385	1400	1,800,000
	No. 1 & Appearance	1500	1750	1000	95	385	1250	1,800,000
	No. 2	1250	1450	825	95	385	1050	1,700,000
	No. 3	725	850	475	95	385	675	1,500,000
Douglas Fir South	Select Structural	1700	1950	1150	90	335	1250	1,400,000
	No. 1 & Appearance	1450	1650	975	90	335	1150	1,400,000
	No. 2	1200	1350	775	90	335	950	1,300,000
	No. 3	700	800	450	90	335	600	1,100,000
Hem-Fir	Select Structural	1400	1650	950	75	245	1150	1,500,000
	No. 1 & Appearance	1200	1400	800	75	245	1000	1,500,000
	No. 2	1000	1150	650	75	245	850	1,400,000
	No. 3	575	675	375	75	245	550	1,200,000
Mountain Hemlock	Select Structural	1500	1700	1000	95	370	1100	1,300,000
	No. 1 & Appearance	1250	1450	850	95	370	1000	1,300,000
	No. 2	1050	1200	675	95	370	825	1,100,000
	No. 3	625	700	400	95	370	525	1,000,000
Mountain Hemlock—Hem-Fir	Select Structural	1400	1650	950	75	245	1100	1,300,000
	No. 1 & Appearance	1200	1400	800	75	245	1000	1,300,000
	No. 2	1000	1150	650	75	245	825	1,100,000
	No. 3	575	675	375	75	245	525	1,000,000
Subalpine Fir (White Woods) (Mixed Species)	Select Structural	1050	1200	700	60	195	800	900,000
	No. 1 & Appearance	900	1050	600	60	195	700	900,000
	No. 2	750	850	475	60	195	600	900,000
	No. 3	425	500	275	60	195	375	800,000
Engelmann Spruce (Engelmann Spruce-Lodgepole Pine)	Select Structural	1150	1350	775	70	195	800	1,200,000
	No. 1 & Appearance	975	1150	650	70	195	725	1,200,000
	No. 2	800	925	525	70	195	600	1,100,000
	No. 3	475	550	300	70	195	375	1,000,000
Lodgepole Pine	Select Structural	1300	1500	875	70	250	1000	1,300,000
	No. 1 & Appearance	1100	1300	750	70	250	900	1,300,000
	No. 2	925	1050	600	70	250	750	1,200,000
	No. 3	525	625	350	70	250	475	1,000,000
Ponderosa Pine-Sugar Pine (Ponderosa Pine-Lodgepole Pine)	Select Structural	1200	1400	825	70	250	950	1,200,000
	No. 1 & Appearance	1050	1200	700	70	250	850	1,200,000
	No. 2	850	975	550	70	250	700	1,100,000
	No. 3	500	575	325	70	250	450	1,000,000
Idaho White Pine	Select Structural	1250	1450	825	65	240	1000	1,400,000
	No. 1 & Appearance	1050	1200	700	65	240	925	1,400,000
	No. 2	875	1000	575	65	240	775	1,300,000
	No. 3	500	575	325	65	240	475	1,100,000
Western Cedars	Select Structural	1250	1450	850	75	295	1100	1,100,000
	No. 1 & Appearance	1050	1250	725	75	295	975	1,100,000
	No. 2	875	1000	575	75	295	825	1,000,000
	No. 3	525	600	325	75	295	525	900,000

[1]These design values apply to lumber when used at a maximum moisture content of 19% such as in most covered structures. For other conditions of use, see Table 15.

Courtesy Western Wood Products Assn.

Table A4

BEAMS and STRINGERS—5″ and Thicker

Width More than 2″ Greater than Thickness

Recommended Design Values in Pounds Per Square Inch[1]

Species or Group	Grade	Extreme Fiber Stress in Bending "Fb" Single Members	Tension Parallel to Grain "Ft"	Horizontal Shear "Fv"	Compression Perpendicular "Fc⊥"	Compression Parallel to Grain "Fc"	Modulus of Elasticity "E"
Douglas Fir-Larch	Select Structural	1600	1050	85	385	1100	1,600,000
	No. 1	1350	900	85	385	925	1,600,000
Douglas Fir South	Select Structural	1550	1050	85	335	1000	1,200,000
	No. 1	1300	850	85	335	850	1,200,000
Hem-Fir	Select Structural	1250	850	70	245	900	1,400,000
	No. 1	1050	700	70	245	775	1,400,000
Mountain Hemlock	Select Structural	1350	900	90	370	875	1,100,000
	No. 1	1100	750	90	370	750	1,100,000
Mountain Hemlock—Hem-Fir	Select Structural	1250	850	70	245	875	1,100,000
	No. 1	1050	700	70	245	750	1,100,000
Subalpine Fir (White Woods) (Mixed Species)	Select Structural	950	625	60	195	625	900,000
	No. 1	800	525	60	195	525	900,000
Engelmann Spruce (Engelmann Spruce-Lodgepole Pine)	Select Structural	1050	700	65	195	650	1,100,000
	No. 1	875	575	65	195	550	1,100,000
Lodgepole Pine	Select Structural	1150	775	65	250	800	1,100,000
	No. 1	975	650	65	250	675	1,100,000
Ponderosa Pine-Sugar Pine (Ponderosa Pine-Lodgepole Pine)	Select Structural	1100	725	65	250	750	1,100,000
	No. 1	925	625	65	250	625	1,100,000
Idaho White Pine	Select Structural	1100	750	60	240	800	1,200,000
	No. 1	925	625	60	240	675	1,200,000
Western Cedars	Select Structural	1100	750	70	295	875	1,000,000
	No. 1	950	625	70	295	725	1,000,000

[1]These design values apply to lumber when used at a maximum moisture content of 19% such as in most covered structures. For other conditions of use, see Table 15.

Courtesy Western Wood Products Assn.

Table A5

POSTS and TIMBERS—5″ x 5″ and Larger
Width Not More than 2″ Greater than Thickness
Recommended Design Values in Pounds Per Square Inch[1]

Species or Group	Grade	Extreme Fiber Stress in Bending "Fb" — Single Members	Tension Parallel to Grain "Ft"	Horizontal Shear "Fv"	Compression — Perpendicular "Fc⊥"	Compression — Parallel to Grain "Fc"	Modulus of Elasticity "E"
Douglas Fir-Larch	Select Structural	1500	1000	85	385	1150	1,600,000
	No. 1	1200	825	85	385	1000	1,600,000
Douglas Fir South	Select Structural	1400	950	85	335	1050	1,200,000
	No. 1	1150	775	85	335	925	1,200,000
Hem-Fir	Select Structural	1200	800	70	245	950	1,400,000
	No. 1	975	650	70	245	850	1,400,000
Mountain Hemlock	Select Structural	1250	825	90	370	925	1,100,000
	No. 1	1000	675	90	370	800	1,100,000
Mountain Hemlock—Hem-Fir	Select Structural	1200	800	70	245	925	1,100,000
	No. 1	975	650	70	245	800	1,100,000
Subalpine Fir (White Woods) (Mixed Species)	Select Structural	875	600	60	195	675	900,000
	No. 1	725	475	60	195	575	900,000
Engelmann Spruce (Engelmann Spruce-Lodgepole Pine)	Select Structural	950	650	65	195	675	1,100,000
	No. 1	775	525	65	195	600	1,100,000
Lodgepole Pine	Select Structural	1100	725	65	250	850	1,100,000
	No. 1	875	600	65	250	725	1,100,000
Ponderosa Pine-Sugar Pine (Ponderosa Pine-Lodgepole Pine)	Select Structural	1000	675	65	250	800	1,100,000
	No. 1	825	550	65	250	700	1,100,000
Idaho White Pine	Select Structural	1050	700	60	240	850	1,200,000
	No. 1	850	575	60	240	750	1,200,000
Western Cedars	Select Structural	1050	700	70	295	900	1,000,000
	No. 1	850	575	70	295	800	1,000,000

[1]These design values apply to lumber when used at a maximum moisture content of 19% such as in most covered structures. For other conditions of use, see Table 15.

Table A6

MACHINE STRESS-RATED LUMBER—2" Thick or Less
Design Value In Pounds Per Square Inch

"f—E" Classification	Extreme Fiber in Bending "Fb" (3)	Modulus of Elasticity "E"	Tension Parallel to Grain "Ft"	Compression Parallel to Grain "Fc"	Compression Perpendicular to Grain "Fc⊥" (DRY)				
					Douglas Fir & Larch	Hem-Fir	Pine(1)	Engelmann Spruce	Cedar(2)
900f — 1.0 E	900	1,000,000	350	725	385	245	240	195	295
1200f — 1.2 E	1200	1,200,000	600	950	385	245	240	195	295
1500f — 1.4 E	1500	1,400,000	900	1200	385	245	240	195	295
1800f — 1.6 E	1800	1,600,000	1175	1450	385	245	240	195	295
2100f — 1.8 E	2100	1,800,000	1575	1700	385	245	240	195	295
2400f — 2.0 E	2400	2,000,000	1925	1925	385	245	240	195	295
2700f — 2.2 E	2700	2,200,000	2150	2150	385	245	240	195	295
3000f — 2.4 E	3000	2,400,000	2400	2400	385	245	240	195	295
3300f — 2.6 E	3300	2,600,000	2650	2650	385	245	240	195	295

(1) Idaho White, Lodgepole, Ponderosa or Sugar Pine.
(2) Incense or Western Red Cedar.
(3) The tabulated Extreme Fiber in Bending values "Fb" are applicable to lumber loaded on edge. When loaded flatwise, these values must be increased by the following factors:

Horizontal Shear "Fv" (DRY)				
95	75	65	70	75

Nominal Width	Flatwise Loading Design Values (Multiply tabulated values by factors shown below)
4"	1.10
6"	1.15
8"	1.19
10"	1.22
12"	1.25
14"	1.28

Courtesy Western Wood Products Assn.

Table A7
DECKING (MC-15)
2" to 4" Thick, 4" to 12" Wide
Design Values In Pounds Per Square Inch
For Flatwise Use Only
Maximum Moisture Content 15%*

Species	Grade	Extreme Fiber in Bending "Fb" Repetitive Member Uses	Modulus of Elasticity "E"
Douglas Fir—Larch	Selected Decking	2150	1,900,000
	Commercial Decking	1800	1,700,000
Douglas Fir South	Selected Decking	2050	1,500,000
	Commercial Decking	1750	1,300,000
Hem-Fir	Selected Decking	1750	1,600,000
	Commercial Decking	1450	1,500,000
Mountain Hemlock	Selected Decking	1800	1,300,000
	Commercial Decking	1500	1,200,000
Mountain Hemlock—Hem-Fir	Selected Decking	1750	1,300,000
	Commercial Decking	1450	1,200,000
Subalpine Fir (White Woods) (Mixed Species)	Selected Decking	1300	1,000,000
	Commercial Decking	1050	900,000
Engelmann Spruce (Engelmann Spruce—Lodgepole Pine)	Selected Decking	1400	1,300,000
	Commercial Decking	1150	1,200,000
Lodgepole Pine	Selected Decking	1550	1,400,000
	Commercial Decking	1300	1,200,000
Ponderosa Pine—Sugar Pine (Ponderosa Pine—Lodgepole Pine)	Selected Decking	1450	1,300,000
	Commercial Decking	1250	1,100,000
Idaho White Pine	Selected Decking	1500	1,500,000
	Commercial Decking	1250	1,300,000
Western Cedars	Selected Decking	1500	1,100,000
	Commercial Decking	1250	1,000,000

*For other conditions of use, see Table 15.

Courtesy Western Wood Products Assn.

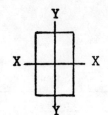

TABLE A8

PROPERTIES OF SECTIONS
BOARDS, DIMENSION, AND TIMBERS

Nominal Size	Actual Size inches b x h	Area sq. in.	Axis X - X I in.⁴	Axis X - X S in.³	Axis Y - Y I in.⁴	Axis Y - Y S in.³	Weight per Foot* lbs.
1 x 3	$\frac{3}{4}$ x $2\frac{1}{2}$	1.88	0.98	0.78	0.09	0.23	0.47
1 x 4	$\frac{3}{4}$ x $3\frac{1}{2}$	2.63	2.68	1.53	0.12	0.33	0.64
1 x 6	$\frac{3}{4}$ x $5\frac{1}{2}$	4.13	10.40	3.78	0.19	0.52	1.00
1 x 8	$\frac{3}{4}$ x $7\frac{1}{4}$	5.44	23.82	6.57	0.26	0.68	1.32
1 x 10	$\frac{3}{4}$ x $9\frac{1}{4}$	6.94	49.47	10.70	0.33	0.87	1.69
1 x 12	$\frac{3}{4}$ x $11\frac{1}{4}$	8.44	88.99	15.82	0.40	1.06	2.05
2 x 3	$1\frac{1}{2}$ x $2\frac{1}{2}$	3.75	1.95	1.56	0.70	0.94	0.91
2 x 4	$1\frac{1}{2}$ x $3\frac{1}{2}$	5.25	5.36	3.06	0.98	1.31	1.28
2 x 6	$1\frac{1}{2}$ x $5\frac{1}{2}$	8.25	20.80	7.56	1.55	2.06	2.00
2 x 8	$1\frac{1}{2}$ x $7\frac{1}{4}$	10.88	47.64	13.14	2.04	2.72	2.64
2 x 10	$1\frac{1}{2}$ x $9\frac{1}{4}$	13.88	98.93	21.39	2.60	3.47	3.37
2 x 12	$1\frac{1}{2}$ x $11\frac{1}{4}$	16.88	177.98	31.64	3.16	4.22	4.10
2 x 14	$1\frac{1}{2}$ x $13\frac{1}{4}$	19.88	290.78	43.89	3.73	4.97	4.83
3 x 3	$2\frac{1}{2}$ x $2\frac{1}{2}$	6.25	3.25	2.60	3.25	2.60	1.52
3 x 4	$2\frac{1}{2}$ x $3\frac{1}{2}$	8.75	8.93	5.10	4.56	3.65	2.13
3 x 6	$2\frac{1}{2}$ x $5\frac{1}{2}$	13.75	34.66	12.60	7.16	5.73	3.34
3 x 8	$2\frac{1}{2}$ x $7\frac{1}{4}$	18.13	79.39	21.90	9.44	7.55	4.41
3 x 10	$2\frac{1}{2}$ x $9\frac{1}{4}$	23.13	164.89	35.65	12.04	9.64	5.62
3 x 12	$2\frac{1}{2}$ x $11\frac{1}{4}$	28.13	296.63	52.73	14.65	11.72	6.84
3 x 14	$2\frac{1}{2}$ x $13\frac{1}{4}$	33.13	484.63	73.15	17.25	13.80	8.05
3 x 16	$2\frac{1}{2}$ x $15\frac{1}{4}$	38.13	738.87	96.90	20.18	16.15	9.27
4 x 4	$3\frac{1}{7}$ x $3\frac{1}{2}$	12.25	12.51	7.15	12.51	7.15	2.98
4 x 6	$3\frac{1}{2}$ x $5\frac{1}{2}$	19.25	48.53	17.65	19.65	11.23	4.68
4 x 8	$3\frac{1}{2}$ x $7\frac{1}{4}$	25.38	111.15	30.66	25.90	14.80	6.17
4 x 10	$3\frac{1}{2}$ x $9\frac{1}{4}$	32.38	230.84	49.91	33.05	18.89	7.87

TABLE A8 (continued)

Nominal Size	Actual Size inches b x h	Area sq. in.	Axis X - X		Axis Y - Y		Weight per Foot* lbs.
			I in.	S in.	I in.	S in.	
4 x 12	3½ x 11¼	39.38	415.28	73.83	40.20	22.97	9.57
4 x 14	3½ x 13¼	46.38	678.46	102.41	47.44	27.11	11.28
4 x 16	3½ x 15¼	53.38	1034.40	135.66	54.60	31.20	12.98
6 x 6	5½ x 5½	30.25	76.26	27.73	76.26	27.73	7.35
6 x 8	5½ x 7½	41.25	193.36	51.56	103.98	37.81	10.03
6 x 10	5½ x 9½	52.25	392.96	82.73	131.71	47.90	12.70
6 x 12	5½ x 11½	63.25	697.07	121.23	159.44	57.98	15.37
6 x 14	5½ x 13½	74.25	1127.67	167.06	187.17	68.06	18.05
6 x 16	5½ x 15½	85.25	1706.78	220.23	214.90	78.15	20.72
6 x 18	5½ x 17½	96.25	2456.38	280.73	242.63	88.23	23.39
8 x 8	7½ x 7½	56.25	263.67	70.31	263.67	70.31	13.67
8 x 10	7½ x 9½	71.25	535.86	112.81	333.98	89.06	17.32
8 x 12	7½ x 11½	86.25	950.55	165.31	404.30	107.81	20.96
8 x 14	7½ x 13½	101.25	1537.73	227.81	474.61	126.56	24.61
8 x 16	7½ x 15½	116.25	2327.42	300.31	544.92	145.31	28.26
8 x 18	7½ x 17½	131.25	3349.61	382.81	615.23	164.06	31.90
10 x 10	9½ x 9½	90.25	678.76	142.90	678.76	142.90	21.94
10 x 12	9½ x 11½	109.25	1204.03	209.40	821.65	172.98	26.55
10 x 14	9½ x 13½	128.25	1947.80	288.56	964.55	203.06	31.17
10 x 16	9½ x 15½	147.25	2948.07	380.40	1107.44	233.15	35.79
10 x 18	9½ x 17½	166.25	4242.84	484.90	1250.34	263.23	40.41
12 x 12	11½ x 11½	132.25	1457.51	253.48	1457.51	253.48	32.14
12 x 14	11½ x 13½	155.25	2357.86	349.31	1710.98	297.56	37.73
12 x 16	11½ x 15½	178.25	3568.71	466.48	1964.46	341.65	43.33
12 x 18	11½ x 17½	201.25	5136.07	586.98	2217.94	385.73	48.92

*Based on 35 lbs./cu.ft. actual volume and weight.

NOTE: Although the maximum size in this table is 12" x 18" larger timber sizes, while uncommon, can sometimes be obtained. Glued-laminated members deeper than 18" are quite common. Glued-laminated timber sizes always differ from those tabulated. See Chapter 15.

TABLE A9. ALLOWABLE UNIT STRESSES[1]/ FOR LAMINATED TIMBER MEMBERS STRESSED PRINCIPALLY IN BENDING,[2]/ LOADED PERPENDICULAR TO THE WIDE FACE OF LAMINATIONS (NORMAL DURATION OF LOAD CONDITIONS)

Combination Symbol	Use Condition	F_b psi	F_t psi	F_c psi	$F_{c\perp}$ - psi Tension face	$F_{c\perp}$ - psi Comp. face	F_v psi	E psi
				DOUGLAS FIR AND LARCH				
26F[3]/	Dry	2600	1600	1500	450	410	165	1,800,000
	Wet	2000	1300	1100	305	275	145	1,500,000
24F	Dry	2400	1600	1500	450	385	165	1,800,000
	Wet	1800	1300	1100	305	260	145	1,500,000
22F	Dry	2200	1600	1500	450*	385*	165	1,800,000
	Wet	1600	1300	1100	305*	260*	145	1,500,000
20F	Dry	2000	1600	1500	385*	385*	165	1,700,000
	Wet	1600	1300	1100	260*	260*	145	1,400,000
18F	Dry	1800	1600	1500	385	385	165	1,700,000
	Wet	1400	1300	1100	260	260	145	1,400,000
16F	Dry	1600	1600	1500	385	385	165	1,600,000
	Wet	1300	1300	1100	260	260	145	1,300,000
				SOUTHERN PINE				
26F[3]/	Dry	2600	1600	1500	385*	385*	200	1,800,000
	Wet	2100	1300	1100	260*	260*	175	1,500,000
24F	Dry	2400	1600	1500	385*	385*	200	1,800,000
	Wet	1900	1300	1100	260*	260*	175	1,500,000
22F	Dry	2200	1600	1500	385*	385*	200	1,700,000
	Wet	1800	1300	1100	260*	260*	175	1,400,000
20F	Dry	2000	1600	1500	385	385	200	1,700,000
	Wet	1600	1300	1100	260*	260*	175	1,400,000
18F	Dry	1800	1600	1500	385	385	200	1,600,000
	Wet	1400	1300	1100	260	260	175	1,300,000

1. Stresses apply to members 12 inches and less in depth. For deeper members the laminated beam depth factor adjustment must be applied.
2. For members stressed principally in tension or compression, see Table A10.
3. The 26F grade is not as widely available as the other grades.
* Certain combinations of laminating lumber permit the use of higher stresses. For this information refer to AITC 117-71 or later revision.

Adapted from AITC 117-71, by permission.

TABLE A.10 ALLOWABLE UNIT STRESSES[1] FOR LAMINATED TIMBER MEMBERS STRESSED PRINCIPALLY IN AXIAL TENSION OR COMPRESSION[2] (NORMAL DURATION OF LOAD CONDITIONS)

Combination Symbol	Use Condition	F_t psi	F_c psi	F_b[3] psi //	F_b[3] psi ⊥	$F_{c\perp}$ psi	F_v[3] psi //	F_v[3] psi ⊥	E psi
DOUGLAS FIR AND LARCH									
5	Dry	2600	2200	2300	2600	450	145	165	2,100,000
	Wet	2000	1600	1600	2000	305	120	145	1,800,000
4	Dry	2400	2000	2100	2400	410	145	165	2,000,000
	Wet	1900	1450	1500	1900	275	120	145	1,700,000
3	Dry	2200	2100	1900	2200	450	145	165	1,900,000
	Wet	1800	1500	1450	1800	305	120	145	1,600,000
2	Dry	1800	1800	1500	1800	385	145	165	1,800,000
	Wet	1400	1300	1100	1400	260	120	145	1,500,000
1	Dry	1200	1500	900	1200	385	145	165	1,600,000
	Wet	950	1100	750	950	260	120	145	1,300,000
SOUTHERN PINE									
5	Dry	2600	2200	2200	2600	450	165	200	2,000,000
	Wet	2100	1600	1750	2100	300	145	175	1,700,000
4	Dry	2400	2100	1900	2400	385	165	200	1,900,000
	Wet	1900	1500	1500	1950	260	145	175	1,600,000
3	Dry	2600	2200	1800	2100	450	165	200	1,800,000
	Wet	2100	1600	1450	1700	300	145	175	1,500,000
2	Dry	2200	1900	1550	1800	385	165	200	1,700,000
	Wet	1800	1400	1250	1450	260	145	175	1,400,000
1	Dry	1600	1400	900	1100	385	165	200	1,500,000
	Wet	1300	1000	700	850	260	145	175	1,300,000

1. The stresses apply to axial stress, and secondary bending stresses in depths 12 inches and less. For depths over 12 inches the laminated beam depth factor adjustment must be applied.

2. Also for secondary bending, see note 1.

3. Symbol // denotes allowable stress when bending load is parallel to wide face of laminations. Symbol ⊥ denotes allowable stress when bending load is perpendicular to the wide face of laminations.

Adapted from AITC 117-71, by permission.

Table A.11 Properties of Sections - Glued Laminated Members

		A = Area			I = Moment of Inertia			S = Section Modulus		
		5.125" WIDTH			6.75" WIDTH			8.75" WIDTH		
No. of Lams	Depth Inches	A in.^{2}	I in.^{4}	S in.^{3}	A in.^{2}	I in.^{4}	S in.^{3}	A in.^{2}	I in.^{4}	S in.^{3}
6	9.0	46.1	311	69	61.8	410	91	78.8	532	118
7	10.5	53.8	494	94	70.9	651	124	91.9	844	161
8	12.0	61.5	738	123	81.0	972	162	105.0	1260	210
9	13.5	69.2	1051	156	91.1	1384	205	118.1	1794	266
10	15.0	76.9	1441	192	101.3	1898	253	131.3	2461	328
11	16.5	84.6	1919	233	111.4	2527	306	144.4	3276	397
12	18.0	92.3	2491	277	121.5	3281	365	157.5	4253	473
13	19.5	99.9	3167	325	131.6	4171	428	170.6	5407	555
14	21.0	107.6	3955	377	141.8	5209	496	183.8	6753	643
15	22.5	115.3	4865	432	151.9	6407	570	196.9	8306	738
16	24.0	123.0	5904	492	162.0	7776	648	210.0	10080	840
17	25.5	130.7	7082	555	172.1	9327	732	223.1	12091	948
18	27.0	138.4	8406	623	182.3	11072	820	236.3	14352	1063
19	28.5	146.1	9886	694	192.4	13021	914	249.4	16880	1185'
20	30.0	153.8	11531	769	202.5	15188	1013	262.5	19688	1313
21	31.5	161.4	13349	848	212.6	17581	1116	275.6	22791	1447
22	33.0	169.1	15348	930	222.8	20215	1225	288.8	26204	1588
23	34.5	176.8	17538	1017	232.9	23098	1339	301.9	29942	1736
24	36.0	184.5	19926	1107	243.0	26224	1458	315.0	34020	1890

For other widths, multiply values in table by width-to-width ratio.

For other depths, multiply values in table by width-to-width ratio.

For A; (Width-to-Width ratio)^3 for I; (Width-to-Width)^2 for S

Supplement

to

1971 EDITION

of

NATIONAL DESIGN SPECIFICATION

for

STRESS-GRADE LUMBER

and ITS FASTENINGS

See November 1972 Addendum

Recommended by

NATIONAL FOREST PRODUCTS ASSOCIATION

1619 Massachusetts Avenue, NW   Washington, D. C. 20036

May 1971

NOTE: This Supplement provides data on working stresses determined in accordance with American Society for Testing and Materials Designations D245-70 "Methods for Establishing Structural Grades and Related Allowable Properties for Visually Graded Lumber" and D2555-70 "Methods for Establishing Clear Wood Strength Values."

ALLOWABLE UNIT STRESSES – STRUCTURAL LUMBER

Table 1a – Allowable Unit Stresses for Structural Lumber – VISUAL GRADING

(Allowable unit stresses listed are for normal loading conditions. See other provisions of Part II for adjustments of tabulated stresses)

Species and commercial grade	Size classification	Extreme fiber in bending "F_b" Single-member uses	Extreme fiber in bending "F_b" Repetitive-member uses	Tension parallel to grain "F_t"	Horizontal shear "F_v"	Compression perpendicular to grain "$F_{c\perp}$"	Compression parallel to grain "F_c"	Modulus of elasticity "E"	Grading rules agency
BALSAM FIR (Surfaced at 15% moisture content. Used at 15% max. m.c.)									
Select Structural		1450	1700	850	65	170	1200	1,200,000	Northeastern
No. 1		1250	1450	725	65	170	975	1,200,000	Lumber
No. 2	2" to 4"	1050	1200	600	65	170	750	1,100,000	Manufacturers
No. 3	thick	575	650	325	65	170	475	1,000,000	Association
Appearance	2" to 4"	1050	1250	725	65	170	1150	1,200,000	and
Construction	wide	750	850	425	65	170	875	1,000,000	Northern
Standard		425	475	250	65	170	725	1,000,000	Hardwood
Utility		200	225	125	65	170	475	1,000,000	and Pine
Stud		575	650	325	65	170	475	1,000,000	Manufacturers
Select Structural	2" to 4"	1250	1450	850	65	170	1050	1,200,000	Association
No. 1	thick	1050	1250	725	65	170	975	1,200,000	(see footnotes
No. 2	6" and	875	1000	575	65	170	800	1,100,000	1, 2, 3, 4, 8,
No. 3	wider	525	600	325	65	170	525	1,000,000	and 9)
Appearance		1050	1250	725	65	170	1150	1,200,000	
BALSAM FIR (Surfaced dry or surfaced green. Used at 19% max. m.c.)									
Select Structural		1350	1550	800	60	170	1050	1,200,000	
No. 1		1150	1300	675	60	170	825	1,200,000	
No. 2	2" to 4"	950	1100	550	60	170	650	1,100,000	Northeastern
No. 3	thick	525	600	300	60	170	400	900,000	Lumber
Appearance	2" to 4"	1000	1150	650	60	170	1000	1,200,000	Manufacturers
Construction	wide	675	800	400	60	170	750	900,000	Association
Standard		375	450	225	60	170	625	900,000	and
Utility		175	200	100	60	170	400	900,000	Northern
Stud		525	600	300	60	170	400	900,000	Hardwood
Select Structural	2" to 4"	1150	1350	775	60	170	925	1,200,000	and Pine
No. 1	thick	1000	1150	650	60	170	825	1,200,000	Manufacturers
No. 2	6" and	825	950	525	60	170	700	1,100,000	Association
No. 3	wider	475	550	300	60	170	450	900,000	
Appearance		1000	1150	650	60	170	1000	1,200,000	(see footnotes
Select Structural	Beams and	1050	––	700	55	170	725	1,000,000	1 through 9)
No. 1	Stringers	875	––	575	55	170	625	1,000,000	
Select Structural	Posts and	975	––	650	55	170	775	1,000,000	
No. 1	Timbers	800	––	525	55	170	675	1,000,000	
Select	Decking	1150	1300	––	––	––	––	1,200,000	NeLMA
Commercial		950	1100	––	––	––	––	1,100,000	
CALIFORNIA REDWOOD (Surfaced at 15% moisture content. Used at 15% max. m.c.)									
Clear Heart Structural	4" & less thick,	2450	2850	1650	155	425	2500	1,400,000	
Clear Structural	any width	2450	2850	1650	155	425	2500	1,400,000	
Select Structural		2200	2550	1300	105	425	2050	1,400,000	
Select Structural, Open grain		1750	2000	1050	105	270	1500	1,200,000	
No. 1		1800	2100	1050	105	425	1650	1,400,000	Redwood
No. 1, Open grain		1450	1650	850	105	270	1200	1,200,000	Inspection
No. 2	4" and less	1500	1700	850	85	425	1300	1,300,000	Service
No. 2, Open grain	thick and	1200	1350	700	85	270	950	1,100,000	
No. 3	wide	850	1000	500	85	425	775	1,200,000	(see footnote
No. 3, Open grain		700	800	400	85	270	575	900,000	3)
Construction		900	1000	500	85	270	1100	900,000	
Standard		500	550	300	85	270	900	900,000	
Utility		250	250	150	85	270	575	900,000	
Stud		700	800	400	85	270	575	900,000	
Select Structural		1900	2150	1250	105	425	1800	1,400,000	
Select Structural, Open grain	4" and less	1500	1700	1000	105	270	1350	1,200,000	
No. 1	thick	1600	1850	1050	105	425	1650	1,400,000	
No. 1, Open grain	6" to 12"	1250	1450	850	105	270	1200	1,200,000	
No. 2	wide	1300	1500	850	85	425	1350	1,300,000	
No. 2, Open grain		1050	1200	700	85	270	1000	1,100,000	
No. 3		750	850	500	85	425	850	1,200,000	
No. 3, Open grain		600	700	400	85	270	625	900,000	
CALIFORNIA REDWOOD (Surfaced dry. Used at 19% max. m.c.)									
Clear Heart Structural	4" & less thick,	2300	2650	1550	145	425	2150	1,400,000	
Clear Structural	any width	2300	2650	1550	145	425	2150	1,400,000	
Select Structural		2050	2350	1200	100	425	1775	1,400,000	
Select Structural, Open grain	4" and less	1600	1850	950	100	270	1300	1,100,000	
No. 1	thick and	1700	1950	1000	100	425	1400	1,400,000	
No. 1, Open grain	wide	1350	1550	800	100	270	1050	1,100,000	Redwood
No. 2		1400	1600	800	80	425	1100	1,300,000	Inspection
No. 2, Open grain		1100	1250	650	80	270	825	1,000,000	Service
No. 3		800	900	450	80	425	675	1,100,000	
No. 3, Open grain		650	700	350	80	270	500	900,000	(see footnote
Construction		800	950	500	80	270	925	900,000	3)
Standard		450	550	250	80	270	775	900,000	
Utility		200	250	150	80	270	500	900,000	
Stud		650	700	350	80	270	500	900,000	

ALLOWABLE UNIT STRESSES – STRUCTURAL LUMBER

Table 1a – Allowable Unit Stresses for Structural Lumber – VISUAL GRADING (cont.)

(Allowable unit stresses listed are for normal loading conditions. See other provisions of Part II for adjustments of tabulated stresses)

Species and commercial grade	Size classification	Extreme fiber in bending "F_b"		Tension parallel to grain "F_t"	Horizontal shear "F_v"	Compression perpendicular to grain "F_{c\perp}"	Compression parallel to grain "F_c"	Modulus of elasticity "E"	Grading rules agency
		Single-member uses	Repetitive-member uses						
CALIFORNIA REDWOOD (Surfaced dry. Used at 19% max. m.c.) (Cont'd)									
Select Structural		1750	2000	1200	100	425	1550	1,400,000	
Select Structural, Open grain	4" and less	1400	1600	950	100	270	1150	1,100,000	
No. 1	thick	1500	1700	1000	100	425	1400	1,400,000	
No. 1, Open grain	6" to 12"	1150	1350	800	100	270	1050	1,100,000	Redwood
No. 2	wide	1200	1400	800	100	425	1200	1,300,000	Inspection
No. 2, Open grain		950	1100	650	80	270	875	1,000,000	Service
No. 3		700	800	450	80	425	725	1,100,000	
No. 3, Open grain		550	650	350	80	270	525	900,000	
CALIFORNIA REDWOOD (Surfaced green. Used any condition)									
Clear Heart Structural	All	1850	2100	1250	135	285	1500	1,300,000	
Clear Structural	sizes	1850	2100	1250	135	285	1500	1,300,000	
Select Structural		1650	1900	950	95	285	1200	1,300,000	
Select Structural, Open grain	4" and less	1300	1500	750	95	180	900	1,000,000	
No. 1	thick and	1350	1550	800	95	285	975	1,300,000	
No. 1, Open grain	wide	1050	1250	650	95	180	725	1,000,000	
No. 2		1100	1300	650	75	285	775	1,100,000	Redwood
No. 2, Open grain		900	1000	500	75	180	575	900,000	Inspection
No. 3		650	750	400	75	285	475	1,000,000	Service
No. 3, Open grain		500	600	300	75	180	350	800,000	
Construction		650	750	400	75	180	650	800,000	
Standard		350	450	200	75	180	525	800,000	
Utility		200	200	100	75	180	350	800,000	
Stud		500	600	300	75	180	350	800,000	
Select Structural		1400	1600	950	95	285	1100	1,300,000	
Select Structural, Open grain	4" and less	1100	1300	750	95	180	800	1,000,000	
No. 1	thick	1200	1350	800	95	285	975	1,300,000	
No. 1, Open grain	6" to 12"	950	1100	650	95	180	725	1,000,000	(see footnote
No. 2	wide	1000	1100	650	75	285	800	1,100,000	3)
No. 2, Open grain		750	900	500	75	180	600	900,000	
No. 3		550	650	400	75	285	500	1,000,000	
No. 3, Open grain		450	500	300	75	180	375	800,000	
Select Structural		1400		950	95	285	1100	1,300,000	
No. 1	5" by 5"	1200		800	95	285	975	1,300,000	
No. 2	and larger	1000		650	95	285	800	1,100,000	
No. 3		550		400	95	285	500	1,000,000	
DOUGLAS FIR-LARCH (Surfaced dry or surfaced green. Used at 19% max. m.c.)									
Dense Select Structural		2450	2800	1400	95	455	1850	1,900,000	
Select Structural		2100	2400	1200	95	385	1600	1,800,000	
Dense No. 1		2050	2400	1200	95	455	1450	1,900,000	
No. 1	2" to 4"	1750	2050	1050	95	385	1250	1,800,000	
Dense No. 2	thick	1700	1950	1000	95	455	1150	1,700,000	
No. 2	2" to 4"	1450	1650	850	95	385	1000	1,700,000	
No. 3	wide	800	925	475	95	385	600	1,500,000	
Construction		1050	1200	625	95	385	1150	1,500,000	West Coast
Standard		600	675	350	95	385	925	1,500,000	Lumber
Utility		275	325	175	95	385	600	1,500,000	Inspection
Stud		800	925	475	95	385	600	1,500,000	Bureau
Dense Select Structural		2100	2400	1400	95	455	1650	1,900,000	and
Select Structural	2" to 4"	1800	2050	1200	95	385	1400	1,800,000	Western
Dense No. 1	thick	1800	2050	1200	95	455	1450	1,900,000	Wood
No. 1	6" and	1500	1750	1000	95	385	1250	1,800,000	Products
Dense No. 2	wider	1450	1700	950	95	455	1250	1,700,000	Association
No. 2		1250	1450	825	95	385	1050	1,700,000	
No. 3		725	850	475	95	385	675	1,500,000	(see footnotes
Appearance	2" to 4" thick 2" to 4" wide	1750	2050	1050	95	385	1500	1,800,000	2 through 9)
Appearance	2" to 4" thick 6" and wider	1500	1750	1000	95	385	1500	1,800,000	
Dense Select Structural		1900	––	1100	85	455	1300	1,700,000	
Select Structural	Beams and	1600	––	950	85	385	1100	1,600,000	
Dense No. 1	Stringers	1550	––	775	85	455	1100	1,700,000	
No. 1		1300	––	675	85	385	925	1,600,000	West Coast
Dense Select Structural		1750	––	1150	85	455	1400	1,700,000	Lumber
Select Structural	Posts and	1500	––	1000	85	385	1200	1,600,000	Inspection
Dense No. 1	Timbers	1400	––	950	85	455	1200	1,700,000	Bureau
No. 1		1200	––	825	85	385	1000	1,600,000	(see footnotes
Select Dex	Decking	1750	2000	––	––	385	––	1,800,000	2 through 9)
Commercial Dex		1450	1650	––	––	385	––	1,800,000	

Table 1a – Allowable Unit Stresses for Structural Lumber – VISUAL GRADING (cont.)

(Allowable unit stresses listed are for normal loading conditions. See other provisions of Part II for adjustments of tabulated stresses)

Species and commercial grade	Size classification	Extreme fiber in bending "F$_b$" Single-member uses	Extreme fiber in bending "F$_b$" Repetitive-member uses	Tension parallel to grain "F$_t$"	Horizontal shear "F$_v$"	Compression perpendicular to grain "F$_{c\perp}$"	Compression parallel to grain "F$_c$"	Modulus of elasticity "E"	Grading rules agency
DOUGLAS FIR-LARCH (Surfaced dry or surfaced green. Used at 19% max. m.c.) (Cont'd)									
Dense Select Structural	Beams and Stringers	1900	--	1250	85	455	1300	1,700,000	
Select Structural		1600	--	1050	85	385	1100	1,600,000	
Dense No. 1		1550	--	1050	85	455	1100	1,700,000	
No. 1		1350	--	900	85	385	925	1,600,000	Western
Dense Select Structural	Posts and Timbers	1750	--	1150	85	455	1350	1,700,000	Wood
Select Structural		1500	--	1000	85	385	1150	1,600,000	Products
Dense No. 1		1400	--	950	85	455	1200	1,700,000	Association
No. 1		1200	--	825	85	385	1000	1,600,000	
Selected Decking	Decking	--	2000	--	-	--	--	1,800,000	(see footnotes
Commercial Decking		--	1650	--				1,700,000	2 through 11)
Selected Decking	Decking	--	2150	(Surfaced at 15% max. m.c. and used at 15% max. m.c.)				1,900,000	
Commercial Decking		--	1800					1,700,000	
DOUGLAS FIR SOUTH (Surfaced dry or surfaced green. Used at 19% max. m.c.)									
Select Structural	2" to 4" thick 2" to 4" wide	2000	2300	1150	90	335	1400	1,400,000	
No. 1/Appearance		1700	1950	975	90	335	1150/1350	1,400,000	
No. 2		1400	1600	825	90	335	900	1,300,000	
No. 3		775	875	450	90	335	550	1,100,000	
Construction		1000	1150	600	90	335	1000	1,100,000	
Standard		550	650	325	90	335	850	1,100,000	
Utility		275	300	150	90	335	550	1,100,000	Western
Studs		775	875	450	90	335	550	1,100,000	Wood
Select Structural	2" to 4" thick 6" and wider	1700	1950	1150	90	335	1250	1,400,000	Products
No. 1/Appearance		1450	1650	975	90	335	1150/1350	1,400,000	Association
No. 2		1200	1350	775	90	335	950	1,300,000	
No. 3		700	800	450	90	335	600	1,100,000	(see footnotes
Select Structural	Beams and Stringers	1550	--	1050	85	335	1000	1,200,000	2 through 11)
No. 1		1300	--	850	85	335	850	1,200,000	
Select Structural	Posts and Timbers	1400	--	950	85	335	1050	1,200,000	
No. 1		1150	--	775	85	335	925	1,200,000	
Selected Decking	Decking	--	1900	--	-	--	--	1,400,000	
Commercial Decking		--	1600	--	-	--	--	1,300,000	
Selected Decking	Decking	--	2050	(Surfaced at 15% max. m.c. and used at 15% max. m.c.)				1,500,000	
Commercial Decking		--	1750					1,300,000	
EASTERN HEMLOCK — TAMARACK (Surfaced at 15% moisture content. Used at 15% max. m.c.)									
Select Structural	2" to 4" thick 2" to 4" wide	1950	2200	1150	90	365	1600	1,300,000	Northeastern
No. 1		1650	1900	975	90	365	1250	1,300,000	Lumber
No. 2		1350	1550	800	90	365	1000	1,200,000	Manufacturers
No. 3		750	850	500	90	365	600	1,000,000	Association
Appearance		1400	1650	950	90	365	1500	1,300,000	and
Construction		975	1150	575	90	365	1150	1,000,000	Northern
Standard		550	625	325	90	365	925	1,000,000	Hardwood
Utility		250	300	150	90	365	600	1,000,000	and Pine
Stud		750	850	450	90 .	365	600	1,000,000	Manufacturers
Select Structural	2" to 4" thick 6" and wider	1650	1900	1100	90	365	1400	1,300,000	Association
No. 1		1400	1650	950	90	365	1250	1,300,000	
No. 2		1150	1300	750	90	365	1050	1,200,000	(see footnotes
No. 3		675	775	450	90	365	675	1,000,000	2, 3, 4, 8 and 9)
Appearance		1400	1650	950	90	365	1500	1,300,000	
EASTERN HEMLOCK — TAMARACK (Surfaced dry or surfaced green. Used at 19% max. m.c.)									
Select Structural	2" to 4" thick 2" to 4" wide	1800	2050	1050	85	365	1350	1,300,000	
No. 1		1500	1750	900	85	365	1050	1,300,000	
No. 2		1250	1450	725	85	365	850	1,100,000	
No. 3		700	800	400	85	365	525	1,000,000	Northeastern
Appearance		1300	1500	875	85	365	1300	1,300,000	Lumber
Construction		900	1050	525	85	365	975	1,000,000	Manufacturers
Standard		500	575	300	85	365	800	1,000,000	Association
Utility		250	275	150	85	365	525	1,000,000	and
Stud		700	800	400	85	365	525	1,000,000	Northern
Select Structural	2" to 4" thick 6" and wider	1550	1750	1050	85	365	1200	1,300,000	Hardwood
No. 1		1300	1500	875	85	365	1050	1,300,000	and Pine
No. 2		1050	1200	700	85	365	900	1,100,000	Manufacturers
No. 3		625	725	400	85	365	575	1,000,000	Association
Appearance		1300	1500	875	85	365	1300	1,300,000	
Select Structural	Beams and Stringers	1400	--	925	80	365	950	1,200,000	(see footnotes
No. 1		1150	--	775	80	365	800	1,200,000	2 through 9)
Select Structural	Posts and Timbers	1300	--	875	80	365	1000	1,200,000	
No. 1		1050	--	700	80	365	875	1,200,000	
Select	Decking	1500	1700	--	--	--	--	1,300,000	NeLMA
Commercial		1250	1450	--	--	--	--	1,100,000	

ALLOWABLE UNIT STRESSES – STRUCTURAL LUMBER

Table 1a – Allowable Unit Stresses for Structural Lumber – VISUAL GRADING (cont.)

(Allowable unit stresses listed are for normal loading conditions. See other provisions of Part II for adjustments of tabulated stresses)

Species and commercial grade	Size classification	Allowable unit stresses in pounds per square inch		Tension parallel to grain "F_t"	Horizontal shear "F_v"	Compression perpendicular to grain "$F_{c\perp}$"	Compression parallel to grain "F_c"	Modulus of elasticity "E"	Grading rules agency
		Extreme fiber in bending "F_b"							
		Single-member uses	Repetitive-member uses						
EASTERN SPRUCE (Surfaced at 15% moisture content. Used at 15% max. m.c.)									
Select Structural		1650	1900	950	70	255	1350	1,400,000	Northeastern
No. 1		1400	1600	800	70	255	1050	1,400,000	Lumber
No. 2	2″ to 4″	1150	1300	675	70	255	825	1,300,000	Manufacturers
No. 3	thick	625	725	375	70	255	500	1,200,000	Association
Appearance	2″ to 4″	1200	1350	800	70	255	1250	1,400,000	and
Construction	wide	825	950	475	70	255	950	1,200,000	Northern
Standard		450	525	275	70	255	775	1,200,000	Hardwood
Utility		200	250	125	70	255	500	1,200,000	and Pine
Stud		625	725	375	70	255	500	1,200,000	Manufacturers
Select Structural	2″ to 4″	1400	1600	950	70	255	1150	1,400,000	Association
No. 1	thick	1200	1350	800	70	255	1050	1,400,000	
No. 2	6″ and	950	1100	650	70	255	875	1,300,000	(see footnotes
No. 3	wider	575	650	375	70	255	550	1,200,000	1, 2, 3, 4, 8
Appearance		1200	1350	800	70	255	1250	1,400,000	and 9)
EASTERN SPRUCE (Surfaced dry or surfaced green. Used at 19% max. m.c.)									
Select Structural		1500	1750	875	65	255	1150	1,400,000	
No. 1		1300	1500	750	65	255	900	1,400,000	
No. 2	2″ to 4″	1050	1200	625	65	255	700	1,200,000	
No. 3	thick	575	675	325	65	255	425	1,100,000	
Appearance	2″ to 4″	1100	1250	750	65	255	1050	1,400,000	Northeastern
Construction	wide	775	875	450	65	255	800	1,100,000	Lumber
Standard		425	500	250	65	255	675	1,100,000	Manufacturers
Utility		200	225	100	65	255	425	1,100,000	Association
Stud		575	675	325	65	255	425	1,100,000	and
Select Structural	2″ to 4″	1300	1500	875	65	255	1000	1,400,000	Northern
No. 1	thick	1100	1250	750	65	255	900	1,400,000	Hardwood
No. 2	6″ and	900	1000	600	65	255	750	1,200,000	and Pine
No. 3	wider	525	600	325	65	255	475	1,100,000	Manufacturers
Appearance		1100	1250	750	65	255	1050	1,400,000	Association
Select Structural	Beams and	1150	––	775	60	255	800	1,200,000	(see footnotes
No. 1	Stringers	950	––	650	60	255	675	1,200,000	1 through 9)
Select Structural	Posts and	1100	––	725	60	255	850	1,200,000	
No. 1	Timbers	875	––	600	60	255	725	1,200,000	
Truss	2″ to 4″ thick 2″ to 4″ wide	1785	2050	1000	65	255	1200	1,400,000	Northeastern Lumber Manufacturers Association
1500 f	2″ to 4″ thick 6″ and wider	1500	1700	1000	65	255	1100	1,400,000	(see footnotes 1 through 9)
Select	Decking	1250	1450	––	––	––	––	1,400,000	
Commercial		1050	1200	––	––	––	––	1,200,000	
EASTERN WHITE PINE (Surfaced at 15% moisture content. Used at 15% max. m.c.)									
Appearance		1100	1250	725	70	220	1150	1,300,000	NeLMA and
Construction	2″ to 4″	750	850	425	70	220	875	1,000,000	NHPMA
Standard	thick	425	475	250	70	220	725	1,000,000	
Utility	2″ to 4″	200	225	125	70	220	475	1,000,000	(see footnotes
Stud	wide	575	650	325	70	220	475	1,000,000	2, 3, 4, 8 and 9)
EASTERN WHITE PINE (Surfaced dry or surfaced green. Used at 19% max. m.c.)									
Appearance		1000	1150	675	70	220	1000	1,200,000	NeLMA and
Construction	2″ to 4″	700	800	400	70	220	750	1,000,000	NHPMA
Standard	thick	375	450	225	70	220	625	1,000,000	
Utility	2″ to 4″	175	200	100	70	220	400	1,000,000	(see footnotes
Stud	wide	525	600	300	70	220	400	1,000,000	2 through 9)
Select	Decking	900	1050	––	––	––	––	1,200,000	NeLMA
Commercial		775	875	––	––	––	––	1,100,000	

ALLOWABLE UNIT STRESSES – STRUCTURAL LUMBER
Table 1a – Allowable Unit Stresses for Structural Lumber – VISUAL GRADING (cont.)
(Allowable unit stresses listed are for normal loading conditions. See other provisions of Part II for adjustments of tabulated stresses)

Species and commercial grade	Size classification	Allowable unit stresses in pounds per square inch		Tension parallel to grain "F_t"	Horizontal shear "F_v"	Compression perpendicular to grain "$F_{c\perp}$"	Compression parallel to grain "F_c"	Modulus of elasticity "E"	Grading rules agency
		Extreme fiber in bending "F_b"							
		Single-member uses	Repetitive-member uses						
ENGELMANN SPRUCE (ENGELMANN SPRUCE–LODGEPOLE PINE) (Surfaced dry or surfaced green. Used at 19% max. m.c.)									
Select Structural	2" to 4" thick	1350	1550	775	70	195	900	1,200,000	
No. 1/Appearance		1150	1300	675	70	195	725/875	1,200,000	
No. 2		950	1100	550	70	195	575	1,100,000	
No. 3	2" to 4" wide	525	600	300	70	195	350	1,000,000	Western
Construction		675	775	400	70	195	650	1,000,000	Wood
Standard		375	425	225	70	195	525	1,000,000	Products
Utility		175	200	100	70	195	350	1,000,000	Association
Stud		525	600	300	70	195	350	1,000,000	
Select Structural	2" to 4" thick	1150	1350	775	70	195	800	1,200,000	(see footnotes
No. 1/Appearance		975	1150	650	70	195	725/875	1,200,000	2 through 11)
No. 2	6" and wider	800	925	525	70	195	600	1,100,000	
No. 3		475	550	300	70	195	375	1,000,000	
Select Structural	Beams and Stringers	1050	––	700	65	195	650	1,100,000	
No. 1		875	––	575	65	195	550	1,100,000	
Select Structural	Posts and Timbers	950	––	650	65	195	675	1,100,000	
No. 1		775	––	525	65	195	600	1,100,000	
Selected Decking	Decking	––	1300	––	–	––	––	1,200,000	
Commercial Decking		––	1100	––	–	––	––	1,100,000	
Selected Decking	Decking	––	1400	(Surfaced at 15% max. m.c. and used at 15% max. m.c.)				1,300,000	
Commercial Decking		––	1150					1,200,000	
HEM-FIR (Surfaced dry or surfaced green. Used at 19% max. m.c.)									
Select Structural		1650	1900	975	75	245	1300	1,500,000	
No. 1		1400	1600	825	75	245	1000	1,500,000	
No. 2		1150	1300	675	75	245	800	1,400,000	
No. 3	2" to 4" thick	625	725	375	75	245	500	1,200,000	
Construction	2" to 4" wide	825	975	475	75	245	925	1,200,000	West Coast
Standard		450	525	275	75	245	750	1,200,000	Lumber
Utility		225	250	125	75	245	500	1,200,000	Inspection
Stud		625	725	375	75	245	500	1,200,000	Bureau
Select Structural	2" to 4" thick	1400	1650	950	75	245	1150	1,500,000	and
No. 1		1200	1400	800	75	245	1000	1,500,000	Western
No. 2	6" and wider	1000	1150	650	75	245	850	1,400,000	Wood
No. 3		575	675	375	75	245	550	1,200,000	Products Association
Appearance	2" to 4" thick 2" to 4" wide	1400	1600	825	75	245	1200	1,500,000	(see footnotes 2 through 9)
Appearance	2" to 4" thick 6" and wider	1200	1400	800	75	245	1200	1,500,000	
Select Structural	Beams and Stringers	1250	––	750	70	245	900	1,300,000	West Coast
No. 1		1000	––	525	70	245	750	1,300,000	Lumber
Select Structural	Posts and Timbers	1200	––	800	70	245	950	1,300,000	Inspection
No. 1		975	––	650	70	245	850	1,300,000	Bureau
Select Dex	Decking	1400	1600	––	––	245	––	1,500,000	(see footnotes
Commercial Dex		1150	1300	––	––	245	––	1,400,000	2 through 9)
Select Structural	Beams and Stringers	1250	––	850	70	245	900	1,300,000	Western
No. 1		1050	––	700	70	245	775	1,300,000	Wood
Select Structural	Posts and Timbers	1200	––	800	70	245	950	1,300,000	Products
No. 1		975	––	650	70	245	850	1,300,000	Association
Selected Decking	Decking	––	1600	––	–	––	––	1,500,000	(see footnotes
Commercial Decking		––	1300	––	–	––	––	1,400,000	2 through 11)
Selected Decking	Decking	––	1750	(Surfaced at 15% max. m.c. and used at 15% max. m.c.)				1,600,000	
Commercial Decking		––	1450					1,500,000	
IDAHO WHITE PINE (Surfaced dry or surfaced green. Used at 19% max. m.c.)									
Select Structural		1450	1650	850	65	240	1150	1,400,000	
No. 1/Appearance	2" to 4" thick	1250	1400	725	65	240	925/1100	1,400,000	
No. 2		1000	1150	600	65	240	725	1,300,000	
No. 3	2" to 4" wide	550	650	325	65	240	450	1,100,000	
Construction		725	850	425	65	240	825	1,100,000	
Standard		400	475	250	65	240	675	1,100,000	
Utility		200	225	125	65	240	450	1,100,000	Western
Stud		550	650	325	65	240	450	1,100,000	Wood
Select Structural	2" to 4" thick	1250	1450	825	65	240	1000	1,400,000	Products
No. 1/Appearance		1050	1200	700	65	240	925/1100	1,400,000	Association
No. 2	6" and wider	875	1000	575	65	240	775	1,300,000	
No. 3		500	575	325	65	240	475	1,100,000	(see footnotes
Select Structural	Beams and Stringers	1100	––	750	60	240	800	1,200,000	2 through 11)
No. 1		925	––	625	60	240	675	1,200,000	
Select Structural	Posts and Timbers	1050	––	700	60	240	850	1,200,000	
No. 1		850	––	575	60	240	750	1,200,000	
Selected Decking	Decking	––	1400	––	–	––	––	1,400,000	
Commercial Decking		––	1150	––	–	––	––	1,300,000	
Selected Decking	Decking	––	1500	(Surfaced at 15% max. m.c. and used at 15% max. m.c.)				1,500,000	
Commercial Decking		––	1250					1,300,000	

ALLOWABLE UNIT STRESSES – STRUCTURAL LUMBER
Table 1a – Allowable Unit Stresses for Structural Lumber – VISUAL GRADING (cont.)
(Allowable unit stresses listed are for normal loading conditions. See other provisions of Part II for adjustments of tabulated stresses)

Species and commercial grade	Size classification	Extreme fiber in bending "F_b" Single-member uses	Extreme fiber in bending "F_b" Repetitive-member uses	Tension parallel to grain "F_t"	Horizontal shear "F_v"	Compression perpendicular to grain "$F_{c\perp}$"	Compression parallel to grain "F_c"	Modulus of elasticity "E"	Grading rules agency
LODGEPOLE PINE (Surfaced dry or surfaced green. Used at 19% max. m.c.)									
Select Structural	2" to 4"	1500	1750	875	70	250	1150	1,300,000	
No. 1/Appearance	thick	1300	1500	750	70	250	900/1050	1,300,000	
No. 2	2" to 4"	1050	1200	625	70	250	700	1,200,000	
No. 3	wide	600	675	350	70	250	425	1,000,000	
Construction		775	875	450	70	250	800	1,000,000	
Standard		425	500	250	70	250	675	1,000,000	
Utility		200	225	125	70	250	425	1,000,000	
Stud		600	675	350	70	250	425	1,000,000	
Select Structural	2" to 4"	1300	1500	875	70	250	1000	1,300,000	Western Wood Products Association
No. 1/Appearance	thick	1100	1300	750	70	250	900/1050	1,300,000	
No. 2	6" and	925	1050	600	70	250	750	1,200,000	
No. 3	wider	525	625	350	70	250	475	1,000,000	(see footnotes 2 through 11)
Select Structural	Beams and	1150	––	775	65	250	800	1,100,000	
No. 1	Stringers	975	––	650	65	250	675	1,100,000	
Select Structural	Posts and	1100	––	725	65	250	850	1,100,000	
No. 1	Timbers	875	––	600	65	250	725	1,100,000	
Selected Decking	Decking	––	1450	––	–	––	––	1,300,000	
Commercial Decking		––	1200	––	–	––	––	1,200,000	
Selected Decking	Decking	––	1550	(Surfaced at 15% max. m.c. and used at 15% max. m.c.)				1,400,000	
Commercial Decking		––	1300					1,200,000	
MOUNTAIN HEMLOCK (Surfaced dry or surfaced green. Used at 19% max. m.c.)									
Select Structural	2" to 4"	1750	2000	1000	95	370	1250	1,300,000	
No. 1	thick	1450	1700	850	95	370	1000	1,300,000	
No. 2	2" to 4"	1200	1400	700	95	370	775	1,100,000	
No. 3	wide	675	775	400	95	370	475	1,000,000	West Coast Lumber Inspection Bureau and Western Wood Products Association
Construction		875	1000	525	95	370	900	1,000,000	
Standard	2" to 4"	500	575	275	95	370	725	1,000,000	
Utility	thick	225	275	125	95	370	475	1,000,000	
Stud	4" wide	675	775	400	95	370	475	1,000,000	
Select Structural	2" to 4"	1500	1700	1000	95	370	1100	1,300,000	
No. 1	thick	1250	1450	850	95	370	1000	1,300,000	
No. 2	6" and	1050	1200	675	95	370	825	1,100,000	
No. 3	wider	625	700	400	95	370	525	1,000,000	(see footnotes 2 through 9)
Appearance	2" to 4" wide 2" to 4" thick	1450	1700	850	95	370	1200	1,300,000	
Appearance	2" to 4" thick 6" and wider	1250	1450	850	95	370	1200	1,300,000	
Select Structural	Beams and	1350	––	775	90	370	875	1,100,000	West Coast Lumber Inspection Bureau
No. 1	Stringers	1100	––	550	90	370	750	1,100,000	
Select Structural	Posts and	1250	––	825	90	370	925	1,100,000	
No. 1	Timbers	1000	––	675	90	370	800	1,100,000	
Select Dex	Decking	1450	1650	––	––	370	––	1,300,000	(see footnotes 2 through 9)
Commercial Dex		1200	1400	––	––	370	––	1,100,000	
Select Structural	Beams and	1350	––	900	90	370	875	1,100,000	
No. 1	Stringers	1100	––	750	90	370	750	1,100,000	
Select Structural	Posts and	1250	––	825	90	370	925	1,100,000	Western Wood Products Association
No. 1	Timbers	1000	––	675	90	370	800	1,100,000	
Selected Decking	Decking	––	1650	––	–	––	––	1,300,000	
Commercial Decking		––	1400	––	–	––	––	1,100,000	(see footnotes 2 through 11)
Selected Decking	Decking	––	1800	(Surfaced at 15% max. m.c. and used at 15% max. m.c.)				1,300,000	
Commercial Decking		––	1500					1,200,000	
MOUNTAIN HEMLOCK–HEM-FIR (Surfaced dry or surfaced green. Used at 19% max. m.c.)									
Select Structural		1650	1900	975	75	245	1250	1,300,000	
No. 1/Appearance	2" to 4"	1400	1600	825	75	245	1000/1200	1,300,000	
No. 2	thick	1150	1300	675	75	245	775	1,100,000	
No. 3	2" to 4"	625	725	375	75	245	475	1,000,000	
Construction	wide	825	975	475	75	245	900	1,000,000	
Standard		450	525	275	75	245	725	1,000,000	
Utility		225	250	125	75	245	475	1,000,000	
Stud		625	725	375	75	245	475	1,000,000	Western Wood Products Association
Select Structural	2" to 4"	1400	1650	950	75	245	1100	1,300,000	
No. 1/Appearance	thick	1200	1400	800	75	245	1000/1200	1,300,000	
No. 2	6" and	1000	1150	650	75	245	825	1,100,000	
No. 3	wider	575	675	375	75	245	525	1,000,000	(see footnotes 2 through 11)
Select Structural	Beams and	1250	––	850	70	245	875	1,100,000	
No. 1	Stringers	1050	––	700	70	245	750	1,100,000	
Select Structural	Posts and	1200	––	800	70	245	925	1,100,000	
No. 1	Timbers	975	––	650	70	245	800	1,100,000	
Selected Decking	Decking	––	1600	––	–	––	––	1,300,000	
Commercial Decking		––	1300	––	–	––	––	1,100,000	
Selected Decking	Decking	––	1750	(Surfaced at 15% max. m.c. and used at 15% max. m.c.)				1,300,000	
Commercial Decking		––	1450					1,200,000	

ALLOWABLE UNIT STRESSES – STRUCTURAL LUMBER

Table 1a – Allowable Unit Stresses for Structural Lumber – VISUAL GRADING (cont.)

(Allowable unit stresses listed are for normal loading conditions. See other provisions of Part II for adjustments of tabulated stresses)

Species and commercial grade	Size classification	Extreme fiber in bending "F_b" Single-member uses	Extreme fiber in bending "F_b" Repetitive-member uses	Tension parallel to grain "F_t"	Horizontal shear "F_v"	Compression perpendicular to grain "$F_{c\perp}$"	Compression parallel to grain "F_c"	Modulus of elasticity "E"	Grading rules agency
NORTHERN PINE (Surfaced at 15% moisture content. Used at 15% max. m.c.)									
Select Structural		1750	2000	1050	75	280	1450	1,500,000	Northeastern
No. 1		1500	1700	875	75	280	1150	1,500,000	Lumber
No. 2	2" to 4"	1250	1400	725	75	280	900	1,300,000	Manufacturers
No. 3	thick	675	775	400	75	280	550	1,200,000	Association
Appearance	2" to 4"	1300	1500	850	75	280	1350	1,500,000	and
Construction	wide	900	1050	525	75	280	1000	1,200,000	Northern
Standard		500	575	300	75	280	850	1,200,000	Hardwood
Utility		225	275	150	75	280	550	1,200,000	and Pine
Stud		675	775	400	75	280	550	1,200,000	Manufacturers
Select Structural	2" to 4"	1500	1750	1000	75	280	1250	1,500,000	Association
No. 1	thick	1300	1500	850	75	280	1150	1,500,000	
No. 2	6" and	1050	1200	700	75	280	950	1,300,000	(see footnotes
No. 3	wider	625	725	400	75	280	600	1,200,000	2, 3, 4, 8 and 9)
Appearance		1300	1500	850	75	280	1350	1,500,000	
NORTHERN PINE (Surfaced dry or surfaced green. Used at 19% max. m.c.)									
Select Structural		1650	1850	950	70	280	1200	1,400,000	
No. 1		1400	1600	825	70	280	975	1,400,000	
No. 2	2" to 4"	1150	1300	675	70	280	775	1,300,000	Northeastern
No. 3	thick	625	725	375	70	280	475	1,100,000	Lumber
Appearance	2" to 4"	1200	1400	800	70	280	1150	1,400,000	Manufacturers
Construction	wide	825	950	475	70	280	875	1,100,000	Association
Standard		450	525	275	70	280	725	1,100,000	and
Utility		225	250	125	70	280	475	1,100,000	Northern
Stud		625	725	375	70	280	475	1,100,000	Hardwood
Select Structural	2" to 4"	1400	1600	950	70	280	1100	1,400,000	and Pine
No. 1	thick	1200	1400	800	70	280	975	1,400,000	Manufacturers
No. 2	6" and	950	1100	650	70	280	825	1,300,000	Association
No. 3	wider	575	650	375	70	280	525	1,100,000	
Appearance		1200	1400	800	70	280	1150	1,400,000	(see footnotes
Select Structural	Beams and	1250	––	850	65	280	850	1,300,000	2 through 9)
No. 1	Stringers	1050	––	700	65	280	725	1,300,000	
Select Structural	Posts and	1150	––	800	65	280	900	1,300,000	
No. 1	Timbers	950	––	650	65	280	800	1,300,000	
Select	Decking	1350	1550	––	––	––	––	1,400,000	NeLMA
Commercial		1150	1300	––	––	––	––	1,300,000	
NORTHERN WHITE CEDAR (Surfaced dry or surfaced green. Used at 19% max. m.c.)									
Select Structural		1150	1350	700	65	205	875	800,000	
No. 1		1000	1150	600	65	205	675	800,000	
No. 2	2" to 4"	825	950	500	65	205	550	700,000	
No. 3	thick	450	525	275	65	205	325	600,000	
Appearance	2" to 4"	850	1000	575	65	205	825	800,000	
Construction	wide	600	675	350	65	205	625	600,000	
Standard		325	375	200	65	205	500	600,000	
Utility		150	175	100	65	205	325	600,000	Northeastern
Stud		450	525	275	65	205	325	600,000	Lumber
Select Structural	2" to 4"	1000	1150	675	65	205	775	800,000	Manufacturers
No. 1	thick	850	1000	575	65	205	675	800,000	Association
No. 2	6" and	700	825	450	65	205	575	700,000	
No. 3	wider	425	475	275	65	205	375	600,000	(see footnotes
Appearance		850	1000	575	65	205	825	800,000	2 through 9)
Select	Decking	975	1100	––	––	––	––	800,000	
Commercial		825	950	––	––	––	––	700,000	
Select Structural	Beams and	900	––	600	60	205	600	700,000	
No. 1	Stringers	750	––	500	60	205	500	700,000	
Select Structural	Posts and	850	––	575	60	205	650	700,000	
No. 1	Timbers	675	––	450	60	205	550	700,000	

Table 1a – Allowable Unit Stresses for Structural Lumber – VISUAL GRADING (cont.)

(Allowable unit stresses listed are for normal loading conditions. See other provisions of Part II for adjustments of tabulated stresses)

Species and commercial grade	Size classification	Extreme fiber in bending "F_b" Single-member uses	Extreme fiber in bending "F_b" Repetitive-member uses	Tension parallel to grain "F_t"	Horizontal shear "F_v"	Compression perpendicular to grain "$F_{c\perp}$"	Compression parallel to grain "F_c"	Modulus of elasticity "E"	Grading rules agency
PONDEROSA PINE–SUGAR PINE (PONDEROSA PINE–LODGEPOLE PINE) (Surfaced dry or surfaced green. Used at 19% max. m.c.)									
Select Structural		1400	1650	825	70	250	1050	1,200,000	
No. 1/Appearance	2" to 4"	1200	1400	700	70	250	850/1000	1,200,000	
No. 2	thick	1000	1150	575	70	250	675	1,100,000	
No. 3	2" to 4"	550	625	325	70	250	400	1,000,000	
Construction	wide	725	825	425	70	250	775	1,000,000	Western
Standard		400	450	225	70	250	625	1,000,000	Wood
Utility		200	225	100	70	250	400	1,000,000	Products
Stud		550	625	325	70	250	400	1,000,000	Association
Select Structural	2" to 4"	1200	1400	825	70	250	950	1,200,000	
No. 1/Appearance	thick	1050	1200	700	70	250	850/1000	1,200,000	(see footnotes
No. 2	6" and	850	975	550	70	250	700	1,100,000	2 through 11)
No. 3	wider	500	575	325	70	250	450	1,000,000	
Select Structural	Beams and	1100	––	725	65	250	750	1,100,000	
No. 1	Stringers	925	––	625	65	250	625	1,100,000	
Select Structural	Posts and	1000	––	675	65	250	800	1,100,000	
No. 1	Timbers	825	––	550	65	250	700	1,100,000	
Selected Decking	Decking	––	1350	––	–	––	––	1,200,000	
Commercial Decking		––	1150	––	–	––	––	1,100,000	
Selected Decking	Decking	––	1450	(Surfaced at 15% max. m.c. and used at 15% max. m.c.)				1,300,000	
Commercial Decking		––	1250					1,100,000	
SITKA SPRUCE (Surfaced dry or surfaced green. Used at 19% max. m.c.)									
Select Structural		1550	1800	925	75	280	1150	1,500,000	
No. 1		1350	1550	775	75	280	925	1,500,000	
No. 2	2" to 4"	1100	1250	650	75	280	725	1,300,000	
No. 3	thick	600	700	350	75	280	450	1,300,000	
Appearance	2" to 4"	1350	1550	750	75	280	1100	1,500,000	
Construction	wide	800	925	475	75	280	825	1,200,000	West
Standard		450	500	250	75	280	675	1,200,000	Coast
Utility		200	250	125	75	280	450	1,200,000	Lumber
Stud		600	700	350	75	280	450	1,200,000	Inspection
Select Structural	2" to 4"	1350	1550	900	75	280	1000	1,500,000	Bureau
No. 1	thick	1150	1300	775	75	280	925	1,500,000	
No. 2	6" and	925	1050	625	75	280	775	1,300,000	(see footnotes
No. 3	wider	525	600	350	75	280	500	1,200,000	2 through 9)
Appearance		1150	1300	750	75	280	1100	1,500,000	
Select Structural	Beams and	1200	––	675	70	280	825	1,300,000	
No. 1	Stringers	1000	––	500	70	280	675	1,300,000	
Select Structural	Posts and	1150	––	750	70	280	875	1,300,000	
No. 1	Timbers	925	––	600	70	280	750	1,300,000	
Select Dex	Decking	1300	1500	––	––	280	––	1,500,000	
Commercial Dex		1100	1250	––	––	280	––	1,300,000	
SOUTHERN PINE (Surfaced at 15% moisture content, K.D. Used at 15% max. m.c.)									
Select Structural		2250	2600	1350	95	405	1850	1,900,000	
Dense Select Structural		2650	3050	1550	95	475	2150	2,000,000	
No. 1		1900	2200	1100	95	405	1450	1,900,000	
No. 1 Dense	2" to 4"	2250	2600	1300	95	475	1700	2,000,000	
No. 2	thick	1350	1550	775	80	345	975	1,500,000	
No. 2 Medium grain	2" to 4"	1550	1800	925	95	405	1150	1,700,000	
No. 2 Dense	wide	1850	2150	1050	95	475	1350	1,800,000	
No. 3		875	1000	525	80	345	700	1,500,000	
No. 3 Dense		1050	1200	600	95	475	825	1,600,000	
Construction		1150	1300	670	75	345	1300	1,500,000	
Standard		640	750	375	75	345	1050	1,500,000	
Utility		300	350	175	75	345	700	1,500,000	
Stud		875	1000	525	80	345	700	1,500,000	
Select Structural		1950	2250	1300	95	405	1650	1,900,000	
Dense Select Structural		2250	2600	1500	95	475	1900	2,000,000	
No. 1		1650	1900	1100	95	405	1450	1,900,000	Southern
No. 1 Dense	2" to 4"	1900	2200	1300	95	475	1700	2,000,000	Pine
No. 2	thick	1150	1300	750	80	345	1050	1,500,000	Inspection
No. 2 Medium grain	6" and	1350	1550	900	95	405	1250	1,700,000	Bureau
No. 2 Dense	wider	1550	1800	1050	95	475	1450	1,800,000	
No. 3		800	900	525	80	345	750	1,500,000	(See footnotes
No. 3 Dense		925	1050	625	95	475	875	1,600,000	3 and 9)
Dense Std. Factory	2" to 4"	2200	2550	1300	95	475	1700	2,000,000	
No. 1 Factory	thick	1500	1750	900	95	405	1150	1,700,000	
No. 1 Dense Factory	2" to 4"	1800	2050	1050	95	475	1350	1,800,000	
No. 2 Factory	wide	1500	1750	900	95	405	1150	1,700,000	
No. 2 Dense Factory	Decking	1800	2050	1050	95	475	1350	1,800,000	
Dense Std. Factory	2" to 4"	1900	2200	1300	95	475	1650	2,000,000	
No. 1 Factory	thick	1350	1550	900	95	405	1250	1,700,000	
No. 1 Dense Factory	6" and	1550	1800	1050	95	475	1450	1,800,000	
No. 2 Factory	wider	1350	1550	900	95	405	1250	1,700,000	
No. 2 Dense Factory	Decking	1550	1800	1050	95	475	1450	1,800,000	

ALLOWABLE UNIT STRESSES – STRUCTURAL LUMBER

Table 1a – Allowable Unit Stresses for Structural Lumber – VISUAL GRADING (cont.)

(Allowable unit stresses listed are for normal loading conditions. See other provisions of Part II for adjustments of tabulated stresses)

Species and commercial grade	Size classification	Allowable unit stresses in pounds per square inch							Grading rules agency
		Extreme fiber in bending "F_b"		Tension parallel to grain "F_t"	Horizontal shear "F_v"	Compression perpendicular to grain "$F_{c\perp}$"	Compression parallel to grain "F_c"	Modulus of elasticity "E"	
		Single-member uses	Repetitive-member uses						
SOUTHERN PINE (Surfaced at 15% moisture content, K.D. Used at 15% max. m.c.) (Cont'd)									
Select Dense		2000	2300	1350	105	475	1850	2,000,000	Southern Pine Inspection Bureau (See footnotes 3 and 9)
Select	3" to 4" thick Decking	1700	1950	1150	105	405	1600	1,900,000	
No. 1 Dense		1750	2000	1150	90	475	1400	1,800,000	
No. 1		1500	1750	1000	90	405	1150	1,700,000	
No. 2 Dense		1750	2000	1150	90	475	1400	1,800,000	
No. 2		1500	1750	1000	90	405	1150	1,700,000	
Dense Structural 86	2" to 4" thick	3000	3450	2000	160	475	2350	2,000,000	
Dense Structural 72		2500	2900	1650	135	475	2000	2,000,000	
SOUTHERN PINE (Surfaced dry. Used at 19% max. m.c.)									
Select Structural		2100	2400	1250	90	405	1600	1,800,000	
Dense Select Structural		2450	2800	1450	90	475	1850	1,900,000	
No. 1	2" to 4" thick	1750	2000	1000	90	405	1250	1,800,000	
No. 1 Dense	2" to 4" wide	2050	2350	1200	90	475	1450	1,900,000	
No. 2		1250	1450	725	75	345	850	1,400,000	
No. 2 Medium grain		1450	1650	850	90	405	1000	1,600,000	
No. 2 Dense		1700	1950	1000	90	475	1150	1,700,000	
No. 3		825	950	475	75	345	600	1,500,000	
No. 3 Dense		950	1100	550	90	475	700	1,400,000	
Construction		1050	1200	620	75	345	1100	1,400,000	
Standard		590	700	340	75	345	925	1,400,000	
Utility		275	325	165	75	345	600	1,400,000	
Stud		825	950	475	75	345	600	1,400,000	Southern Pine Inspection Bureau (See footnotes 3 and 9)
Select Structural		1800	2050	1200	90	405	1400	1,800,000	
Dense Select Structural		2100	2400	1400	90	475	1650	1,900,000	
No. 1	2" to 4" thick	1500	1750	1000	90	405	1250	1,800,000	
No. 1 Dense	6" and wider	1800	2050	1200	90	475	1450	1,900,000	
No. 2		1050	1200	700	75	345	900	1,400,000	
No. 2 Medium grain		1250	1450	825	90	405	1050	1,600,000	
No. 2 Dense		1450	1650	975	90	475	1250	1,700,000	
No. 3		725	825	475	75	345	650	1,400,000	
No. 3 Dense		850	975	575	90	475	750	1,500,000	
Dense Std. Factory	2" to 4" thick	2000	2300	1200	90	475	1450	1,900,000	
No. 1 Factory	2" to 4" wide	1400	1600	825	90	405	1000	1,600,000	
No. 1 Dense Factory		1650	1900	975	90	475	1150	1,700,000	
No. 2 Factory		1400	1600	825	90	405	1000	1,600,000	
No. 2 Dense Factory		1700	1950	975	90	475	1150	1,700,000	
Dense Std. Factory	2" to 4" thick	1750	2000	1200	90	475	1450	1,900,000	
No. 1 Factory	6" and wider	1250	1450	825	90	405	1050	1,600,000	
No. 1 Dense Factory		1450	1650	975	90	475	1250	1,700,000	
No. 2 Factory		1250	1450	825	90	405	1050	1,600,000	
No. 2 Dense Factory		1450	1650	975	90	475	1250	1,700,000	
Dense Structural 86	2" to 4" thick	2750	3150	1850	150	475	2050	1,900,000	
Dense Structural 72		2300	2650	1550	125	475	1700	1,900,000	
SOUTHERN PINE (Surfaced green. Used any condition)									
Select Structural		1700	1950	975	80	270	1050	1,600,000	
Dense Select Structural		1950	2250	1150	80	315	1250	1,600,000	
No. 1		1400	1600	825	80	270	850	1,600,000	
No. 1 Dense	2½" to 4" thick	1650	1900	975	80	315	975	1,600,000	
No. 2	2½" to 4" wide	1000		575	70	230	550	1,300,000	
No. 2 Medium grain		1150	1300	675	80	270	650	1,400,000	
No. 2 Dense		1350	1500	800	80	315	775	1,500,000	
No. 3		650	750	375	70	230	400	1,300,000	
No. 3 Dense		775	900	450	80	315	475	1,300,000	
Construction		850	975	490	70	230	750	1,300,000	
Standard		475	550	275	70	230	620	1,300,000	
Utility		225	250	125	70	230	400	1,300,000	
Stud		650	750	375	70	230	400	1,300,000	Southern Pine Inspection Bureau (See footnotes 3 and 9)
Select Structural		1450	1650	950	80	270	925	1,600,000	
Dense Select Structural		1650	1900	1100	80	315	1100	1,600,000	
No. 1		1200	1400	800	80	270	825	1,600,000	
No. 1 Dense	2½" to 4" thick	1400	1600	950	80	315	975	1,600,000	
No. 2	6" and wider	850	975	550	70	230	600	1,300,000	
No. 2 Medium grain		1000	1150	650	80	270	700	1,400,000	
No. 2 Dense		1150	1300	775	80	315	825	1,500,000	
No. 3		575	650	375	70	230	425	1,300,000	
No. 3 Dense		675	775	450	80	315	500	1,300,000	
Dense Std. Factory	2½" to 4" thick	1600	––	950	80	315	975	1,600,000	
No. 1 Factory	2½" to 4" wide	1150	––	650	80	270	650	1,400,000	
No. 1 Dense Factory		1300	––	775	80	315	775	1,500,000	
No. 2 Factory		1150	––	650	80	270	650	1,400,000	
No. 2 Dense Factory		1300	––	775	80	315	775	1,500,000	

ALLOWABLE UNIT STRESSES – STRUCTURAL LUMBER

Table 1a – Allowable Unit Stresses for Structural Lumber – VISUAL GRADING (cont.)

(Allowable unit stresses listed are for normal loading conditions. See other provisions of Part II for adjustments of tabulated stresses)

Species and commercial grade	Size classification	Extreme fiber in bending "F_b"		Tension parallel to grain "F_t"	Horizontal shear "F_v"	Compression perpendicular to grain "$F_{c\perp}$"	Compression parallel to grain "F_c"	Modulus of elasticity "E"	Grading rules agency
		Single-member uses	Repetitive-member uses						
SOUTHERN PINE (Surfaced green. Used any condition) (Cont'd)									
Dense Std. Factory	2½" to 4" thick	1400	––	950	80	315	975	1,600,000	
No. 1 Factory	6" and wider	1000	––	650	80	270	700	1,400,000	
No. 1 Dense Factory		1150	––	775	80	315	825	1,500,000	
No. 2 Factory		1000	––	650	80	270	700	1,400,000	
No. 2 Dense Factory		1150	––	775	80	315	825	1,500,000	Southern Pine Inspection Bureau
No. 1 SR	5" and thicker	1300	––	850	110	270	925	1,600,000	(See footnotes 3 and 9)
No. 1 Dense SR		1500	––	1000	110	315	1050	1,600,000	
No. 2 SR		1100	––	725	95	270	675	1,400,000	
No. 2 Dense SR		1300	––	850	95	315	775	1,500,000	
Dense Structural 65		1650	––	1100	105	315	1000	1,600,000	
Dense Structural 86	2½" and thicker	2200	––	1450	140	315	1350	1,600,000	
Dense Structural 72		1850	––	1250	120	315	1150	1,600,000	
SUBALPINE FIR (WHITE WOODS) (WESTERN WOODS) (Surfaced dry or surfaced green. Used at 19% max. m. c.)									
Select Structural	2" to 4" thick	1250	1400	725	60	195	900	900,000	
No. 1/Appearance	2" to 4" wide	1050	1200	600	60	195	700/850	900,000	
No. 2		850	1000	500	60	195	550	900,000	
No. 3		475	550	275	60	195	350	800,000	
Construction		625	725	375	60	195	650	800,000	
Standard		350	400	200	60	195	525	800,000	
Utility		175	200	100	60	195	350	800,000	
Stud		475	550	275	60	195	350	800,000	Western Wood Products Association
Select Structural	2" to 4" thick	1050	1200	700	60	195	800	900,000	(see footnotes 2 through 11)
No. 1/Appearance	6" and wider	900	1050	600	60	195	700/850	900,000	
No. 2		750	850	475	60	195	600	900,000	
No. 3		425	500	275	60	195	375	800,000	
Select Structural	Beams and Stringers	950	––	625	60	195	625	900,000	
No. 1		800	––	525	60	195	525	900,000	
Select Structural	Posts and Timbers	875	––	600	60	195	675	900,000	
No. 1		725	––	475	60	195	575	900,000	
Selected Decking	Decking	––	1200	––	–	––	––	900,000	
Commercial Decking		––	1000	––	–	––	––	900,000	
Selected Decking	Decking	––	1300	(Surfaced at 15% max. m.c. and used at 15% max. m.c.)				1,000,000	
Commercial Decking		––	1050					900,000	
WESTERN CEDARS (Surfaced dry or surfaced green. Used at 19% max. m.c.)									
Select Structural	2" to 4" thick	1450	1700	850	75	295	1250	1,100,000	West Coast Lumber Inspection Bureau and Western Wood Products Association
No. 1	2" to 4" wide	1250	1450	725	75	295	975	1,100,000	
No. 2		1000	1200	600	75	295	775	1,000,000	
No. 3		575	650	325	75	295	475	900,000	
Construction		750	850	425	75	295	875	900,000	
Standard		425	475	250	75	295	725	900,000	
Utility		200	225	125	75	295	475	900,000	
Stud		575	650	325	75	295	475	900,000	(see footnotes 2 through 9)
Select Structural	2" to 4" thick	1250	1450	850	75	295	1100	1,100,000	
No. 1	6" and wider	1050	1250	725	75	295	975	1,100,000	
No. 2		875	1000	575	75	295	825	1,000,000	
No. 3		525	600	325	75	295	525	900,000	
Appearance	2" to 4" thick / 2" to 4" wide	1250	1450	725	75	295	1150	1,100,000	
Appearance	2" to 4" thick / 6" and wider	1050	1250	725	75	295	1150	1,100,000	
Select Structural	Beams and Stringers	1100	––	675	70	295	875	1,000,000	West Coast Lumber Inspection Bureau
No. 1		900	––	475	70	295	725	1,000,000	
Select Structural	Posts and Timbers	1050	––	700	70	295	900	1,000,000	(see footnotes 2 through 9)
No. 1		850	––	575	70	295	800	1,000,000	
Select Dex	Decking	1200	1400	––	––	295	––	1,100,000	
Commercial Dex		1050	1200	––	––	295	––	1,000,000	
Select Structural	Beams and Stringers	1100	––	750	70	295	875	1,000,000	Western Wood Products Association
No. 1		950	––	625	70	295	725	1,000,000	
Select Structural	Posts and Timbers	1050	––	700	70	295	900	1,000,000	
No. 1		850	––	575	70	295	800	1,000,000	(see footnotes 2 through 11)
Selected Decking	Decking	––	1400	––	–	––	––	1,100,000	
Commercial Decking		––	1200	––	–	––	––	1,000,000	
Selected Decking	Decking	––	1500	(Surfaced at 15% max. m.c. and used at 15% max. m.c.)				1,100,000	
Commercial Decking		––	1250					1,000,000	

ALLOWABLE UNIT STRESSES – STRUCTURAL LUMBER

Table 1a – Allowable Unit Stresses for Structural Lumber – VISUAL GRADING (cont.)

(Allowable unit stresses listed are for normal loading conditions. See other provisions of Part II for adjustments of tabulated stresses)

Species and commercial grade	Size classification	Extreme fiber in bending F_b Single-member uses	Extreme fiber in bending F_b Repetitive-member uses	Tension parallel to grain F_t	Horizontal shear F_v	Compression perpendicular to grain $F_{c\perp}$	Compression parallel to grain F_c	Modulus of elasticity E	Grading rules agency
COAST SITKA SPRUCE (Surfaced dry or surfaced green. Used at 19% max. m.c.)									
Select Structural	2" to 4" thick 2" to 4" wide	1500	1700	875	65	290	1100	1,700,000	National Lumber Grades Authority
No. 1		1250	1450	750	65	290	875	1,700,000	
No. 2		1050	1200	625	65	290	700	1,500,000	
No. 3		575	675	350	65	290	425	1,300,000	
Appearance		1250	1450	725	65	290	1050	1,700,000	
Construction		750	875	450	65	290	800	1,300,000	(A Canadian Agency. See footnotes 2 through 9 and 12)
Standard		425	500	250	65	290	650	1,300,000	
Utility		200	225	125	65	290	425	1,300,000	
Stud		600	675	350	65	290	425	1,300,000	
Select Structural	2" to 4" thick 6" and wider	1300	1500	875	65	290	975	1,700,000	
No. 1		1100	1250	725	65	290	875	1,700,000	
No. 2		900	1050	600	65	290	750	1,500,000	
No. 3		525	600	350	65	290	475	1,300,000	
Appearance		1100	1250	725	65	290	1050	1,700,000	
Select Structural	Beams and Stringers	1150	––	675	60	290	775	1,500,000	
No. 1 Structural		950	––	475	60	290	650	1,500,000	
Select Structural	Posts and Timbers	1100	––	725	60	290	825	1,500,000	
No. 1 Structural		875	––	575	60	290	725	1,500,000	
Select	Wall and Roof Plank	1250	1450	––	––	290	––	1,700,000	
Commercial		1050	1200	––	––	290	––	1,500,000	
DOUGLAS FIR-LARCH (NORTH) (Surfaced dry or surfaced green. Used at 19% max. m.c.)									
Dense Select Structural	2" to 4" thick 2" to 4" wide	2400	2800	1400	95	455	1800	1,900,000	National Lumber Grades Authority
Select Structural		2100	2400	1200	95	385	1550	1,800,000	
Dense No. 1		2050	2400	1200	95	455	1450	1,900,000	
No. 1		1750	2050	1050	95	385	1250	1,800,000	
Dense No. 2		1700	1950	1000	95	455	1200	1,700,000	
No. 2		1450	1650	850	95	385	1000	1,700,000	
No. 3		800	925	475	95	385	600	1,500,000	
Appearance		1750	2050	1050	95	385	1500	1,800,000	
Construction		1050	1200	625	95	385	1150	1,500,000	
Standard		600	675	350	95	385	925	1,500,000	
Utility		275	325	175	95	385	600	1,500,000	(A Canadian Agency. See footnotes 2 through 9 and 12)
Stud		800	925	475	95	385	600	1,500,000	
Dense Select Structural	2" to 4" thick 6" and wider	2100	2400	1400	95	455	1650	1,900,000	
Select Structural		1800	2050	1200	95	385	1400	1,800,000	
Dense No. 1		1800	2050	1200	95	455	1450	1,900,000	
No. 1		1500	1750	1000	95	385	1250	1,800,000	
Dense No. 2		1450	1700	950	95	455	1250	1,700,000	
No. 2		1250	1450	825	95	385	1050	1,700,000	
No. 3		725	850	475	95	385	675	1,500,000	
Appearance		1500	1750	1000	95	385	1500	1,800,000	
Dense Select Structural	Beams and Stringers	1900	––	1100	85	445	1300	1,700,000	
Select Structural		1600	––	950	85	380	1100	1,600,000	
Dense No. 1 Structural		1550	––	775	85	455	1100	1,700,000	
No. 1 Structural		1350	––	675	85	385	925	1,600,000	
Dense Select Structural	Posts and Timbers	1750	––	1150	85	455	1350	1,700,000	
Select Structural		1500	––	1000	85	385	1150	1,600,000	
Dense No. 1 Structural		1400	––	950	85	455	1200	1,700,000	
No. 1 Structural		1200	––	825	85	385	1000	1,600,000	
Select	Wall and Roof Plank	1750	2000	––	––	385	––	1,800,000	
Commercial		1450	1650	––	––	385	––	1,700,000	
EASTERN WHITE PINE (NORTH) (Surfaced dry or surfaced green. Used at 19% max. m.c.)									National Lumber Grades Authority
Appearance	2" to 4" thick 2" to 4" wide	1000	1150	675	65	220	1000	1,200,000	
Construction		700	800	400	65	220	750	1,000,000	
Standard		375	450	225	65	220	625	1,000,000	(A Canadian Agency. See footnotes 2 through 9 and 12)
Utility		175	200	100	65	220	400	1,000,000	
Stud		525	600	300	65	220	400	1,000,000	
Select	Wall and Roof Plank	900	1050	––	––	––	––	1,200,000	
Commercial		775	875	––	––	––	––	1,100,000	

ALLOWABLE UNIT STRESSES – STRUCTURAL LUMBER

Table 1a – Allowable Unit Stresses for Structural Lumber – VISUAL GRADING (cont.)

(Allowable unit stresses listed are for normal loading conditions. See other provisions of Part II for adjustments of tabulated stresses)

Species and commercial grade	Size classification	Extreme fiber in bending "F_b" Single-member uses	Extreme fiber in bending "F_b" Repetitive-member uses	Tension parallel to grain "F_t"	Horizontal shear "F_v"	Compression perpendicular to grain "$F_{c\perp}$"	Compression parallel to grain "F_c"	Modulus of elasticity "E"	Grading rules agency
EASTERN HEMLOCK – TAMARACK (NORTH) (Surfaced dry or surfaced green. Used at 19% max. m.c.)									
Select Structural		1800	2050	1050	85	365	1350	1,300,000	
No. 1		1500	1750	900	85	365	1050	1,300,000	
No. 2	2" to 4" thick	1250	1450	725	85	365	850	1,100,000	
No. 3	2" to 4" wide	700	800	400	85	365	525	1,000,000	
Appearance		1300	1500	875	85	365	1300	1,300,000	
Construction		900	1050	525	85	365	975	1,000,000	
Standard		500	575	300	85	365	800	1,000,000	
Utility		250	275	150	85	365	525	1,000,000	National Lumber Grades Authority (A Canadian Agency. See footnotes 2 through 9 and 12)
Stud		700	800	400	85	365	525	1,000,000	
Select Structural	2" to 4" thick	1550	1750	1050	85	365	1200	1,300,000	
No. 1	6" and wider	1300	1500	875	85	365	1050	1,300,000	
No. 2		1050	1200	700	85	365	900	1,100,000	
No. 3		625	725	-400	85	365	575	1,000,000	
Appearance		1300	1500	875	85	365	1300	1,300,000	
Select Structural	Beams and Stringers	1450	––	850	85	405	950	1,300,000	
No. 1 Structural		1200	––	600	85	405	800	1,300,000	
Select Structural	Posts and Timbers	1300	––	875	80	365	1000	1,200,000	
No. 1 Structural		1050	––	700	80	365	875	1,200,000	
Select	Wall and Roof Plank	1500	1700	––	––	––	––	1,300,000	
Commercial		1250	1450	––	––	––	––	1,100,000	
HEM-FIR (NORTH) (Surfaced dry or surfaced green. Used at 19% max. m.c.)									
Select Structural		1650	1900	975	75	245	1300	1,500,000	
No. 1		1400	1600	825	75	245	1000	1,500,000	
No. 2	2" to 4" thick	1150	1300	675	75	245	800	1,400,000	
No. 3	2" to 4" wide	625	725	375	75	245	500	1,200,000	
Appearance		1400	1600	825	75	245	1200	1,500,000	
Construction		825	950	475	75	245	925	1,200,000	
Standard		450	525	275	75	245	750	1,200,000	
Utility		225	250	125	75	245	500	1,200,000	National Lumber Grades Authority (A Canadian Agency. See footnotes 2 through 9 and 12)
Stud		625	725	375	75	245	500	1,200,000	
Select Structural	2" to 4" thick	1400	1650	950	75	245	1150	1,500,000	
No. 1	6" and wider	1200	1400	800	75	245	1000	1,500,000	
No. 2		1000	1150	660	75	245	850	1,400,000	
No. 3		575	675	375	75	245	550	1,200,000	
Appearance		1200	1400	800	75	245	1200	1,500,000	
Select Structural	Beams and Stringers	1250	––	750	70	245	900	1,400,000	
No. 1 Structural		1000	––	525	70	245	750	1,400,000	
Select Structural	Posts and Timbers	1200	––	800	70	245	950	1,400,000	
No. 1 Structural		975	––	650	70	245	850	1,400,000	
Select	Wall and Roof Plank	1350	1550	––	––	245	––	1,500,000	
Commercial		1150	1300	––	––	245	––	1,400,000	
PONDEROSA PINE (Surfaced dry or surfaced green. Used at 19% max. m.c.)									
Select Structural		1400	1650	825	70	250	1050	1,200,000	
No. 1		1200	1400	700	70	250	850	1,200,000	
No. 2	2" to 4" thick	1000	1150	575	70	250	675	1,100,000	
No. 3	2" to 4" wide	550	625	325	70	250	400	1,000,000	
Appearance		1200	1400	700	70	250	850	1,200,000	
Construction		725	825	425	70	250	775	1,000,000	
Standard		400	450	225	70	250	625	1,000,000	
Utility		200	225	100	70	250	400	1,000,000	National Lumber Grades Authority (A Canadian Agency. See footnotes 2 through 9 and 12)
Stud		550	625	325	70	250	400	1,000,000	
Select Structural	2" to 4" thick	1200	1400	825	70	250	950	1,200,000	
No. 1	6" and wider	1050	1200	700	70	250	850	1,200,000	
No. 2		850	975	550	70	250	700	1,100,000	
No. 3		500	575	325	70	250	450	1,000,000	
Appearance		1050	1200	700	70	250	850	1,200,000	
Select Structural	Beams and Stringers	1100	––	725	65	250	750	1,100,000	
No. 1 Structural		925	––	500	65	250	625	1,100,000	
Select Structural	Posts and Timbers	1000	––	675	65	250	800	1,100,000	
No. 1 Structural		825	––	550	65	250	700	1,100,000	
Select	Wall and Roof Plank	––	1450	––	––	––	––	1,300,000	
Commercial		––	1250	––	––	––	––	1,100,000	

ALLOWABLE UNIT STRESSES – STRUCTURAL LUMBER

Table 1a – Allowable Unit Stresses for Structural Lumber – VISUAL GRADING (cont.)

(Allowable unit stresses listed are for normal loading conditions. See other provisions of Part II for adjustments of tabulated stresses)

Species and commercial grade	Size classification	Extreme fiber in bending "F_b" Single-member uses	Extreme fiber in bending "F_b" Repetitive-member uses	Tension parallel to grain "F_t"	Horizontal shear "F_v"	Compression perpendicular to grain "$F_{c\perp}$"	Compression parallel to grain "F_c"	Modulus of elasticity "E"	Grading rules agency
RED PINE (Surfaced dry or surfaced green. Used at 19% max. m.c.)									
Select Structural		1400	1600	800	70	280	1050	1,300,000	
No. 1		1200	1350	700	70	280	825	1,300,000	
No. 2	2" to 4"	975	1100	575	70	280	650	1,200,000	
No. 3	thick	525	625	325	70	280	400	1,000,000	
Appearance	2" to 4"	1200	1350	675	70	280	925	1,300,000	
Construction	wide	700	800	400	70	280	750	1,000,000	
Standard		400	450	225	70	280	600	1,000,000	National
Utility		175	225	100	70	280	400	1,000,000	Lumber
Stud		525	600	325	70	280	400	1,000,000	Grades
Select Structural	2" to 4"	1200	1350	800	70	280	900	1,300,000	Authority
No. 1	thick	1000	1150	675	70	280	825	1,300,000	
No. 2	6" and	825	950	550	70	280	675	1,200,000	(A Canadian
No. 3	wider	500	550	325	70	280	425	1,000,000	Agency. See
Appearance		1000	1150	675	70	280	925	1,300,000	footnotes 2
Select Structural	Beams and	1050	--	625	65	280	725	1,100,000	through 9
No. 1 Structural	Stringers	875	--	450	65	280	600	1,100,000	and 12)
Select Structural	Posts and	1000	--	675	65	280	775	1,100,000	
No. 1 Structural	Timbers	800	--	550	65	280	675	1,100,000	
Select	Wall and	1150	1350	--	--	280	--	1,300,000	
Commercial	Roof Plank	975	1100	--	--	280	--	1,300,000	
SPRUCE–PINE–FIR (Surfaced dry or surfaced green. Used at 19% max. m.c.)									
Select Structural		1450	1650	850	70	265	1100	1,500,000	
No. 1		1200	1400	725	70	265	875	1,500,000	
No. 2	2" to 4"	1000	1150	600	70	265	675	1,300,000	
No. 3	thick	550	650	325	70	265	425	1,200,000	
Appearance	2" to 4"	1200	1400	700	70	265	1050	1,500,000	
Construction	wide	725	850	425	70	265	775	1,200,000	
Standard		400	475	225	70	265	650	1,200,000	National
Utility		175	225	100	70	265	425	1,200,000	Lumber
Stud		550	650	325	70	265	425	1,200,000	Grades
Select Structural	2" to 4"	1250	1450	825	70	265	975	1,500,000	Authority
No. 1	thick	1050	1200	700	70	265	875	1,500,000	
No. 2	6" and	875	1000	575	70	265	725	1,300,000	(A Canadian
No. 3	wider	500	575	325	70	265	450	1,200,000	Agency. See
Appearance		1050	1200	700	70	265	1050	1,500,000	footnotes 2
Select Structural	Beams and	1100	--	650	65	265	775	1,300,000	through 9
No. 1 Structural	Stringers	900	--	450	65	265	625	1,300,000	and 12)
Select Structural	Posts and	1050	--	700	65	265	800	1,300,000	
No. 1 Structural	Timbers	850	--	550	65	265	700	1,300,000	
Select	Wall and	1200	1400	--	--	265	--	1,500,000	
Commercial	Roof Plank	1000	1150	--	--	265	--	1,300,000	
WESTERN CEDARS (NORTH) (Surfaced dry or surfaced green. Used at 19% max. m.c.)									
Select Structural		1450	1700	850	70	285	1200	1,100,000	
No. 1		1250	1450	725	70	285	975	1,100,000	
No. 2	2" to 4"	1000	1200	600	70	285	775	1,000,000	
No. 3	thick	575	650	325	70	285	475	900,000	
Appearance	2" to 4"	1250	1450	725	70	285	1150	1,100,000	
Construction	wide	750	850	425	70	285	875	900,000	
Standard		425	475	250	70	285	725	900,000	National
Utility		200	225	125	70	285	475	900,000	Lumber
Stud		575	650	325	70	285	475	900,000	Grades
Select Structural	2" to 4"	1250	1450	850	70	285	1100	1,100,000	Authority
No. 1	thick	1050	1250	725	70	285	975	1,100,000	
No. 2	6" and	875	1000	575	70	285	825	1,000,000	(A Canadian
No. 3	wider	525	600	325	70	285	525	900,000	Agency. See
Appearance		1050	1250	725	70	285	1150	1,100,000	footnotes 2
Select Structural	Beams and	1100	--	675	65	285	850	1,000,000	through 9
No. 1 Structural	Stringers	900	--	475	65	285	700	1,000,000	and 12)
Select Structural	Posts and	1050	--	700	65	285	900	1,000,000	
No. 1 Structural	Timbers	850	--	575	65	285	800	1,000,000	
Select	Wall and	1200	1400	--	--	285	--	1,100,000	
Commercial	Roof Plank	1050	1200	--	--	285	--	1,000,000	

ALLOWABLE UNIT STRESSES – STRUCTURAL LUMBER

Table 1a – Allowable Unit Stresses for Structural Lumber – VISUAL GRADING (cont.)

(Allowable unit stresses listed are for normal loading conditions. See other provisions of Part II for adjustments of tabulated stresses)

Species and commercial grade	Size classification	Extreme fiber in bending "F_b"		Tension parallel to grain "F_t"	Horizontal shear "F_v"	Compression perpendicular to grain "$F_{c\perp}$"	Compression parallel to grain "F_c"	Modulus of elasticity "E"	Grading rules agency
		Single-member uses	Repetitive-member uses						
WESTERN WHITE PINE (Surfaced dry or surfaced green. Used at 19% max. m.c.)									
Select Structural		1350	1550	775	65	235	1100	1,400,000	
No. 1		1150	1300	675	65	235	875	1,400,000	
No. 2	2" to 4"	925	1050	550	65	235	675	1,300,000	
No. 3	thick	525	600	300	65	235	425	1,200,000	
Appearance	2" to 4"	1150	1300	650	65	235	1050	1,400,000	
Construction	wide	675	775	400	65	235	775	1,200,000	
Standard		375	425	225	65	235	650	1,200,000	
Utility		175	200	100	65	235	425	1,200,000	National
Stud		525	600	300	65	235	425	1,200,000	Lumber
Select Structural	2" to 4"	1150	1300	775	65	235	975	1,400,000	Grades
No. 1	thick	975	1150	650	65	235	875	1,400,000	Authority
No. 2	6" and	800	925	525	65	235	725	1,300,000	
No. 3	wider	475	550	300	65	235	450	1,200,000	(A Canadian
Appearance		975	1150	650	65	235	1050	1,400,000	Agency. See
Select Structural	Beams and	1050	––	600	60	235	775	1,300,000	footnotes 2
No. 1 Structural	Stringers	850	––	425	60	235	625	1,300,000	through 9
Select Structural	Posts and	975	––	650	60	235	800	1,300,000	and 12)
No. 1 Structural	Timbers	775	––	525	60	235	700	1,300,000	
Select	Wall and	1100	1300	––	––	235	––	1,400,000	
Commercial	Roof Plank	925	1050	––	––	235	––	1,300,000	

1. Where Eastern Spruce and Balsam Fir are shipped in a combination, the tabulated values for Balsam Fir shall apply.

2. The recommended design values shown in Table 1a are applicable to lumber that will be used under dry conditions such as in most covered structures. For 2" to 4" thick lumber the DRY surfaced size should be used. In calculating design values, the natural gain in strength and stiffness that occurs as lumber dries has been taken into consideration as well as the reduction in size that occurs when unseasoned lumber shrinks. The gain in load carrying capacity due to increased strength and stiffness resulting from drying more than offsets the design effect of size reductions due to shrinkage. For 5" and thicker lumber, the surfaced sizes also may be used because design values have been adjusted to compensate for any loss in size by shrinkage which may occur.

3. Values for "F_b", "F_t", and "F_c" for the grades of Construction, Standard and Utility apply only to 4" widths.

4. The values in Table 1a are based on edgewise use. For dimension 2" to 4" in thickness, when used flatwise, the recommended design values for fiber stress in bending may be multiplied by the following factors:

Width	Thickness		
	2"	3"	4"
2" to 4"	1.10	1.04	1.00
6" and wider	1.22	1.16	1.11

5. When 2" to 4" thick lumber is manufactured at a maximum moisture content of 15 percent and used in a condition where the moisture content does not exceed 15 percent the design values for surfaced dry or surfaced green lumber shown in Table 1a may be multiplied by the following factors:

Extreme fiber in bending "F_b"	Tension parallel to grain "F_t"	Horizontal shear "F_v"	Compression perpendicular to grain "$F_{c\perp}$"	Compression parallel to grain "F_c"	Modulus of elasticity "E"
1.08	1.08	1.05	1.00	1.17	1.05

6. When 2" to 4" thick lumber is designed for use where the moisture content will exceed 19 percent for an extended period of time, the values shown in Table 1a should be multiplied by the following factors:

Extreme fiber in bending "F_b"	Tension parallel to grain "F_t"	Horizontal shear "F_v"	Compression perpendicular to grain "$F_{c\perp}$"	Compression parallel to grain "F_c"	Modulus of elasticity "E"
0.86	0.84	0.97	0.67	0.70	0.97

7. When lumber 5" and thicker is designed for use where the moisture content will exceed 19 percent for an extended period of time, the values shown in Table 1a should be multiplied by the following factors:

Extreme fiber in bending "F_b"	Tension parallel to grain "F_t"	Horizontal shear "F_v"	Compression perpendicular to grain "$F_{c\perp}$"	Compression parallel to grain "F_c"	Modulus of elasticity "E"
1.00	1.00	1.00	0.67	0.91	1.00

8. The tabulated horizontal shear values shown herein are based on the conservative assumption of the most severe checks, shakes or splits possible, as if a piece were split full length. When lumber 4" and thinner is manufactured unseasoned the tabulated values should be multiplied by a factor of 0.92.

Specific horizontal shear values for any grade and species of lumber may be established by use of the following tables when the length of split or check is known:

When length of split on wide face is:	Multiply tabulated "F_v" value by: (Nominal 2" Lumber)
No split	2.00
½ x wide face	1.67
¾ x wide face	1.50
1 x wide face	1.33
1½ x wide face or more	1.00

When length of split on wide face is:	Multiply tabulated "F_v" value by: (3" and Thicker Lumber)
No split	2.00
½ x narrow face	1.67
1 x narrow face	1.33
1½ x narrow face or more	1.00

9. Stress rated boards of nominal 1", 1¼" and 1½" thickness, 2" and wider, are permitted the recommended design values shown for Select Structural, No. 1, Appearance, No. 2 and No. 3 grades as shown in 2" to 4" thick, 2" to 4" wide and 2" to 4" thick, 6" and wider categories when graded in accordance with those grade requirements.

10. For species combinations shown in parentheses, the lowest design values for any species in the combination are tabulated. White Woods may include Engelmann Spruce, any true firs, any hemlock and any pine. Mixed Species may include any western species.

11. When Decking is surfaced at 15 percent moisture content and used where the moisture content will exceed 15 percent for an extended period of time, the tabulated design values should be multiplied by the following factors: Extreme Fiber in Bending "F_b"—0.79; Modulus of Elasticity "E"—0.92.

12. National Lumber Grades Authority is the Canadian rules writing agency responsible for preparation, maintenance and dissemination of a uniform softwood lumber grading rule for all Canadian species.

ALLOWABLE UNIT STRESSES – STRUCTURAL LUMBER

Table 1b – Allowable Unit Stresses for Structural Lumber – MACHINE STRESS RATED

(The allowable unit stresses listed are for normal loading conditions. See other provisions of Part II for adjustments of tabulated stresses)

Grading rules agency Grade designation	Size classification	Extreme fiber in bending "F_b" (4)		Tension parallel to grain "F_t"	Compression parallel to grain "F_c"	Compression perpendicular to grain "$F_{c\perp}$" (DRY) (1)					Modulus of elasticity "E"
		Single-member uses	Repetitive-member uses			Douglas Fir-Larch	Hem-Fir	Pine (2)	Engelmann Spruce	Cedar (3)	
WESTERN WOOD PRODUCTS ASSOCIATION											
1200f-1.2E	Machine	1200	1400	600	950	385	245	240	195	295	1,200,000
1500f-1.4E	Rated Lum-	1500	1750	900	1200	385	245	240	195	295	1,400,000
1650f-1.5E	ber 2"	1650	1900	1020	1320	385	245	240	195	295	1,500,000
1800f-1.6E	thick or	1800	2050	1175	1450	385	245	240	195	295	1,600,000
2100f-1.8E	less	2100	2400	1575	1700	385	245	240	195	295	1,800,000
2400f-2.0E	All widths	2400	2750	1925	1925	385	245	240	195	295	2,000,000
2700f-2.2E		2700	3100	2150	2150	385	245	240	195	295	2,200,000
3000f-2.4E		3000	3450	2400	2400	385	245	240	195	295	2,400,000
3300f-2.6E		3300	3800	2650	2650	385	245	240	195	295	2,600,000
900f-1.0E	Machine	900	1050	350	725	385	245	240	195	295	1,000,000
900f-1.2E	Rated Joists	900	1050	350	725	385	245	240	195	295	1,200,000
1200f-1.5E	2" thick	1200	1400	600	950	385	245	240	195	295	1,500,000
1350f-1.8E	or less	1350	1550	750	1075	385	245	240	195	295	1,800,000
1800f-2.1E	All widths	1800	2050	1175	1450	385	245	240	195	295	2,100,000
WEST COAST LUMBER INSPECTION BUREAU											
900f-1.0E		900	1050	350	725	385	245				1,000,000
1200f-1.2E	Machine	1200	1400	600	950	385	245				1,200,000
1500f-1.4E	Rated	1500	1750	900	1200	385	245				1,400,000
1650f-1.5E	Lumber	1650	1900	1020	1320	385	245				1,500,000
1800f-1.6E	2" thick	1800	2050	1175	1450	385	245				1,600,000
2100f-1.8E	or less	2100	2400	1575	1700	385	245				1,800,000
2400f-2.0E	All widths	2400	2750	1925	1925	385	245				2,000,000
2700f-2.2E		2700	3100	2150	2150	385	245				2,200,000
900f-1.0E	Machine	900	1050	350	725	385	245				1,000,000
900f-1.2E	Rated Joists	900	1050	350	725	385	245				1,200,000
1200f-1.5E	2" thick	1200	1400	600	950	385	245				1,500,000
1500f-1.8E	or less	1500	1750	900	1200	385	245				1,800,000
1800f-2.1E	6" and wider	1800	2050	1175	1450	385	245				2,100,000

Table 1b Footnotes Applicable to MACHINE STRESS-RATED LUMBER

1. Allowable unit stresses for Horizontal Shear "F_v" (DRY) for all grade designations are as follows:

Douglas Fir-Larch	Hem-Fir	Pine	Engelmann Spruce	Cedar
95	75	65	70	75

2. Pine includes Idaho White, Lodgepole, Ponderosa or Sugar Pine.

3. Cedar includes Incense or Western Red Cedar.

4. Tabulated Extreme Fiber in Bending values "F_b" are applicable to lumber loaded on edge. When loaded flatwise, these values should be multiplied by the following factors:

Nominal Width (in)	4"	6"	8"	10"	12"	14"
Factor	1.10	1.15	1.19	1.22	1.25	1.28

Table 1a – Allowable Unit Stresses for Structural Lumber – VISUAL GRADING (cont.)

(Allowable unit stresses listed are for normal loading conditions. See other provisions of Part II for adjustments of tabulated stresses)

Species and commercial grade	Size classification	Allowable unit stresses in pounds per square inch							Grading rules agency
		Extreme fiber in bending "F_b"		Tension parallel to grain "F_t"	Horizontal shear "F_v"	Compression perpendicular to grain "$F_{c\perp}$"	Compression parallel to grain "F_c"	Modulus of elasticity "E"	
		Single-member uses	Repetitive-member uses						
ASPEN (BIGTOOTH–QUAKING) (Surfaced at 15% moisture content. Used at 15% max. m.c.)									
Select Structural	2" to 4"	1400	1600	825	65	185	1000	1,200,000	
No. 1		1200	1400	700	65	185	800	1,200,000	
No. 2	thick	1000	1150	575	65	185	625	1,100,000	Northern Hardwood and Pine Manufacturers Association and Western Wood Products Association
No. 3	2" to 4"	550	625	325	65	185	375	900,000	
Appearance	wide	1200	1400	700	65	185	950	1,200,000	
Stud		550	625	325	65	185	375	900,000	
Construction	2" to 4"	725	825	425	65	185	725	900,000	
Standard	thick	400	450	225	65	185	600	900,000	
Utility	4" wide	200	225	100	65	185	375	900,000	
Select Structural		1200	1400	825	65	185	875	1,200,000	(see footnotes 2, 3, 4, 8 and 9)
No. 1	2" to 4"	1050	1200	700	65	185	800	1,200,000	
No. 2	thick	850	975	550	65	185	675	1,100,000	
No. 3	6" and	500	575	325	65	185	425	900,000	
Appearance	wider	1050	1200	700	65	185	950	1,200,000	
ASPEN (BIGTOOTH–QUAKING) (Surfaced dry or surfaced green. Used at 19% max. m.c.)									
Select Structural	2" to 4"	1300	1500	775	60	185	850	1,100,000	
No. 1		1100	1300	650	60	185	675	1,100,000	
No. 2	thick	925	1050	525	60	185	550	1,000,000	Northern Hardwood and Pine Manufacturers Association and Western Wood Products Association
No. 3	2" to 4"	500	575	300	60	185	325	900,000	
Appearance	wide	1100	1300	650	60	185	825	1,100,000	
Stud		500	575	300	60	185	325	900,000	
Construction	2" to 4"	650	750	400	60	185	625	900,000	
Standard	thick	375	425	225	60	185	500	900,000	
Utility	4" wide	175	200	100	60	185	325	900,000	
Select Structural		1150	1300	750	60	185	750	1,100,000	(see footnotes 2 through 9)
No. 1	2" to 4"	950	1100	650	60	185	675	1,100,000	
No. 2	thick	775	900	525	60	185	575	1,000,000	
No. 3	6" and	450	525	300	60	185	375	900,000	
Appearance	wider	950	1100	650	60	185	825	1,100,000	
BLACK COTTONWOOD (Surfaced dry or surfaced green. Used at 19% max. m.c.)									
Select Structural	2" to 4"	1000	1200	600	50	100	725	1,200,000	
No. 1		875	1000	500	50	100	575	1,200,000	
No. 2	thick	725	825	425	50	100	450	1,100,000	
No. 3	2" to 4"	400	450	225	50	100	275	900,000	
Appearance	wide	875	1000	500	50	100	700	1,200,000	National Lumber Grades Authority
Stud		400	450	225	50	100	275	900,000	
Construction	2" to 4"	525	600	300	50	100	525	900,000	
Standard	thick	300	325	175	50	100	425	900,000	(A Canadian Agency. See footnotes 2 through 8 and 12)
Utility	4" wide	150	200	75	50	100	275	900,000	
Select Structural		875	1000	600	50	100	650	1,200,000	
No. 1	2" to 4"	750	875	500	50	100	575	1,200,000	
No. 2	thick	625	700	400	50	100	475	1,100,000	
No. 3	6" and	350	425	225	50	100	300	900,000	
Appearance	wider	750	875	500	50	100	700	1,200,000	
COAST SPECIES (Surfaced dry or surfaced green. Used at 19% max. m.c.)									
Select Structural	2" to 4"	1500	1700	875	65	245	1100	1,500,000	
No. 1		1250	1450	750	65	245	875	1,500,000	
No. 2	thick	1050	1200	625	65	245	700	1,400,000	
No. 3	2" to 4"	575	675	350	65	245	425	1,200,000	
Appearance	wide	1250	1450	725	65	245	1050	1,500,000	
Stud		575	675	350	65	245	425	1,200,000	National Lumber Grades Authority
Construction	2" to 4"	750	875	450	65	245	800	1,200,000	
Standard	thick	425	500	250	65	245	650	1,200,000	(A Canadian Agency. See footnotes 2 through 8 and 12)
Utility	4" wide	200	225	125	65	245	425	1,200,000	
Select Structural		1300	1500	875	65	245	975	1,500,000	
No. 1	2" to 4"	1100	1250	725	65	245	875	1,500,000	
No. 2	thick	900	1050	600	65	245	750	1,400,000	
No. 3	6" and	525	600	350	65	245	475	1,200,000	
Appearance	wider	1100	1250	725	65	245	1050	1,500,000	
Select	Decking	1250	1450	––	–––	245	––	1,500,000	
Commercial		1050	1200	––	–––	245	––	1,400,000	

ALLOWABLE UNIT STRESSES – STRUCTURAL LUMBER

Table 1a – Allowable Unit Stresses for Structural Lumber – VISUAL GRADING (cont.)

(Allowable unit stresses listed are for normal loading conditions. See other provisions of Part II for adjustments of tabulated stresses)

Species and commercial grade	Size classification	Extreme fiber in bending "F_b" Single-member uses	Extreme fiber in bending "F_b" Repetitive-member uses	Tension parallel to grain "F_t"	Horizontal shear "F_v"	Compression perpendicular to grain "$F_{c\perp}$"	Compression parallel to grain "F_c"	Modulus of elasticity "E"	Grading rules agency
NORTHERN ASPEN (Surfaced dry or surfaced green. Used at 19% max. m.c.									
Select Structural		1300	1500	750	60	195	850	1,400,000	
No. 1	2" to 4"	1100	1250	650	60	195	675	1,400,000	
No. 2	thick	900	1050	525	60	195	525	1,200,000	
No. 3	2" to 4"	500	575	275	60	195	325	1,100,000	
Appearance	wide	1100	1250	650	60	195	800	1,400,000	National Lumber Grades Authority
Stud		500	575	275	60	195	325	1,100,000	
Construction	2" to 4"	650	750	375	60	195	600	1,100,000	(A Canadian
Standard	thick	350	425	200	60	195	500	1,100,000	Agency. See
Utility	4" wide	175	200	100	60	195	325	1,100,000	footnotes 2
Select Structural		1100	1250	750	60	195	750	1,400,000	through 8
No. 1	2" to 4"	950	1100	625	60	195	675	1,400,000	and 12)
No. 2	thick	775	900	500	60	194	550	1,200,000	
No. 3	6" and	450	525	275	60	195	350	1,100,000	
Appearance	wider	950	1100	625	60	195	800	1,400,000	
NORTHERN SPECIES (Surfaced dry or surfaced green. Used at 19% max. m.c.									
Select Structural		1350	1550	775	65	220	1050	1,100,000	
No. 1	2" to 4"	1150	1300	675	65	220	825	1,100,000	
No. 2	thick	925	1050	550	65	220	650	1,000,000	
No. 3	2" to 4"	525	600	300	65	220	400	900,000	
Appearance	wide	1000	1150	650	65	220	850	1,100,000	National Lumber Grades Authority
Stud		525	600	300	65	220	400	900,000	
Construction	2" to 4"	675	775	400	65	220	750	900,000	(A Canadian
Standard	thick	375	425	225	65	220	600	900,000	Agency. See
Utility	4" wide	175	200	100	65	220	400	900,000	footnotes 2
Select Structural		1150	1300	775	65	220	900	1,100,000	through 8
No. 1	2" to 4"	975	1150	650	65	220	825	1,100,000	and 12)
No. 2	thick	800	925	525	65	220	675	1,000,000	
No. 3	6" and	475	550	300	65	220	425	900,000	
Appearance	wider	975	1100	650	65	220	850	1,100,000	
Select	Decking	900	1050	—	—	220	—	1,100,000	
Commercial		775	875	—	—	220	—	1,000,000	
WESTERN HEMLOCK (Surfaced dry or surfaced green. Used at 19% max. m.c.)									
Select Structural		1800	2100	1050	90	280	1450	1,600,000	
No. 1	2" to 4"	1550	1800	900	90	280	1150	1,600,000	
No. 2	thick	1300	1450	750	90	280	900	1,400,000	West Coast Lumber Inspection Bureau
No. 3	2" to 4"	700	800	425	90	280	550	1,300,000	
Appearance	wide	1550	1800	900	90	280	1350	1,600,000	
Stud		700	800	425	90	280	550	1,300,000	
Construction	2" to 4"	925	1050	550	90	280	1050	1,300,000	and Western Wood Products Association
Standard	thick	525	600	300	90	280	850	1,300,000	
Utility	4" wide	250	275	150	90	280	550	1,300,000	
Select Structural		1550	1800	1050	90	280	1300	1,600,000	(See footnotes 2 through 9)
No. 1	2" to 4"	1350	1550	900	90	280	1150	1,600,000	
No. 2	thick	1100	1250	725	90	280	975	1,400,000	
No. 3	6" and	650	750	425	90	280	625	1,300,000	
Appearance	wider	1350	1550	900	90	280	1350	1,600,000	
Select Structural	Beams and	1450	—	825	85	280	1000	1,400,000	West Coast Lumber Inspection Bureau
No. 1	Stringers	1150	—	575	85	280	850	1,400,000	
Select Structural	Posts and	1300	—	875	85	280	1100	1,400,000	
No. 1	Timbers	1050	—	700	85	280	950	1,400,000	
Select Dex	Decking	1500	1750	—	—	280	—	1,600,000	(See footnotes 2 through 9)
Commercial Dex		1300	1450	—	—	280	—	1,400,000	
Select Structural	Beams and	1400	—	950	85	280	1000	1,400,000	
No. 1	Stringers	1150	—	775	85	280	850	1,400,000	
Select Structural	Posts and	1300	—	875	85	280	1100	1,400,000	Western Wood Products Association
No. 1	Timbers	1050	—	700	85	280	950	1,400,000	
Selected Decking	Decking		1750			280		1,600,000	(See footnotes 2 through 11)
Commercial Decking			1450			280		1,400,000	
Selected Decking	Decking		1900	(Surfaced at 15% max. m.c. and used at 15% max. m.c.)		280		1,700,000	
Commercial Decking			1600			280		1,500,000	

Table 1a – Allowable Unit Stresses for Structural Lumber – VISUAL GRADING (cont.)

(Allowable unit stresses listed are for normal loading conditions. See other provisions of Part II for adjustments of tabulated stresses)

Species and commercial grade	Size classification	Extreme fiber in bending "F_b"		Tension parallel to grain "F_t"	Horizontal shear "F_v"	Compression perpendicular to grain "$F_{c\perp}$"	Compression parallel to grain "F_c"	Modulus of elasticity "E"	Grading rules agency
		Single-member uses	Repetitive-member uses						
EASTERN WHITE PINE (Surfaced dry or surfaced green. Used at 19% max. m.c.)									
Select Structural	2" to 4"	1350	1550	800	70	220	1050	1,200,000	
No. 1	thick	1150	1350	675	70	220	850	1,200,000	
No. 2	2" to 4"	950	1100	550	70	220	675	1,100,000	
No. 3	wide	525	600	300	70	220	400	1,000,000	
Appearance		1150	1350	675	70	220	1000	1,200,000	Northeastern Lumber Manufacturers Association
Select Structural	2" to 4"	1150	1350	775	70	220	950	1,200,000	
No. 1	thick	1000	1150	675	70	220	850	1,200,000	
No. 2	6" and	825	950	550	70	220	700	1,100,000	(See footnotes 2 through 9)
No. 3	wider	475	550	300	70	220	450	1,000,000	
Appearance		1000	1150	675	70	220	1000	1,200,000	
Select Structural	Beams and	1050	–	700	65	220	675	1,100,000	
No. 1	Stringers	875	–	600	65	220	575	1,100,000	
Select Structural	Posts and	975	–	650	65	220	725	1,100,000	
No. 1	Timbers	800	–	525	65	220	625	1,100,000	

Table 1b – Allowable Unit Stresses for Structural Lumber – MACHINE STRESS RATED

(The allowable unit stresses listed are for normal loading conditions. See other provisions of Part II for adjustment of tabulated stresses)

Grading rules agency / Grading designation	Size classification	Extreme fiber in bending "F_b" (4)		Tension Parallel to grain "F_t"	Compression parallel to grain "F_c"	Compression perpendicular to grain "$F_{c\perp}$"	Modulus of Elasticity "E"
		Single member uses	Repetitive member uses				
SOUTHERN PINE INSPECTION BUREAU							
1200f–1.2E		1200	1375	600	950	405	1,200,000
1500f–1.4E		1500	1725	900	1200	405	1,400,000
1650f–1.5E		1650	1900	1020	1320	405	1,500,000
1800f–1.6E	Machine Rated Lumber	1800	2100	1175	1450	405	1,600,000
2100f–1.8E		2100	2400	1575	1700	405	1,800,000
2400f–2.0E	2" thick or less	2400	2750	1925	1925	405	2,000,000
2700f–2.2E	2" to 4" wide	2700	3100	2150	2150	405	2,200,000
3000f–2.4E		3000	3450	2400	2400	405	2,400,000
3300f–2.6E		3300	3800	2650	2650	405	2,600,000
900f–1.0E		900	1025	350	725	405	1,000,000
900f–1.2E	Machine Rated Lumber	900	1025	350	725	405	1,200,000
1200f–1.5E		1200	1375	600	950	405	1,500,000
1350f–1.8E	2" thick or less.	1350	1550	750	1075	405	1,800,000
1800f–2.1E	6" and wider	1800	2050	1175	1450	405	2,100,000

Allowable unit stress for Horizontal Shear "F_v": KD = 95 psi.
S-DRY = 90 psi.

5-71-10M
8-71-5M
11-71-5M
4-72-10M
11-72-10M

2-04-1-11

APPENDIX B

DESIGN PROPERTIES FOR BOLTS, LAG BOLTS AND COMMON WOOD SCREWS

Table B1. Grouping of Species for Determining Allowable Loads for Lag Screws, Nails, Spikes, Wood Screws, Drift Bolts.

Group	Species of Wood	Specific Gravity * (G)
I	Ash, commercial white	0.63
	Beech	.67
	Birch, sweet	.71
	Birch, yellow	.65
	Elm, rock	.67
	Hickory, true	.80
	Maple (hard), black	.60
	Maple (hard), sugar	.67
	Oak, commercial red	.66
	Oak, commercial white	.71
	Pecan	.73
II	Douglas fir	0.51
	Larch	.55
	Pine, southern	.55
III	Cedar, Alaska	0.47
	Cedar, Port Orford	.45
	Cypress, southern	.49
	Hemlock, western	.47
	Pine, Norway	.47
	Redwood (old growth)	.44
	Sweet gum	.53
IV	Basswood	0.35
	Cedar, northern white	.32
	Cedar, southern white	.34
	Cedar, western red	.36
	Cottonwood, black	.34
	Fir, Balsam	.37
	Fir, commercial white	.40
	Hemlock, eastern	.44
	Pine, lodgepole	.44
	Pine, ponderosa	.44
	Pine, sugar	.39
	Pine, eastern white	.39
	Pine, western white	.41
	Spruce, Engelmann	.40
	Spruce, red, white, Sitka	.42
	Yellow poplar	.45

* Based on weight and volume when oven-dry.

Courtesy National Forest Products Assn.

Table B2. Allowable Loads in Pounds on One Bolt Loaded at Both Ends (Double Shear)* for Following Species.
[The allowable bolt loads below are for normal loading conditions. See other provisions of Ch. 12 for adjustments of these tabulated allowable bolt loads.]

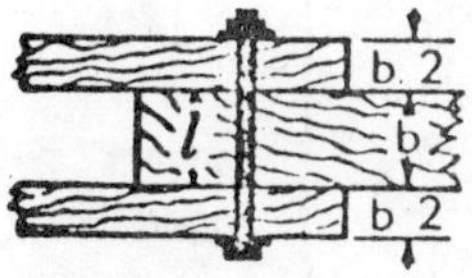

Length of bolt in main member *l* (Inches)	Diameter of bolt *d* (Inches)	*l/d*	Projected area of bolt $A=l\times d$ (Sq. In.)	1 BEECH, BIRCH, ELM, Rock, MAPLE, Hard — Parallel to grain *P*	1 — Perpendicular to grain *Q*	2 CEDAR, Alaska, SPRUCE, Eastern and Sitka — Parallel to grain *P*	2 — Perpendicular to grain *Q*	3 CYPRESS, Southern — Parallel to grain *P*	3 — Perpendicular to grain *Q*	4 DOUGLAS FIR, LARCH, Western, PINE, Southern — Parallel to grain *P*	4 — Perpendicular to grain *Q*	5 FIR, White, HEMLOCK, Eastern — Parallel to grain *P*	5 — Perpendicular to grain *Q*	6 CEDAR, Port Orford, HEMLOCK, Western — Parallel to grain *P*	6 — Perpendicular to grain *Q*
	½	3.3	.8125	1,120	750	750	380	1,010	450	1,010	480	680	450	850	450
	⅝	2.6	1.0156	1,430	850	930	420	1,290	510	1,290	540	850	510	1,070	510
1⅝	¾	2.2	1.2188	1,720	950	1,120	470	1,550	570	1,550	600	1,010	570	1,280	570
	⅞	1.9	1.4219	2,000	1,040	1,310	520	1,810	620	1,810	670	1,190	620	1,500	620
	1	1.6	1.625	2,290	1,140	1,500	570	2,070	680	2,070	730	1,360	680	1,720	680
	½	4.0	1.00	1,300	920	900	460	1,180	550	1,180	590	840	550	1,030	550
	⅝	3.2	1.25	1,730	1,050	1,160	520	1,560	630	1,560	670	1,050	630	1,320	630
2	¾	2.7	1.50	2,110	1,160	1,390	580	1,910	700	1,910	740	1,250	700	1,580	700
	⅞	2.3	1.75	2,460	1,280	1,620	640	2,230	770	2,230	820	1,470	770	1,850	770
	1	2.0	2.00	2,820	1,400	1,850	700	2,550	840	2,550	890	1,670	840	2,110	840
	½	5.3	1.3125	1,400	1,210	1,030	610	1,280	730	1,280	780	1,010	730	1,180	730
	⅝	4.2	1.6406	2,090	1,370	1,460	690	1,890	820	1,890	880	1,360	820	1,670	820
2⅝	¾	3.5	1.9688	2,670	1,530	1,810	760	2,430	920	2,430	980	1,650	920	2,060	920
	⅞	3.0	2.2969	3,200	1,680	2,120	840	2,900	1,010	2,900	1,080	1,920	1,010	2,420	1,010
	1	2.6	2.625	3,690	1,830	2,430	920	3,340	1,100	3,340	1,170	2,190	1,100	2,770	1,100
	½	6.0	1.50	1,420	1,330	1,050	690	1,290	830	1,290	890	1,070	830	1,200	830
	⅝	4.8	1.875	2,190	1,570	1,560	780	1,980	940	1,980	1,000	1,510	940	1,790	940
3	¾	4.0	2.25	2,930	1,740	2,030	870	2,660	1,050	2,660	1,120	1,870	1,050	2,320	1,050
	⅞	3.4	2.625	3,590	1,920	2,420	960	3,250	1,150	3,250	1,230	2,190	1,150	2,760	1,150
	1	3.0	3.00	4,180	2,100	2,770	1,050	3,790	1,260	3,790	1,340	2,510	1,260	3,170	1,260
	½	7.3	1.8125	1,420	1,390	1,050	830	1,290	950	1,290	1,020	1,070	950	1,200	950
	⅝	5.8	2.2656	2,220	1,850	1,640	950	2,010	1,140	2,010	1,210	1,660	1,140	1,870	1,140
3⅝	¾	4.8	2.7188	3,190	2,110	2,280	1,050	2,860	1,270	2,860	1,350	2,190	1,270	2,600	1,270
	⅞	4.1	3.1719	4,090	2,320	2,840	1,160	3,680	1,390	3,680	1,490	2,630	1,390	3,240	1,390
	1	3.6	3.625	4,880	2,530	3,320	1,270	4,430	1,520	4,430	1,620	3,030	1,520	3,790	1,520
	½	8.0	2.00	1,420	1,390	1,050	890	1,290	980	1,290	1,040	1,070	980	1,200	980
	⅝	6.4	2.50	2,220	1,750	1,640	1,050	2,010	1,250	2,010	1,330	1,670	1,250	1,870	1,250
4	¾	5.3	3.00	3,190	2,310	2,340	1,160	2,890	1,400	2,890	1,490	2,330	1,400	2,680	1,400
	⅞	4.6	3.50	4,230	2,560	3,000	1,280	3,830	1,540	3,830	1,640	2,850	1,540	3,430	1,540
	1	4.0	4.00	5,210	2,790	3,600	1,400	4,720	1,680	4,720	1,790	3,330	1,680	4,120	1,680
	½	9.0	2.25	1,420	1,340	1,050	900	1,290	960	1,290	1,020	1,070	960	1,200	960
	⅝	7.2	2.8125	2,220	1,980	1,640	1,170	2,010	1,350	2,010	1,440	1,670	1,350	1,870	1,350
4½	¾	6.0	3.375	3,190	2,520	2,360	1,310	2,890	1,570	2,890	1,680	2,420	1,570	2,700	1,570
	⅞	5.1	3.9375	4,350	2,880	3,160	1,440	3,920	1,730	3,920	1,840	3,110	1,730	3,610	1,730
	1	4.5	4.50	5,520	3,140	3,900	1,570	4,980	1,890	4,980	2,010	3,670	1,890	4,450	1,890
	1⅛	4.0	5.0625	6,590	3,420	4,560	1,710	5,980	2,050	5,980	2,190	4,210	2,050	5,210	2,050
	⅝	8.8	3.4375	2,220	1,910	1,640	1,270	2,010	1,360	2,010	1,450	1,670	1,360	1,870	1,360
	¾	7.3	4.125	3,190	2,660	2,380	1,590	2,890	1,820	2,890	1,940	2,420	1,820	2,700	1,820
5½	⅞	6.3	4.8125	4,350	3,310	3,230	1,760	3,940	2,100	3,940	2,250	3,310	2,100	3,670	2,100
	1	5.5	5.50	5,650	3,800	4,170	1,920	5,120	2,300	5,120	2,460	4,180	2,300	4,670	2,300
	1⅛	4.9	6.1875	7,110	4,190	5,110	2,090	6,440	2,510	6,440	2,680	4,960	2,510	5,840	2,510
	⅝	10.4	4.0625	2,220	1,800	1,650	1,230	2,010	1,300	2,010	1,390	1,670	1,300	1,870	1,300
	¾	8.7	4.875	3,190	2,560	2,330	1,700	2,890	1,820	2,890	1,940	2,420	1,820	2,700	1,820
6½	⅞	7.4	5.6875	4,350	3,410	3,230	2,070	3,940	2,350	3,940	2,510	3,310	2,350	3,670	2,350
	1	6.5	6.50	5,680	4,180	4,210	2,270	5,140	2,700	5,140	2,880	4,290	2,700	4,810	2,700
	1⅛	5.8	7.3125	7,200	4,820	5,290	2,470	6,500	2,970	6,500	3,170	5,370	2,970	6,050	2,970
	⅝	12.0	4.6875	2,220	1,670	1,650	1,200	2,010	1,220	2,010	1,300	1,670	1,220	1,870	1,220
	¾	10.0	5.625	3,190	2,420	2,380	1,660	2,890	1,760	2,890	1,880	2,420	1,760	2,700	1,760
7½	⅞	8.6	6.5625	4,350	3,300	3,230	2,180	3,940	2,340	3,940	2,500	3,310	2,340	3,670	2,340
	1	7.5	7.50	5,680	4,230	4,210	2,590	5,140	2,940	5,140	3,130	4,290	2,940	4,810	2,940
	1⅛	6.7	8.4375	7,200	5,140	5,340	2,850	6,500	3,370	6,500	3,610	5,450	3,370	6,110	3,370
	¾	12.7	7.125	3,190	2,150	2,380	1,570	2,890	1,580	2,890	1,690	2,420	1,580	2,700	1,580
	⅞	10.9	8.3125	4,350	2,980	3,230	2,080	3,940	2,190	3,940	2,350	3,310	2,190	3,670	2,190
9½	1	9.5	9.50	5,680	3,960	4,210	2,680	5,140	2,860	5,140	3,050	4,290	2,860	4,810	2,860
	1⅛	8.4	10.6875	7,200	5,120	5,340	3,350	6,500	3,630	6,500	3,830	5,450	3,630	6,110	3,630
	1¼	7.6	11.875	8,870	6,190	6,570	3,820	8,040	4,310	8,040	4,590	6,780	4,310	7,510	4,310
	1	11.5	11.50	5,680	3,640	4,210	2,580	5,140	2,680	5,140	2,850	4,290	2,680	4,810	2,680
11½	1⅛	10.2	12.9375	7,200	4,710	5,340	3,260	6,500	3,440	6,500	3,660	5,450	3,440	6,100	3,440
	1¼	9.2	14.375	8,870	5,890	6,570	3,950	8,040	4,210	8,040	4,490	6,780	4,210	7,510	4,210

* Three (3) member joint.

Table B2. Allowable Loads in Pounds on One Bolt Loaded at Both Ends (Double Shear)* for Following Species.---Continued
[The allowable bolt loads below are for normal loading conditions. See other provisions of Ch. 12 for adjustments of these tabulated allowable bolt loads.]

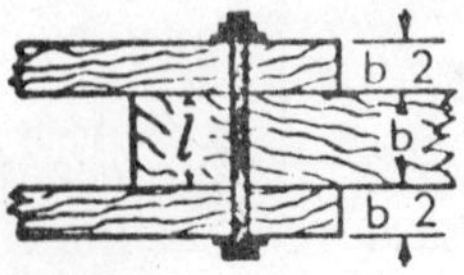

Length of bolt in main member l (Inches)	Diameter of bolt d (Inches)	l/d	Projected area of bolt $A=l\times d$ (Sq. In.)	7 HICKORY, PECAN Parallel to grain P	Perpendicular to grain Q	8 ASH, White, OAK, Red and White Parallel to grain P	Perpendicular to grain Q	9 PINE, Norway, Ponderosa, Sugar, White Parallel to grain P	Perpendicular to grain Q	10 CEDAR, Western, Red, PINE, Lodgepole Parallel to grain P	Perpendicular to grain Q	11 REDWOOD Parallel to grain P	Perpendicular to grain Q	12 SPRUCE, Englemann Parallel to grain P	Perpendicular to grain Q
1⅜	½	3.3	.8125	1,400	900	940	750	710	380	680	330	940	380	580	270
	⅝	2.6	1.0156	1,780	1,020	1,200	850	890	420	850	370	1,200	420	710	310
	¾	2.2	1.2188	2,150	1,130	1,450	950	1,070	470	1,010	420	1,450	470	850	340
	⅞	1.9	1.4219	2,500	1,250	1,690	1,040	1,250	520	1,190	460	1,690	520	1,000	370
	1	1.6	1.625	2,860	1,360	1,930	1,140	1,430	570	1,360	500	1,930	570	1,140	410
2	½	4.0	1.00	1,630	1,110	1,100	920	860	460	840	410	1,100	460	700	330
	⅝	3.2	1.25	2,160	1,250	1,460	1,050	1,100	520	1,050	460	1,460	520	890	380
	¾	2.7	1.50	2,630	1,400	1,780	1,160	1,320	580	1,250	510	1,780	580	1,060	420
	⅞	2.3	1.75	3,080	1,540	2,080	1,280	1,540	640	1,470	560	2,080	640	1,240	460
	1	2.0	2.00	3,520	1,680	2,380	1,400	1,760	700	1,670	610	2,380	700	1,410	500
2⅝	½	5.3	1.3125	1,740	1,450	1,180	1,210	980	610	1,010	530	1,180	610	850	440
	⅝	4.2	1.6406	2,610	1,650	1,760	1,370	1,390	690	1,360	600	1,760	690	1,140	490
	¾	3.5	1.9688	3,340	1,830	2,250	1,530	1,720	760	1,650	670	2,250	760	1,390	550
	⅞	3.0	2.2969	4,000	2,020	2,700	1,680	2,020	840	1,920	740	2,700	840	1,620	600
	1	2.6	2.625	4,610	2,200	3,110	1,830	2,310	920	2,190	810	3,110	920	1,850	660
3	½	6.0	1.50	1,770	1,600	1,200	1,330	1,000	690	1,070	610	1,200	690	900	500
	⅝	4.8	1.875	2,740	1,880	1,850	1,570	1,490	780	1,510	690	1,850	780	1,270	560
	¾	4.0	2.25	3,660	2,090	2,470	1,740	1,930	870	1,870	770	2,470	870	1,580	630
	⅞	3.4	2.625	4,480	2,300	3,020	1,920	2,300	960	2,190	840	3,020	960	1,850	690
	1	3.0	3.00	5,230	2,510	3,530	2,100	2,640	1,050	2,510	920	3,530	1,050	2,110	750
3⅝	½	7.3	1.8125	1,770	1,670	1,200	1,390	1,000	830	1,070	730	1,200	830	900	600
	⅝	5.8	2.2656	2,760	2,220	1,860	1,850	1,560	950	1,660	830	1,860	950	1,400	680
	¾	4.8	2.7188	3,980	2,530	2,680	2,110	2,170	1,050	2,190	930	2,680	1,050	1,850	760
	⅞	4.1	3.1719	5,110	2,780	3,450	2,320	2,700	1,160	2,630	1,020	3,450	1,160	2,220	840
	1	3.6	3.625	6,110	3,040	4,120	2,530	3,160	1,270	3,030	1,110	4,120	1,270	2,550	910
4	½	8.0	2.00	1,770	1,660	1,200	1,390	1,000	890	1,070	780	1,200	890	900	670
	⅝	6.4	2.50	2,770	2,340	1,870	1,950	1,560	1,050	1,670	920	1,870	1,050	1,420	750
	¾	5.3	3.00	3,990	2,780	2,690	2,310	2,230	1,160	2,330	1,020	2,690	1,160	1,960	840
	⅞	4.6	3.50	5,290	3,070	3,570	2,560	2,860	1,280	2,850	1,130	3,570	1,280	2,400	920
	1	4.0	4.00	6,510	3,350	4,400	2,790	3,430	1,400	3,330	1,230	4,400	1,400	2,800	1,010
4½	½	9.0	2.25	1,770	1,610	1,200	1,340	1,000	900	1,070	790	1,200	900	900	710
	⅝	7.2	2.8125	2,770	2,380	1,870	1,980	1,560	1,170	1,670	1,030	1,870	1,170	1,420	850
	¾	6.0	3.375	3,990	3,020	2,690	2,520	2,250	1,310	2,420	1,150	2,690	1,310	2,040	940
	⅞	5.1	3.9375	5,440	3,450	3,670	2,880	3,010	1,440	3,110	1,270	3,670	1,440	2,620	1,040
	1	4.5	4.50	6,900	3,770	4,660	3,140	3,710	1,570	3,670	1,380	4,660	1,570	3,090	1,130
	1⅛	4.0	5.0625	8,240	4,110	5,560	3,420	4,340	1,710	4,210	1,510	5,560	1,710	3,540	1,230
5½	⅝	8.8	3.4375	2,770	2,300	1,870	1,910	1,560	1,270	1,670	1,120	1,870	1,270	1,420	990
	¾	7.3	4.125	3,990	3,190	2,690	2,660	2,250	1,590	2,420	1,400	2,690	1,590	2,040	1,150
	⅞	6.3	4.8125	5,440	3,970	3,670	3,310	3,060	1,760	3,310	1,550	3,670	1,760	2,780	1,270
	1	5.5	5.50	7,070	4,560	4,770	3,800	3,970	1,920	4,180	1,690	4,770	1,920	3,520	1,380
	1⅛	4.9	6.1875	8,890	5,020	6,000	4,190	4,870	2,090	4,960	1,840	6,000	2,090	4,180	1,510
6½	⅝	10.4	4.0625	2,770	2,160	1,870	1,800	1,570	1,230	1,670	1,090	1,870	1,230	1,420	990
	¾	8.7	4.875	3,990	3,070	2,690	2,560	2,250	1,700	2,420	1,490	2,690	1,700	2,040	1,320
	⅞	7.4	5.6875	5,440	4,090	3,670	3,410	3,060	2,070	3,310	1,820	3,670	2,070	2,780	1,500
	1	6.5	6.50	7,100	5,020	4,790	4,180	4,000	2,270	4,290	2,000	4,790	2,270	3,620	1,630
	1⅛	5.8	7.3125	8,970	5,790	6,050	4,820	5,040	2,470	5,370	2,180	6,050	2,470	4,520	1,780
7½	⅝	12.0	4.6875	2,770	2,000	1,870	1,670	1,570	1,200	1,670	1,050	1,870	1,200	1,420	970
	¾	10.0	5.625	3,990	2,900	2,690	2,420	2,250	1,660	2,420	1,460	2,690	1,660	2,040	1,330
	⅞	8.6	6.5625	5,440	3,960	3,670	3,300	3,060	2,180	3,310	1,920	3,670	2,180	2,780	1,680
	1	7.5	7.50	7,100	5,070	4,790	4,230	4,000	2,590	4,290	2,280	4,790	2,590	3,620	1,890
	1⅛	6.7	8.4375	8,970	6,160	6,050	5,140	5,090	2,850	5,450	2,510	6,050	2,850	4,630	2,050
9½	¾	12.7	7.125	3,990	2,580	2,690	2,150	2,250	1,570	2,420	1,380	2,690	1,570	2,040	1,270
	⅞	10.9	8.3125	5,440	3,580	3,670	2,980	3,060	2,080	3,310	1,830	3,670	2,080	2,780	1,680
	1	9.5	9.50	7,100	4,750	4,790	3,960	4,000	2,680	4,290	2,360	4,790	2,680	3,620	2,150
	1⅛	8.4	10.6875	8,970	6,140	6,050	5,120	5,090	3,350	5,450	2,950	6,050	3,350	4,630	2,560
	1¼	7.6	11.875	11,090	7,420	7,480	6,190	6,260	3,820	6,780	3,360	7,480	3,820	5,710	2,800
11½	1	11.5	11.50	7,100	4,370	4,790	3,640	4,000	2,580	4,290	2,270	4,790	2,580	3,620	2,090
	1⅛	10.2	12.9375	8,970	5,650	6,050	4,710	5,090	3,260	5,450	2,860	6,050	3,260	4,630	2,620
	1¼	9.2	14.375	11,090	7,070	7,480	5,890	6,260	3,950	6,780	3,480	7,480	3,950	5,710	3,150

Table B3. LAG BOLTS or LAG SCREWS--Allowable Lateral Loads---Normal Duration.

WOOD SIDE PIECES

[For species in each Group, see Table B1]

Thickness of Side Member (inches)	Length of Lag Bolt (inches)	Diameter of Lag Bolt Shank (inches)	GROUP I Total Lateral Load per Lag Bolt in Single Shear (pounds)		GROUP II Total Lateral Load per Lag Bolt in Single Shear (pounds)		GROUP III Total Lateral Load per Lag Bolt in Single Shear (pounds)		GROUP IV Total Lateral Load per Lag Bolt in Single Shear (pounds)	
			Parallel to Grain	Perpendicular to Grain	Parallel to Grain	Perpendicular to Grain	Parallel to Grain	Perpendicular to Grain	Parallel to Grain	Perpendicular to Grain
1⅝"	4"	¼	220	210	170	170	130	120	100	100
		5/16	290	240	210	170	150	130	120	110
		⅜	330	250	240	180	180	140	140	110
		7/16	370	260	270	190	200	140	160	110
		½	400	260	300	190	220	140	170	110
		⅝	450	270	360	210	250	150	190	120
	5"	¼	230	220	190	180	170	170	150	150
		5/16	340	290	280	240	230	190	180	160
		⅜	450	340	360	270	260	200	210	160
		7/16	540	380	400	280	290	210	230	170
		½	590	380	450	290	320	210	250	170
		⅝	680	410	540	320	370	220	290	180
	6"	¼	260	250	220	210	200	200	180	170
		5/16	380	330	320	270	300	250	260	220
		⅜	490	380	410	320	360	280	290	220
		7/16	610	430	520	360	410	290	320	230
		½	740	480	610	390	440	290	350	230
		⅝	940	560	710	430	490	300	400	240
	7"	¼	280	270	240	230	210	210	190	180
		5/16	410	350	350	300	320	270	280	240
		⅜	540	410	450	340	420	320	370	280
		7/16	670	470	560	390	520	370	420	300
		½	810	520	670	440	570	370	460	300
		⅝	1000	600	810	490	620	370	500	300
2⅝"	6"	⅜	490	380	370	280	270	210	220	170
		7/16	590	420	430	300	320	230	260	180
		½	660	430	480	310	360	230	290	190
		⅝	730	440	560	340	400	240	320	190
		¾	830	450	630	350	450	250	360	200
		⅞	910	470	730	380	490	260	390	200
		1	1010	510	800	400	550	280	440	220
	7"	⅜	490	380	410	310	260	280	290	220
		7/16	660	470	550	390	420	300	340	240
		½	830	540	650	420	460	300	370	240
		⅝	970	580	750	450	520	310	420	250
		¾	1080	600	860	470	590	320	470	260
		⅞	1240	640	970	500	670	350	540	280
		1	1390	700	1080	540	750	380	600	300
	8"	⅜	550	420	460	360	420	320	370	280
		7/16	720	510	610	430	550	390	440	310
		½	900	590	770	500	610	400	490	320
		⅝	1250	750	970	580	680	410	550	330
		¾	1410	780	1110	610	760	420	610	340
		⅞	1570	820	1220	630	850	440	680	350
		1	2000	1000	1380	690	960	480	770	390
	9"	⅜	600	450	500	380	460	350	410	310
		7/16	790	560	670	470	610	430	540	380
		½	990	640	830	540	770	500	610	390
		⅝	1330	800	1120	670	850	510	690	410
		¾	1690	930	1350	740	950	520	760	420
		⅞	1930	1010	1480	770	1050	540	840	440
		1	2150	1070	1670	830	1160	580	940	470

By permission of NFPA.

Table B4. LAG BOLTS or LAG SCREWS---Allowable Lateral Loads---Normal Duration.

1/2" METAL SIDE PIECES

[For species in each Group, see Table B1]

Length of Lag Bolt (inches)	Diameter of Lag Bolt Shank (inches)	GROUP I Total Lateral Load per Lag Bolt in Single Shear (pounds)		GROUP II Total Lateral Load per Lag Bolt in Single Shear (pounds)		GROUP III Total Lateral Load per Lag Bolt in Single Shear (pounds)		GROUP IV Total Lateral Load per Lag Bolt in Single Shear (pounds)	
		Parallel to Grain	Perpendicular to Grain	Parallel to Grain	Perpendicular to Grain	Parallel to Grain	Perpendicular to Grain	Parallel to Grain	Perpendicular to Grain
3"	1/4	240	185	210	160	155	120	125	100
	5/16	355	240	265	180	190	130	155	105
	3/8	420	255	320	245	230	140	180	110
	7/16	485	275	370	210	265	150	210	120
	1/2	550	285	415	215	295	155	240	125
	5/8	645	310	490	235	350	170	280	135
4"	1/4*	275	210	235	185	210	165	190	145
	5/16	410	280	355	240	290	200	235	160
	3/8	570	345	480	290	345	210	275	165
	7/16	750	425	575	320	405	230	320	180
	1/2	830	430	625	325	450	235	360	185
	5/8	975	465	740	355	530	255	425	205
5"	5/16	435	295	375	255	335	230	300	205
	3/8	615	375	535	325	470	295	375	230
	7/16	820	465	710	405	535	350	430	245
	1/2	1045	540	850	440	610	315	490	255
	5/8	1330	635	1005	480	720	345	580	280
	3/4	1580	695	1190	525	855	375	690	305
6"	5/16*	445	305	400	270	345	235	305	205
	3/8	630	385	545	330	490	300	430	260
	7/16	850	480	735	415	660	375	545	310
	1/2	1100	570	945	490	770	400	615	320
	5/8	1640	790	1250	600	900	430	720	345
	3/4	1970	865	1480	650	1060	460	850	370
7"	3/8*	645	390	555	340	500	305	440	270
	7/16	865	490	750	425	670	380	590	335
	1/2	1120	580	970	505	865	450	745	385
	5/8	1700	820	1460	700	1020	490	900	430
	3/4	2360	1040	2030	890	1290	570	1040	460
8"	7/16*	875	500	760	430	680	385	600	340
	1/2	1140	590	985	510	880	455	775	400
	5/8	1750	840	1500	720	1325	635	1070	560
	3/4	2475	1090	2130	935	1550	680	1250	555
	7/8	3280	1365	2720	1130	1950	810	1560	715
9"	1/2*	1150	600	990	515	885	460	780	405
	5/8	1770	850	1510	725	1360	650	1200	575
	3/4	2520	1110	2160	950	1780	785	1435	630
	7/8	3350	1390	2880	1200	2060	855	1660	690
10"	5/8*	1800	865	1540	740	1380	660	1220	585
	3/4	2540	1120	2190	965	1970	865	1625	715
	7/8	3420	1420	2960	1230	2340	970	1890	785
	1	4420	1770	3710	1485	2660	1065	2140	855
11"	3/4*	2580	1130	2220	970	2000	880	1765	780
	7/8	3450	1430	2990	1240	2600	1080	2100	870
	1	4500	1800	3880	1550	2970	1190	2370	950
12"	7/8	3470	1440	3000	1250	2690	1120	2320	965
	1	4520	1810	3900	1560	3290	1320	2630	1050
	1 1/8	5660	2260	4900	1960	3570	1430	2870	1150
13"	7/8*	3500	1455	3030	1260	2710	1130	2390	990
	1	4550	1820	3930	1570	3520	1410	2890	1155
	1 1/8	5700	2280	4920	1970	3920	1570	3120	1250
14"	1	4570	1830	3950	1570	3530	1410	3120	1240
	1 1/8	5740	2300	4950	1980	4380	1750	3500	1400
	1 1/4	7020	2800	6060	2420	4830	1930	3910	1560
15"	1	4580	1830	3960	1580	3550	1420	3130	1250
	1 1/8	5770	2310	4980	1990	4460	1790	3820	1530
	1 1/4	7070	2830	6110	2450	5250	2100	4180	1670
16"	1*	4600	1840	3960	1580	3550	1420	3130	1250
	1 1/8*	5800	2320	5000	2000	4470	1790	3950	1580
	1 1/4*	7120	2850	6150	2460	5500	2200	4520	1810

* Greater lengths do not provide higher loads.

Courtesy National Forest Products Assn.

Table B5– LAG BOLTS or LAG SCREWS—Allowable Withdrawal Loads — Normal Duration.

Allowable load in withdrawal, in pounds per inch of penetration of the threaded part into the member holding the point.

D = the shank diameter in inches. G = the specific gravity of the wood, based on weight and volume when oven-dry.

When specific gravity (G) of wood is	SIZE											
	¼	5⁄16	⅜	7⁄16	½	9⁄16	⅝	¾	⅞	1	1⅛	1¼
	D = 0.250	0.3125	0.375	0.4375	0.500	0.5625	0.625	0.750	0.875	1.000	1.125	1.250
.32	115	136	156	175	195	211	229	263	295	326	356	385
.34	126	149	171	192	212	231	251	287	323	356	389	421
.35	132	156	178	200	222	242	262	300	337	373	407	440
.36	138	163	186	209	231	252	273	313	352	389	425	460
.37	143	169	194	218	241	263	285	326	367	405	442	479
.38	149	176	202	227	251	273	298	339	381	421	460	498
.40	161	190	217	244	270	294	319	366	411	454	496	536
.41	167	197	226	254	281	306	332	380	427	472	515	558
.42	173	205	235	263	291	318	344	395	443	490	535	579
.43	180	213	244	274	303	331	358	411	461	509	556	602
.44	186	220	252	283	313	341	369	424	476	526	574	621
.45	192	227	260	292	323	353	382	438	492	544	594	643
.46	199	235	269	302	334	364	395	453	508	562	613	664
.47	205	242	278	312	345	376	407	467	525	580	633	685
.48	212	251	287	322	357	389	421	483	542	599	655	709
.51	232	274	313	352	389	425	460	528	593	655	716	774
.53	246	290	333	374	413	451	488	560	629	695	759	821
.59	289	341	391	439	485	529	573	657	738	815	891	964
.62	311	367	421	473	523	570	618	708	795	878	960	1038
.64	326	385	441	496	548	598	648	743	834	922	1007	1090
.66	342	403	462	519	574	626	678	778	873	965	1054	1141
.67	349	412	472	531	587	640	693	795	893	986	1078	1166
.68	357	422	484	543	601	655	710	814	914	1010	1103	1194
.71	382	452	517	581	642	700	759	870	976	1080	1195	1278
.80	456	539	617	693	767	836	906	1039	1166	1289	1408	1524

SOLUTION OF HANKINSON FORMULA

A. The allowable unit stresses in compression for lumber and allowable loads for connectors, bolts, and lag screws at an angle of load to grain between 0° and 90° are obtained from the Hankinson formula given in figure

B. The Hankinson formula is for the condition where the loaded surface is perpendicular to the direction of the load.

C. Where the resultant force is at an angle other than 90° with the surface under consideration, the angle θ is the angle between the direction of grain and the direction of the force component which is perpendicular to the surface.

D. The bearing surface for a connector, bolt, or lag screw is assumed perpendicular to the force.

E. The following table lists $\sin^2 \theta$ and $\cos^2 \theta$ for various angles of θ.

$\sin^2\theta$	θ	$\cos^2\theta$	$\sin^2\theta$	θ	$\cos^2\theta$
0.00000	0	1.00000	.58682	50	.41318
.00760	5	.99240	.67101	55	.32899
.03015	10	.96985	.75000	60	.25000
.06698	15	.93302	.82140	65	.17860
.11698	20	.88302	.88302	70	.11698
.17860	25	.82140	.93302	75	.06698
.25000	30	.75000	.96985	80	.03015
.32899	35	.67101	.99240	85	.00760
.41318	40	.58682	1.00000	90	.00000
.50000	45	.50000			

Courtesy National Forest Products Assn.

Figure B1. Hankinson Formula

The Hankinson formula may be solved graphically through use of the charts on this page.

Bearing Strength of Wood at Angles to the Grain (Hankinson Formula).

The compressive strength of wood depends on the direction of the grain with respect to the direction of the applied load. It is highest parallel to the grain, and lowest perpendicular to the grain. The variation in strength, at angles between parallel and perpendicular, is determined by the Hankinson formula. The Scholten nomographs, shown here, are a graphical solution of this formula which is —

$$F_n = \frac{F_c \, F_{c\perp}}{F_c \sin^2\theta + F_{c\perp} \cos^2\theta}$$

F_c = Unit stress in compression parallel to the grain.

$F_{c\perp}$ = Unit stress in compression perpendicular to the grain.

θ = Angle between the direction of grain and direction of load normal to the face considered.

F_n = Unit compressive stress at inclination θ with the direction of grain.

The difference between the two charts is in scale, the one on the right to units of 1000 pounds, and the one on the left to units of 100 pounds. These units may be applied to allowable lumber stresses in pounds per square inch, or to total loads in the case of bolts, timber connectors or lag screws.

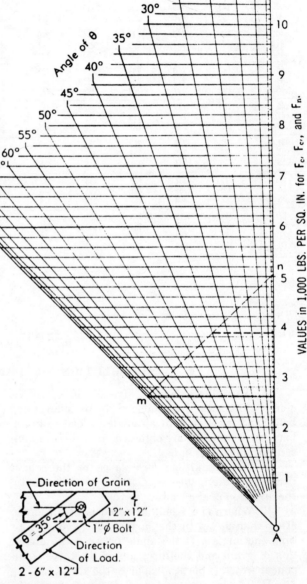

Example for Bolted Joint

Bolt values are obtained from Table 12. Assume P = F_c' = 5030 lbs., Q = $F_{c\perp}$ = 2620 lbs., and θ = 35°. On line A-B, in chart at right, locate 5030 lbs. at point n. On same line A-B, locate 2620 lbs. and project to point m on line A-C. Where line m-n intersects the radial line for 35°, project to line A-B and read the allowable load of 3870 lbs. for the 35° angle of load to grain.

Courtesy National Forest Products Assn.

Table B6

WOOD SCREWS--Allowable Lateral Loads--Normal Duration

Allowable lateral loads (shear) in pounds for screws embedded to approximately 7 times the shank diameter into the member holding the point. For less penetration, reduce loads in proportion. Penetration should not be less than 4 times the shank diameter.

						SIZE OF SCREW						
For species in each group, see Table B1.	g =	6	7	8	9	10	12	14	16	18	20	24
	D =	0.138	0.151	0.164	0.177	0.190	0.216	0.242	0.268	0.294	0.320	0.372
	7D =	.966	1.057	1.148	1.239	1.330	1.512	1.694	1.876	2.058	2.240	2.604
	4D =	.552	.604	.656	.708	.760	.864	.968	1.072	1.176	1.280	1.488
Group I	=	91	109	129	150	173	224	281	345	415	492	664
Group II	=	75	90	106	124	143	185	232	284	342	406	548
Group III	=	62	74	87	101	117	151	190	233	280	332	448
Group IV	=	48	58	68	79	91	118	148	181	218	258	349

Courtesy National Forest Products Assn.

Table B7

WOOD SCREWS--Allowable Withdrawal Loads--Normal Duration

Inserted perpendicular to grain of wood   g = gauge of screw,
                                            D = diameter of screw (inches)

Allowable load in withdrawal in lbs per in. of penetration of threaded portion of screw into the member holding the point.

Specific gravity (G) of wood (See Table B1 for species)		SIZE OF SCREW										
	g =	6	7	8	9	10	12	14	16	18	20	24
	D =	0.138	0.151	0.164	0.177	0.190	0.216	0.242	0.268	0.294	0.320	0.372
.32		40	44	48	52	55	63	71	78	86	93	108
.34		46	50	54	58	63	71	80	88	97	105	123
.35		48	53	57	62	66	75	84	93	103	112	130
.36		51	56	60	65	70	80	89	99	109	118	137
.37		54	59	64	69	74	84	94	104	115	125	145
.38		57	62	67	73	78	89	99	110	121	132	153
.40		63	69	75	81	87	98	110	122	134	146	170
.41		66	72	79	85	91	103	116	128	141	153	178
.42		69	76	82	89	95	109	121	135	148	161	187
.43		73	80	86	93	100	114	127	141	155	169	196
.44		76	83	91	97	105	119	133	148	162	177	205
.45		80	87	95	102	110	125	140	155	170	185	215
.46		83	91	99	107	115	130	146	162	177	193	224
.47		87	95	103	111	120	136	152	169	185	201	234
.48		91	99	108	116	125	142	159	176	193	210	244
.51		102	112	121	131	141	160	179	199	218	237	276
.53		111	121	131	142	152	173	194	215	235	256	298
.59		137	150	163	176	189	214	240	266	292	317	369
.62		151	166	180	194	208	237	265	294	322	351	407
.64		161	176	192	207	222	252	282	312	343	374	434
.66		171	188	204	220	236	268	300	333	365	397	461
.67		177	193	210	227	243	276	310	343	376	410	476
.68		182	199	216	233	251	285	319	353	387	422	490
.71		196	214	233	252	270	307	394	381	418	455	529
.80		252	275	299	323	347	394	441	489	536	584	679

Approximately two-thirds of the length of a standard wood screw is threaded.

Courtesy National Forest Products Assn.

APPENDIX C

BEAM FORMULAS & SHEAR
AND MOMENT DIAGRAMS

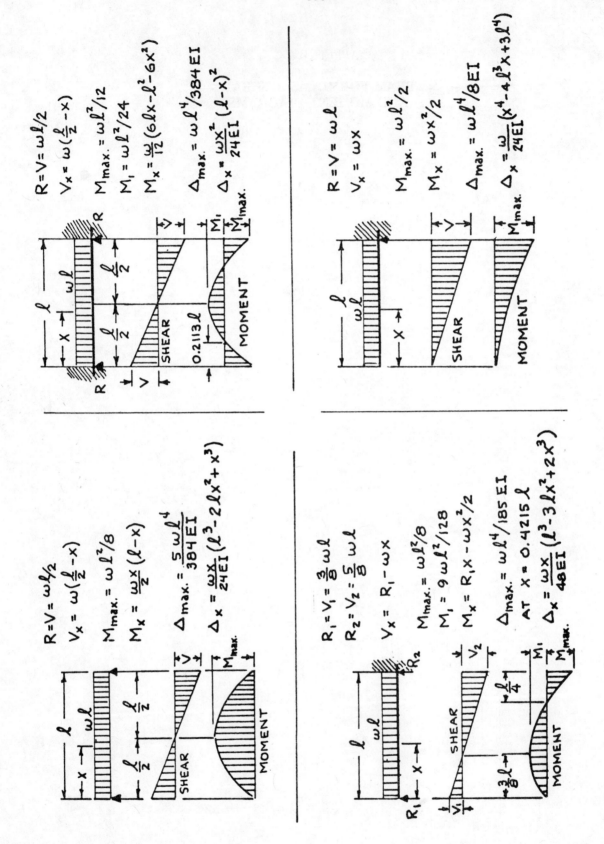

$R = V = \omega l/2$

$V_x = \omega\left(\dfrac{l}{2} - x\right)$

$M_{max.} = \omega l^2/12$

$M_1 = \omega l^2/24$

$M_x = \dfrac{\omega}{12}(6lx - l^2 - 6x^2)$

$\Delta_{max.} = \omega l^4/384EI$

$\Delta_x = \dfrac{\omega x^2}{24EI}(l-x)^2$

0.2113 l

SHEAR

MOMENT

$R = V = \omega l$

$V_x = \omega x$

$M_{max.} = \omega l^2/2$

$M_x = \omega x^2/2$

$\Delta_{max.} = \omega l^4/8EI$

$\Delta_x = \dfrac{\omega}{24EI}(x^4 - 4l^3x + 3l^4)$

SHEAR

MOMENT

$R = V = \omega l/2$

$V_x = \omega\left(\dfrac{l}{2} - x\right)$

$M_{max.} = \omega l^2/8$

$M_x = \dfrac{\omega x}{2}(l-x)$

$\Delta_{max.} = \dfrac{5\,\omega l^4}{384EI}$

$\Delta_x = \dfrac{\omega x}{24EI}(l^3 - 2lx^2 + x^3)$

SHEAR

MOMENT

$R_1 = V_1 = \dfrac{3}{8}\,\omega l$

$R_2 = V_2 = \dfrac{5}{8}\,\omega l$

$V_x = R_1 - \omega x$

$M_{max.} = \omega l^2/8$

$M_1 = 9\,\omega l^2/128$

$M_x = R_1 x - \omega x^2/2$

$\Delta_{max.} = \omega l^4/185\,EI$

At $x = 0.4215\,l$

$\Delta_x = \dfrac{\omega x}{48EI}(l^3 - 3lx^2 + 2x^3)$

SHEAR

MOMENT

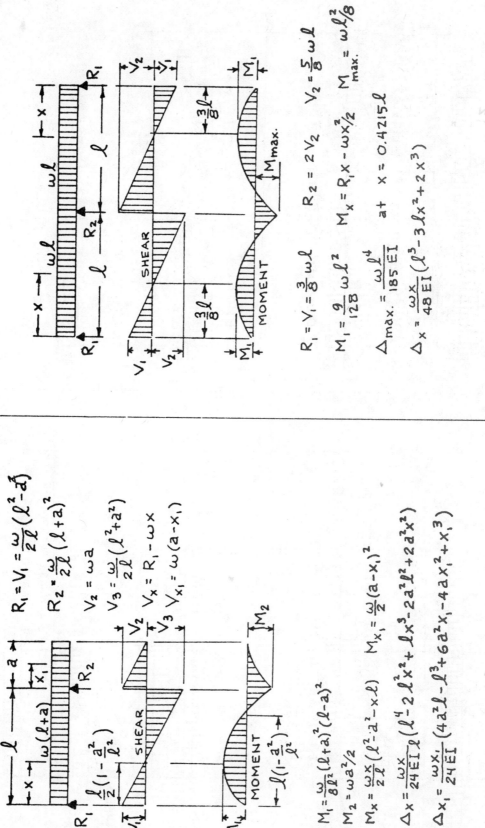

$R_1 = V_1 = \dfrac{3}{8} wl$ $R_2 = 2V_2$ $V_2 = \dfrac{5}{8} wl$

$M_1 = \dfrac{9}{128} wl^2$ $M_x = R_1 x - wx^2/2$ $M_{max.} = wl^2/8$

$\Delta_{max.} = \dfrac{wl^4}{185\,EI}$ at $x = 0.4215\,l$

$\Delta_x = \dfrac{wx}{48\,EI}(l^3 - 3lx^2 + 2x^3)$

$R_1 = V_1 = \dfrac{w}{2l}(l^2 - a^2)$

$R_2 = \dfrac{w}{2l}(l+a)^2$

$V_2 = wa$

$V_3 = \dfrac{w}{2l}(l^2 + a^2)$ $V_x = R_1 - wx$ $V_{x_1} = w(a - x_1)$

$M_1 = \dfrac{w}{8l^2}(l+a)^2(l-a)^2$

$M_2 = wa^2/2$

$M_x = \dfrac{wx}{2l}(l^2 - a^2 - xl)$ $M_{x_1} = \dfrac{w}{2}(a - x_1)^2$

$\Delta_x = \dfrac{wx}{24\,EI\,l}(l^4 - 2l^2x^2 + lx^3 - 2a^2l^2 + 2a^2x^2)$

$\Delta_{x_1} = \dfrac{wx_1}{24\,EI}(4a^2l - l^3 + 6a^2x_1 - 4ax_1^2 + x_1^3)$

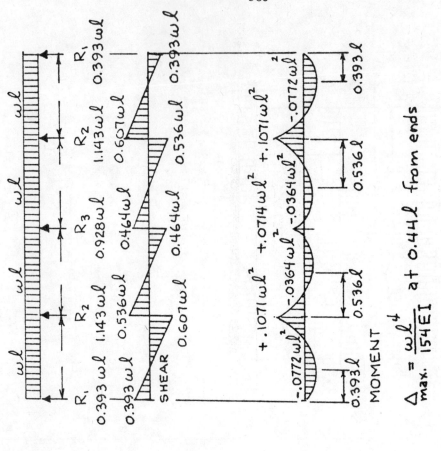

SHEAR

R_1 0.393 ωl · 0.393 ωl · R_2 1.143 ωl 0.607 ωl · R_3 0.928 ωl 0.464 ωl · R_2 1.143 ωl 0.536 ωl · R_1 0.393 ωl

0.607 ωl 0.536 ωl 0.464 ωl 0.464 ωl 0.536 ωl 0.393 ωl

MOMENT

$+.1071 ωl^2$ $+.0714 ωl^2$ $+.1071 ωl^2$
$-.0772 ωl^2$ $-.0364 ωl^2$ $-.0364 ωl^2$ $-.0772 ωl^2$

0.393 l · 0.536 l · 0.536 l · 0.393 l

$$\Delta_{max.} = \frac{ωl^4}{154 EI} \quad \text{at } 0.44 l \text{ from ends}$$

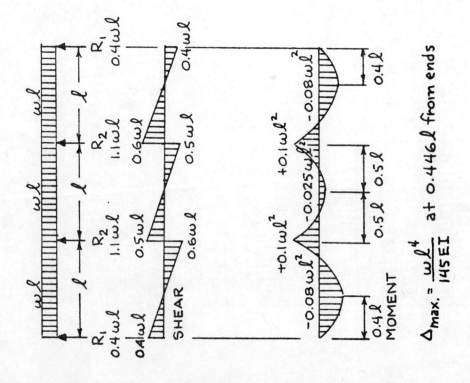

SHEAR

R_1 0.4 ωl · 0.4 ωl · R_2 1.1 ωl 0.6 ωl · R_2 1.1 ωl 0.5 ωl · R_1 0.4 ωl

0.6 ωl 0.5 ωl 0.6 ωl 0.4 ωl

MOMENT

$+0.1 ωl^2$ $+0.1 ωl^2$
$-0.08 ωl^2$ $-0.025 ωl^2$ $-0.08 ωl^2$

0.4 l · 0.5 l · 0.5 l · 0.4 l

$$\Delta_{max.} = \frac{ωl^4}{145 EI} \quad \text{at } 0.446 l \text{ from ends}$$

361

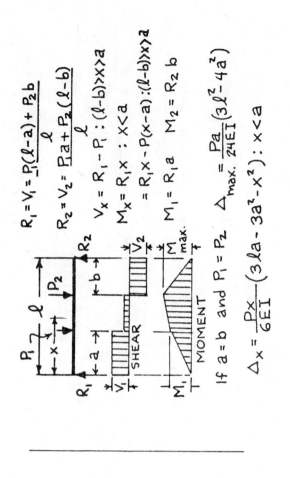

$$R_1 = V_1 = \frac{P_1(\ell-a)+P_2 b}{\ell}$$

$$R_2 = V_2 = \frac{P_1 a + P_2(\ell-b)}{\ell}$$

$$V_x = R_1 - P_1 : (\ell-b)>x>a$$

$$M_x = R_1 x : x<a$$

$$= R_1 x - P(x-a) : (\ell-b)>x>a$$

$$M_1 = R_1 a \qquad M_2 = R_2 b$$

If $a=b$ and $P_1 = P_2$ $\quad \Delta_{max} = \frac{Pa}{24EI}(3\ell^2-4a^2)$

$$\Delta_x = \frac{Px}{6EI}(3\ell a - 3a^2 - x^2) : x<a$$

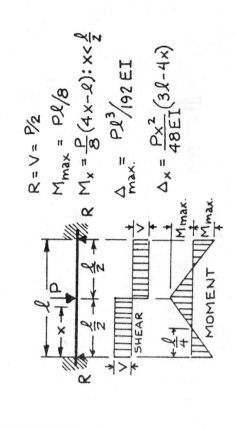

$$R = V = P/2$$

$$M_{max} = P\ell/8$$

$$M_x = \frac{P}{8}(4x-\ell) : x<\frac{\ell}{2}$$

$$\Delta_{max} = \frac{P\ell^3}{192EI}$$

$$\Delta_x = \frac{Px^2}{48EI}(3\ell-4x)$$

$$R = V = P/2$$

$$M_{max} = P\ell/4$$

$$M_x = Px/2$$

$$\Delta_{max} = \frac{P\ell^3}{48EI}$$

$$\Delta_x = \frac{Px}{48EI}(3\ell^2-4x^2)$$

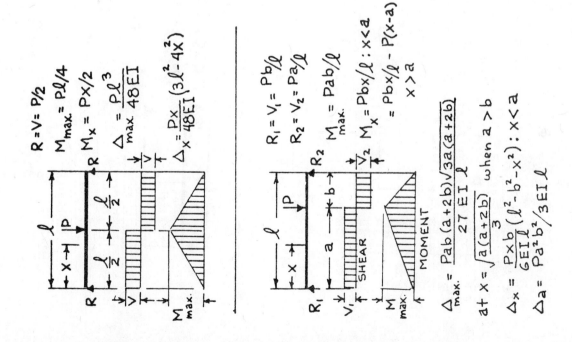

$$R_1 = V_1 = Pb/\ell$$

$$R_2 = V_2 = Pa/\ell$$

$$M_{max} = Pab/\ell$$

$$M_x = Pbx/\ell : x<a$$

$$= Pbx/\ell - P(x-a) : x>a$$

$$\Delta_{max} = \frac{Pab(a+2b)\sqrt{3a(a+2b)}}{27EI\ell} \quad \text{when } a>b$$

$$at \ x = \sqrt{\frac{a(a+2b)}{3}}$$

$$\Delta_x = \frac{Px b}{6EI\ell}(\ell^2-b^2-x^2) : x<a$$

$$\Delta_a = Pa^2 b^2/3EI\ell$$

362

SIMPLE BEAM — ONE CONCENTRATED MOVING LOAD

$$R_{1\,max.} = V_{1\,max.} = P \; ; \; x=0$$

$M_{max.}$ at load when $x = \dfrac{\ell}{2}$

$$= P\ell/4$$

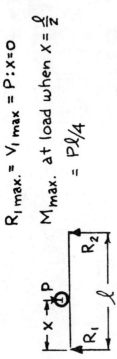

TWO EQUAL CONCENTRATED MOVING LOADS

$$R_{1\,max.} = V_{1\,max.} \text{ at } x=0$$
$$= P\left(2 - \dfrac{a}{\ell}\right)$$

When $a < 0.586\ell$

$M_{max.}$ Under load #1

at $x = \dfrac{\ell}{2} - \dfrac{a}{4}$

$$= \dfrac{P}{2\ell}\left(\ell - \dfrac{a}{2}\right)^2$$

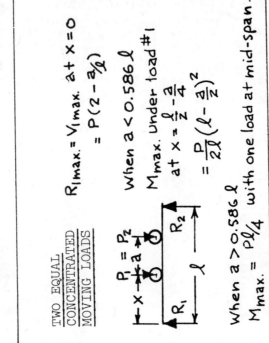

When $a > 0.586\ell$
$M_{max.} = P\ell/4$ with one load at mid-span.

TWO UNEQUAL CONCENTRATED MOVING LOADS

$$R_{1\,max.} = V_{1\,max.} \; (\text{at } x=0)$$
$$= P_1 + P_2\,\dfrac{(\ell - a)}{\ell}$$

M under P_1 at

max. $x = \dfrac{1}{2}\left(\ell - \dfrac{P_2 a}{P_1 + P_2}\right)$

$$= (P_1 + P_2)\,x^2/\ell$$

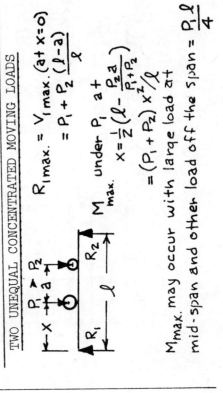

$M_{max.}$ may occur with large load at mid-span and other load off the span $= \dfrac{P_1 \ell}{4}$

$$R = V = P$$
$$M_{max.} = Pb$$
$$M_x = P(x-a)$$
$$\Delta_{max.} = \dfrac{Pb^2}{6EI}(3\ell - b)$$
$$\Delta_a = \dfrac{Pb^3}{3EI}$$
$$\Delta_x = \dfrac{Pb^2}{6EI}(3\ell - 3x - b) \quad \text{when } x < a$$

SHEAR

MOMENT

$$\Delta_x = \dfrac{P(\ell-x)^2}{6EI}(3b - \ell + x) \; ; \; x > a$$

$$R = V = P$$
$$M_{max.} = P\ell$$
$$M_x = Px$$
$$\Delta_{max.} = \dfrac{P\ell^3}{3EI}$$

SHEAR

MOMENT

$$\Delta_x = \dfrac{P}{6EI}(2\ell^3 - 3\ell^2 x + x^3)$$

APPENDIX D

EFFECT OF SHEAR DEFORMATION
ON THE DEFLECTION OF BEAMS

The deflection of beams at the center of the span is usually calculated using equations which ignore the shear component of deflection. For three common loading arrangements, these equations are:

Uniformly distributed load

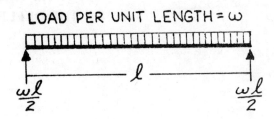

$$\Delta = \frac{5}{384} \cdot \frac{w\ell^4}{EI}$$

Concentrated load at center of span

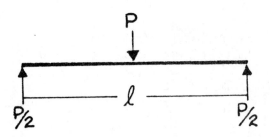

$$\Delta = \frac{P\ell^3}{48EI}$$

Two equal concentrated loads, spaced equidistant from supports

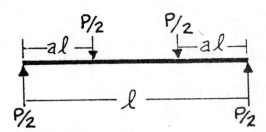

$$\Delta = \frac{P\ell^3}{48EI}(3a - 4a^3)$$

As mentioned in Chapter 9, for most applications of stress graded joists, plank and sawn timber, these equations will predict deflection of wood beams with sufficient precision, if the ℓ/h ratio of the member is in the range of 15 to 25.

In reality, deflection is a function both of elastic modulus (E) and the shear modulus (G) of a material. The more precise equations for beams of rectangular cross-section account for both elements of total deflection. The equations developed by the technique described by Orosz in FPL-0210 and based on energy methods described by Timoshenko in his "Strength of Materials" 3rd edition are:

Uniformly distributed load

$$\Delta = \frac{5}{384}\frac{w\ell^4}{EI}\left[1 + 0.96\left(\frac{h}{\ell}\right)^2\frac{E}{G}\right]$$

Concentrated load at mid-span

$$\Delta = \frac{P\ell^3}{48EI} \left[1 + 1.2\left(\frac{h}{\ell}\right)^2 \frac{E}{G} \right]$$

Two equal concentrated loads, spaced equidistant from supports

$$\Delta \quad \frac{P\ell^3}{48EI} \quad (3a - 4a^3) \left[1 + \frac{2.4}{(3-4a^2)} \left(\frac{h}{\ell}\right)^2 \frac{E}{G} \right]$$

In these equations h = depth of the member, with I = moment of inertia of the member, and other symbols per the sketches on the preceding page.

The added increments of deflection, containing the E/G and h/ℓ terms represent deflection due to shear displacement of material along planes parallel to the neutral axis of the beam.

The principal purpose of this appendix is to draw attention to the magnitude of the shear deformation effect. It will be of particular interest to readers who are likely to be engaged in research, materials testing, or the design of members with proportions outside the range normally encountered in conventional framed structures. The relationships described here will account for differences between observed results and calculated predictions using the equations that consider pure bending deflection and ignore shear deformation.

For commercial species of wood the ratio E/G varies between species, in the range of 6 to 20. The ratio h/ℓ is under the control of the designer. To illustrate the magnitude of the effects these two factors have on the accuracy of deflection computation using the usual formulas that ignore shear deformation, Table D1 is of interest. The errors appear tolerable in the general range for framing. For shorter or deeper members the error is too large to be ignored. Note that for small values of E/G the error diminishes. Steel has an E/G of about 2.6 which justifies the practice of ignoring shear deformation in steel structural design.

In the case of long-thin members, such as decking and roof sheathing, the effect of shear deformation is often too slight to warrant consideration.

Table D1 does not cover the effects for members with two concentrated loads. It should be evident that if these loads are close to the center the error will approximate that for the single concentrated load, and if the loads are near the ends of the beam that error will be small. If the loads are at third-points, the error will be about 78 percent of that shown in the table for concentrated load at mid-span.

Table D1. Deflection Error in Shear Deformation is Ignored

	Shear Deflection as a Percentage of Bending Deflection					
ℓ/h	Uniformly Distributed Load			Concentrated Load at Mid-Span		
	E/G = 6 %	E/G = 13 %	E/G = 20 %	E/G = 6 %	E/G = 13 %	E/G = 20 %
5	23.0	50.0	76.8	18.8	62.0	96.0
10	6.8	12.6	19.2	7.2	15.5	24.0
15	2.6	5.5	8.5	3.2	7.0	10.9
21	1.3	2.8	4.5	1.7	3.5	5.4
25	1.0	2.0	3.2	1.1	2.4	3.8
35	0.5	1.0	1.6	0.6	1.2	1.9

APPENDIX E

DEFLECTION DUE TO WATER LOAD ADDED BY
DEAD LOAD CREEP

The deflection due to creep is either y' due to dead load or due to dead load ÷ 2, depending on whether or not the beam is initially unseasoned when installed. *Assume it is unseasoned.*

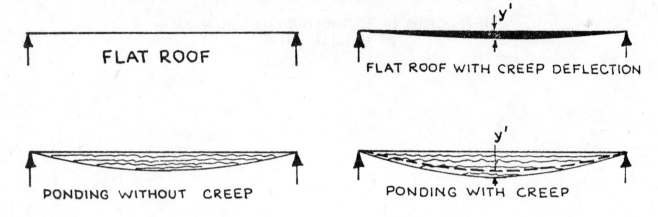

The shape of the elastic curve of the beam after creep has occurred is defined by the equation:

$$y' = \frac{wx}{24EI}\ (\ell^3 - 2\ell x^2 + x^3)$$

where w = Dead load in lbs/inch for the width of roof tributary to the member.

At the point of overflow, the beam will carry the normal ponding load for a level beam and in addition, a load due to the weight of water in the basin formed by the creep deformation.

The creep basin load is a non-uniform load.

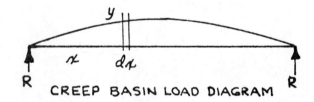

CREEP BASIN LOAD DIAGRAM

The ordinate, y, to the creep deformation curve may be integrated along the span to get the area under the curve. This area multiplied by 0.433 will be the total load per foot width of deck and may be equated to 2R, the sum of the reactions.

$$2R = 0.433 \Sigma ydx = 0.433 \int_0^{\ell} \frac{wx}{24EI} (\ell^3 - 2\ell x^2 + x^3)dx$$

0.433 = weight in lbs./in. of water on a one foot wide surface, one inch in depth.

$$2R = \frac{0.433w}{24EI} \int_0^{\ell} (\ell^3 x 2\ell x^3 + x^4)dx = \frac{0.433w}{24EI} \left[\frac{\ell^3 x^2}{2} \quad \frac{-2\ell x^4}{4} \quad \frac{+x^5}{5} \right]_0^{\ell}$$

$$2R = \frac{0.433w}{24EI} \left(\frac{\ell^5}{2} - \frac{\ell^5}{2} + \frac{\ell^5}{5} \right) = \frac{0.433w\ell^5}{24EI(5)}$$

w is the dead load in lbs per inch of span per foot of deck width.

$$\text{Reaction } R = \frac{0.433w\ell^5}{24EI(10)} = \frac{w\ell^5}{554EI}$$

Moment at any point "x" due to this load

$$M_x = Rx - \int_0^x xydx(0.433) \qquad \text{Per ft. of width}$$

$$= \frac{0.433}{24EI} \frac{w\ell^5 x}{10} - 0.433 \int_0^x \frac{wx}{24EI} (\ell^3 - 2\ell x^2 + x^3)xdx$$

$$= \frac{0.433w}{24EI} \left[\frac{\ell^5 x}{10} - \int_0^x (\ell^3 x^2 - 2\ell x^4 + x^5)dx \right]$$

$$= \frac{0.433w}{24EI} \left[\frac{\ell^5 x}{10} - \frac{\ell^3 x^3}{3} + \frac{2\ell x^5}{5} - \frac{x^6}{6} \right]$$

$$M_{max}_{(\ell/2)} = \frac{0.433w}{24EI} \left[\frac{\ell^6}{20} - \frac{\ell^6}{24} + \frac{2\ell^6}{160} - \frac{\ell^6}{384} \right]$$

$$= \frac{0.433w}{24EI} \frac{(19.2 - 16 + 4.8 - 1)}{384 \ EI} = \frac{w\ell^6}{3040EI}$$

Deflection caused by this load.

$$EI \frac{d^2y}{dx^2} = M_x = \frac{0.433w}{24EI} \left(\frac{\ell^5 x}{10} - \frac{\ell^3 x^3}{3} + \frac{2\ell x^5}{5} - \frac{x^6}{6} \right)$$

$$EI \frac{dy}{dx} = \frac{0.433w}{24EI} \left(\frac{\ell^5 x^2}{20} - \frac{\ell^3 x^4}{12} + \frac{2\ell x^6}{30} - \frac{x^7}{42} \right)$$

$$EI\, y = \frac{0.433w}{24EI} \left(\frac{\ell^5 x^3}{60} - \frac{\ell^3 x^5}{60} + \frac{2\ell x^7}{210} - \frac{x^8}{336} \right)$$

$$y_{\ell/2} = \frac{0.433w}{24\, E^2 I^2} \left(\frac{\ell^5 \ell^3}{8(60)} - \frac{\ell^3 \ell^5}{32(60)} + \frac{2\ell \ell^7}{128(210)} - \frac{\ell^8}{256(336)} \right)$$

$$= \frac{0.433 w \ell^8}{24\, E^2 I^2} \left(\frac{3}{32(60)} + \frac{1}{128(105)} - \frac{1}{256(336)} \right)$$

$$= \frac{0.433 w \ell^8}{24\, E^2 I^2} \left(\frac{1}{640} + \frac{1}{13,440} - \frac{1}{86016} \right) = \frac{w\ell^8}{34103 E^2 I^2}$$